Here Is THE Diet!

"The authors have done a great deal more than simply explain the Prudent Diet and its potential as a preventative of ... coronary heart disease. Basic methods of cooking are explained: steps and ingredients have been reduced to only those essential for a perfect product. Here is **the** diet. The authors have collaborated in a book for every homemaker who wants to feed her family well and healthfully."

—Robert S. Goodhart, M.D.,
New York Academy of Medicine

THE PRUDENT DIET

includes many helpful suggestions for planning everyday family meals, meals for special occasions, foods to choose when eating out and a host of hearty and delicious recipes —healthful dishes for every occasion and for every taste.

Bantam Health Books
Ask your bookseller for the books you have missed

THE CHINESE ART OF HEALING by Stephen Palós
A DICTIONARY OF SYMPTOMS by Dr. Joan Gomez
DIET WATCHERS GUIDE by Anne Gold & Sara Welles Briller
"DOCTOR, MAKE ME BEAUTIFUL" by Dr. James W. Smith and Samm Sinclair Baker
THE DOCTOR'S QUICK WEIGHT LOSS DIET COOKBOOK by Dr. Irwin M. Stillman and Samm Sinclair Baker
THE FAMILY GUIDE TO BETTER FOOD AND BETTER HEALTH by Ronald Deutsch
FOR PEOPLE WHO MAKE LOVE: A GUIDE TO SEXUAL HEALTH by John J. Secondi, M.D.
FROM EDEN TO AQUARIUS: THE BOOK OF NATURAL HEALING by Greg Brodsky
HONEY AND YOUR HEALTH by Dr. Bodog Beck and Dorée Smedley
LIVING WITH YOUR BAD BACK by Theodore Berland
NUTRITION AGAINST DISEASE by Dr. Roger J. Williams
NUTRITION AND YOUR MIND by Dr. George Watson
THE PRUDENT DIET by Iva Bennett and Martha Simon
STOP DIETING! START LOSING! by Ruth West
SWEET AND DANGEROUS by Dr. John Yudkin
THE TRUTH ABOUT VITAMIN E by Martin Ebon
VITAMIN C AND THE COMMON COLD by Dr. Linus Pauling
WHICH VITAMINS DO YOU NEED? by Martin Ebon

THE PRUDENT DIET

By
Iva Bennett
and
Martha Simon

BANTAM BOOKS
Toronto / New York / London

*This book is dedicated to
the memory of the late Dr. Norman Jolliffe,
our chief, teacher, and friend*

This low-priced Bantam Book
has been completely reset in a type face
designed for easy reading, and was printed
from new plates. It contains the complete
text of the original hard-cover edition.
NOT ONE WORD HAS BEEN OMITTED.

THE PRUDENT DIET
*A Bantam Book / published by arrangement with
David White, Inc.*

PRINTING HISTORY
David White edition published May 1973
2nd printing......July 1973
Cook Book Club edition published August 1973
Excerpts appeared in GOOD FOOD magazine January 1974
Bantam edition published July 1974

2nd printing

All rights reserved.
Copyright © 1973 by Iva Bennett and Martha Simon.
This book may not be reproduced in whole or in part, by
mimeograph or any other means, without permission.
For information address: David White, Inc.
60 East 55th Street, New York, N. Y. 10022

Published simultaneously in the United States and Canada

Bantam Books are published by Bantam Books, Inc. Its trademark, consisting of the words "Bantam Books" and the portrayal of a bantam, is registered in the United States Patent Office and in other countries. Marca Registrada. Bantam Books, Inc., 666 Fifth Avenue, New York, New York 10019.

PRINTED IN THE UNITED STATES OF AMERICA

Contents

FOREWORD

PREFACE

PART ONE: THE SEARCH FOR AN ANSWER — 1

1. RESEARCH ON THE RELATION OF DIET TO CORONARY HEART DISEASE — 3
2. THE ANTI-CORONARY CLUB — 7
3. PRACTICAL APPLICATIONS OF THE PRUDENT DIET — 12
4. THE MATHEMATICS OF REDUCING — 23
5. FOOD GROUPS FOR KEY NUTRIENTS — 30
6. SUMMING UP — 33

PART TWO: THE PRUDENT DIET IN PRACTICE — 35

7. PLANNING MEALS FOR PLEASURE AND HEALTH — 37
8. BASIC INFORMATION FOR THE PRUDENT DIET — 47
9. COCKTAILERS AND HORS D'OEUVRE — 54
10. SOUPS — 81
11. FISH AND SHELLFISH — 107
12. POULTRY — 150
13. LEAN MEATS — 170
14. VEGETABLES — 196
15. PANCAKES AND GRAIN DISHES — 226
16. SALADS AND SALAD DRESSINGS — 235
17. SAUCES AND GRAVIES — 250
18. YEAST BREADS AND QUICK BREADS — 260
19. CAKES, PIES, AND COOKIES — 270
20. DESSERTS — 304

GLOSSARY — 321

BIBLIOGRAPHY — 322

INDEX — 325

Charts and Tables

FATTY ACID DISTRIBUTION OF DIETS OF STUDY MEMBERS ENTERING THE ANTI-CORONARY CLUB VS. THE PRUDENT DIET	9
HIDDEN FAT IN SOME COMMON FOODS	13
FATTY ACID COMPOSITION OF CERTAIN FOODS	14
DISTRIBUTION OF FATTY ACIDS—FATS	16
DISTRIBUTION OF FATTY ACIDS—PROTEIN FOODS	18
FOODS SUPPLYING PROTEIN DAILY FOR THE ADULT	20
DIFFERENCES IN CALORIES BY WEIGHT	27
DESIRABLE WEIGHTS	28
DAILY CALORIE ALLOWANCES FOR ADULTS	29
EQUIVALENTS BY WEIGHT AND BY VOLUME	48
TIME AND TEMPERATURE CHARTS FOR PREPARING FISH DISHES	109

Foreword

I take pleasure in the opportunity granted me to write the foreword to this most useful and readable book on the Prudent Diet and how to follow it. Both Mrs. Simon and Mrs. Bennett are well qualified nutrition teachers and excellent cooks. Both have had years of practical experience in the Nutrition Bureau of the Health Department of the City of New York and in that department's Anti-Coronary Club. In this book they have done a great deal more than simply explain the Prudent Diet and its potential as a preventative of atherosclerosis and coronary heart disease. Basic methods of cooking are explained: steps and ingredients have been reduced to only those essential for a perfect product, thus removing the bogey from some great recipes. Most important, they have shown that protective foods and meals can also be delicious and generally acceptable.

Heart disease resulting from coronary atherosclerosis is the prime killer of American men in the forty-to-sixty-five-year age bracket. Initiation of the proper diet and regular physical exercise early in life and faithful adherence thereto throughout adolescence and adulthood offer the greatest promise for significant reduction in premature mortality from this disease. Here is *the* diet. Mrs. Simon and Mrs. Bennett have collaborated in a book for every homemaker who wants to feed her family well and healthfully. (It can be recommended, also, to restaurateurs and other professionals.) Moderation is the keynote. No food has been entirely prohibited.

Here is how it is possible to eat, drink, and be merry, and still be healthy.

> Robert S. Goodhart, M.D., D.M.S., Executive Secretary, Committee on Medical Education, New York Academy of Medicine; Adjunct Professor of Community Medicine, Mount Sinai School of Medicine of the City University of New York

Preface

Dr. Norman Jolliffe's last and possibly most important contribution to the science of public health nutrition was the establishment of the Diet and Coronary Heart Disease Research Study. He started this project in 1957, when he was Director of the Bureau of Nutrition of the New York City Department of Health.[1]* Subsequently, the medical supervision of the project was under Dr. George J. Christakis, the late Dr. Seymour H. Rinzler and Dr. Henry Singman, who is now preparing the final report of this research study for publication.

The results of this fourteen-year study would have surpassed his greatest expectations: the men in the study who have been instructed in the Prudent Diet, compared with a control group that received no dietary instruction, have had less than one-half the incidence of heart attacks.

As public health nutritionists, the authors of this book had the good fortune to work closely with Dr. Jolliffe during his entire association with the Bureau of Nutrition. He urged us to improve, up-date, and enlarge the Health Department booklet "How to Follow the Prudent Diet," which he had helped us develop in 1958. He foresaw the great usefulness of the booklet, which has been reprinted many times and is still much in demand.

The present book is an attempt to carry out his suggestion and to give wide circulation to the principles and practices of the Prudent Diet. The book is divided into two parts. The first, The Search for an Answer,

---

* See Bibliography.

outlines the scientific studies made in many parts of the world which led to the establishment of the Anti-Coronary Club. The theory of the Prudent Diet is explained in some detail, because when the principles underlying the diet are understood, a very wide choice of foods can be made. The second part, The Prudent Diet in Practice, begins with a chapter on planning meals in accordance with the principles of the Prudent Diet, including suggestions for everyday family meals, meals for special occasions, and foods to choose when eating out. The aim is to suggest to homemakers from varied ethnic backgrounds ways to make desirable changes in the family diet while maintaining their own cultural preferences. The remaining chapters consist of recipes, for the most part recipes used by the authors for many years. Foods of all kinds are included, with the emphasis given to those of special importance to the Prudent Diet.

Acknowledgments

We are most grateful to Dr. Robert S. Goodhart for reviewing the manuscript, for his suggestions and criticisms, and for writing the Foreword. We appreciate not only this important contribution, but also his giving so generously of his time.

From the beginning, we were fortunate to have the help of Carmen Gomezplata, literary advisor and longtime friend. She took great pleasure in making use of her expertise for our benefit. Working together was a stimulating experience, valuable far beyond this immediate project. We thank her sincerely.

We owe much to Hedi Borodin, Martha Simon's sister, for being sounding board, critic, and contributor.

Lucky for us, we had as our editor Mona, Mrs. David White. She has an eagle eye for error.

Sincere appreciation is due our good friend, Marshall Neale of Lewis/Neale, Inc., for suggesting a farsighted editor, Mr. David White.

We also wish to thank Miss Dolores Malvido for typing the manuscript.

It is impossible to acknowledge the debt we owe to all who, in person or through their writings, have influenced us. We have learned much from those to whom we have taught the Prudent Diet. Their response and the pleasures our families and friends found in this way of eating encouraged us to write this book.

There is now no question but that diet is an important factor; not the only one, of course, but probably the most important factor accounting for the high death rate from coronary heart disease that afflicts so many American males during their middle age, from 45 to 65.

> DR. NORMAN JOLLIFFE,
> "Diet and Coronary Heart
> Disease," presented before
> the Orange County, New York,
> Heart Association in November, 1956

PART ONE
The Search for an Answer

1

Research on the Relation of Diet to Coronary Heart Disease

On November 4, 1956, Dr. Norman Jolliffe, in an address to the Heart Association of Orange County, New York, on the subject of diet and coronary heart disease, said:

> No prudent person who has had or wishes to avoid coronary heart disease should eat a high-fat diet of the type consumed by most Americans and by many people in other industrialized Western nations. This prudence applies to all males past 18–21 and all women past their menopause. It applies to the obese and the non-obese alike. It applies to those who have never had a coronary attack as well as to those who wish to avoid a recurrence. Although there are differences in susceptibility, it applies to all races and occupations, to the physically active and to the sedentary. It applies not only to the chain-smoking, tense, briefcase-carrying-home executive but to his opposite and the relaxed, satisfied bartender.[1]*

At that time scientific studies on the relationship of diet to blood cholesterol levels and to coronary heart disease were being made throughout the world. Among the most interesting were those of Dr. L. W. Kinsell in California, who demonstrated that diets rich in vegetable oil would cause a fall in blood cholesterol levels.[2] At the University of South Africa, Dr. Bronte-Stewart and his co-workers were conducting nutrition research corroborating Dr. Kinsell's findings.[3] They studied the

---

* See Bibliography.

effect of marine oils as well as vegetable oils and several kinds of highly saturated fats on the blood cholesterol levels of the Bantus, known to be free of coronary heart disease. They found that marine and vegeable oils (sources of polyunsaturated fats) would lower blood cholesterol levels and that foods containing saturated fats would raise them.

Dr. Ancel Keys, the world-traveling researcher, made the observation that countries whose populations had blood cholesterol levels averaging 220 milligrams and above had a high incidence of coronary heart disease, while those with averages of 200 milligrams and below had no such problem.[4]

Scientists engaged in a Public Health Service Study at Framingham, Massachusetts, found three outstanding risk factors related to coronary heart disease: high blood cholesterol, high blood pressure, and overweight.[5,6]

Coronary heart disease today is the number-one killer in the United States of America. The United States has the unhappy distinction of having one of the world's highest death rates from this discase, and New York State and New York City have the highest rates in the United States.[7]

WHO IS MOST VULNERABLE?

Coronary heart disease strikes men in their fifties, forties, and even earlier. Women are more vulnerable after the child-bearing years. Medical experts estimate that it takes about twenty years of atherosclerotic development to lead to a heart attack. Studies of young soldiers killed in the Korean war (and also in Vietnam)[8] have shown that atherosclerosis had made serious inroads among teen-age boys and men in their twenties. Within recent years, studies in New York City, Vermont, and Iowa revealed that school children had overly high blood-cholesterol levels.[9,10]

Are heredity, race, or environment predisposing factors to coronary heart disease? Incidence of coronary heart disease is very high among the whole United States population, which is composed of many different racial and ethnic groups. Most Americans can be said to be prone to this diease. However, individual susceptibility varies. At the extremes, a small percentage of persons, predisposed by genetic factors, is found to be either almost totally resistant or extremely vulnerable to coronary heart disease. These persons are seldom influenced by environmental factors. But research has shown that most people can reduce the risk of coronary heart disease by changing the foods they eat, probably the most important environmental factor that can be influenced.

During the 1960s studies were made of two population groups "on the move." When Japanese moved from Japan, where coronary heart disease was then practically unknown, to Hawaii and California, they adopted the local eating habits of their new environment.[11] Those who settled in Hawaii had a moderate increase in coronary heart disease; their death rate from heart disease became close to that of the Hawaiians. Those who moved to California developed the high incidence rate of coronary heart disease of their American neighbors. A similar observation was made when the Yemenite Jews settled in Israel. In their native country, Yemen, coronary heart disease was practically nonexistent. As they accepted the food habits of the Israelis (similar to those in affluent Western societies), they became prone to the disease.[12] These two outstanding observations indicate that environment (mainly food habits), not heredity or race, makes the major difference in the incidence of coronary heart disease.

In June 1967, the American Medical Association requested the Federal Government to set up a long-term, large-scale study on diet and coronary heart disease. This was just at the completion of a two-year preliminary study to determine the feasibility of such a project. This study, called the National Diet-Heart Study, was supported by the National Institutes of Health, the United States Public Health Service, and the American Heart Association. It showed that the risk factors to coronary heart disease could be reduced among those who followed a diet similar to the Prudent Diet.[13]

A NECESSARY PILOT STUDY

In October 1956, Dr. Jolliffe submitted his proposal for a Diet and Coronary Heart Disease Research Study for New Yorkers to Dr. Leona Baumgartner, then New York City Commissioner of Health, who signed the Executive Order creating such a study in the Health Department of the City of New York. Only one factor —the relationship of diet to coronary heart disease— was to be investigated.[14]

Information about food consumption from areas in the United States and abroad revealed a close link between high saturated fat, high blood cholesterol, and high incidence of coronary heart disease. All the affluent Western societies had certain food habits in common. Over the last fifty years, more and more of the calories people consumed were coming from meat, fat-rich dairy products, and fat-rich desserts, while calories from grains and potatoes declined.

The pilot study suggested by Dr. Jolliffe was needed to answer several very important questions:

Could a diet be devised which was equally desirable from the standpoint of fat composition and nutritional adequacy?

Was it possible to make this diet so palatable that staying on it would be no hardship?

Could a free-living population group be persuaded to follow this diet for an indefinite period?

Would there be a fall in blood-cholesterol levels among those who followed the diet?

Would this fall in cholesterol level be sustained?

Would the lowering of blood cholesterol eventually achieve a reduction in the rate of coronary heart disease?

To help explain the "whys" of the Prudent Diet, a brief history of this study, familiarly known as "The Anti-Coronary Club," follows. Some of the detailed reports of the study are listed in the bibliography.

2
The Anti-Coronary Club

Under Dr. Jolliffe's over-all direction in this study were a chief cardiologist, three nutritionists, a statistician, several physicians, a laboratory technician, and nursing and clerical staff.

The pattern for the Prudent Diet was developed by Dr. Jolliffe, assisted by the participating nutritionists. It is a palatable, nutritionally adequate diet, with dietary fats present in favorable proportions. Important considerations were the decrease in saturated fat and in total fat and the increase in polysaturated fats. The result was a ratio of polyunsaturated to saturated fatty acids (P/S ratio) of 1.3 as compared to a P/S ratio of 0.3 of the average American diet.[15] The diet is composed of foods available in every neighborhood of New York City, permitting a great variety in taste and fitting any budget.

Recruiting volunteers for the study presented less of a problem than was anticipated. A sufficient number of men in their fifties (the most vulnerable age for a heart attack) responded to one news release and one radio announcement over WNYC. The membership in the Anti-Coronary Club rose to over 1,000 men. All new members had been referred by earlier participants.

An orientation program was given to each new group of members. There was an introductory lecture by a physician, who explained the aims of the study and acquainted the men with their responsibilities and privileges. Tests for blood cholesterol, blood-pressure readings, electrocardiograms, diet histories, and general physical examinations were a part of the regular routine. It was emphasized that this was a research project, not a treatment center. Physicians in the community learned to understand and appreciate the functions of the Anti-Coronary Club. If the need for medical care arose, the members of the study were referred to their own physicians, to whom, with the patient's consent, all diagnostic information was made available.

After an initial diet history was taken, each new member and his wife (or another person in charge of preparing his food) whenever possible were instructed individually by the nutritionists on how to follow the diet. The flexibility of the diet makes it feasible to fit the pattern to a great extent to the men's food preferences and their mode of living. Participants were happily surprised to discover the range of food at their disposal. Follow-up diet conferences kept the nutritionists informed of progress. It was emphasized that success with the Prudent Diet would not be effortless. A change from a lifelong pattern of eating is not easy. Self-discipline and stick-to-it-iveness are essential. The greatest asset to a member is a helpful spouse. It has been the experience of the nutritionists that the wife who finds it a challenge to prepare food in accordance with recommendations can often produce meals of excellent quality and of greater variety than before.

Like the subjects of other studies, the men entering the Anti-Coronary Club had high-fats diets. About 40 percent of their total calories were calories from fat. The proportion of saturated fats was high, predominating about three times over the polyunsaturated fats. The following chart illustrates the ratio of polyunsaturated to saturated fats (P/S ratio) of previous diets and of the Prudent Diet.

Staff meetings were held at the Anti-Coronary Club office to keep the medical and nutrition team informed of progress. The statistician's regular analysis of the data was eagerly anticipated. The results often seemed too good to be true. Blood cholesterol came down and stayed down. Would these findings be maintained over the years? The answer is yes. Blood cholesterol came down and stayed down.[16][17]

CHOLESTEROL IN FOODS

Nutritionists are often asked for information regarding a low-cholesterol diet. When someone asks for this type of help, the chances are he wants a diet that will lower cholesterol.

Cholesterol is a fat-like substance present in all

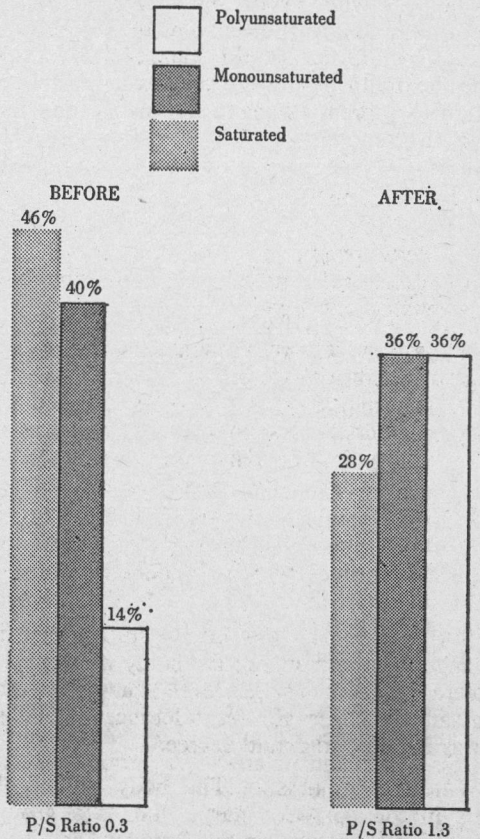

FATTY ACID DISTRIBUTION OF DIETS OF STUDY MEMBERS
ENTERING THE ANTI-CORONARY CLUB VS. THE PRUDENT DIET

human and other animal tissues and fluids. The body makes cholesterol which it needs for many important functions.

In spite of much meticulous research, a direct relationship between the cholesterol in foods we eat and the blood cholesterol level has not been established. All that can be said today is that the amount of cholesterol in the foods we eat has little if any effect upon blood cholesterol levels. However, even if new facts are discovered, you are safe in following the Prudent Diet. Its recommendations as to variety and moderate amount of animal foods (the only source of dietary cholesterol) keep the cholesterol intake at a very moderate level.

SOME UNEXPECTED BENEFITS

As the study progressed, not only did the blood cholesterol levels of the members fall and remain lower, but other benefits developed.

BLOOD PRESSURES CAME DOWN. In addition to the lowering of blood cholesterol levels, a decrease in hypertension (elevated blood pressure) was found among the study members.[17] A similar observation was made in the Feasibility Study.[18] High blood pressure is not only a risk factor in coronary heart disease, it is also a very important factor in proneness to strokes. Therefore, the Prudent Diet has favorably influenced important risk factors in both coronary heart disease and strokes.

BLOOD SUGAR LEVELS WERE LOWERED. Another favorable change occurred among the study members—glucose tolerance (blood sugar levels) improved among those members whose glucose tolerance (blood sugar level) was elevated to a mild degree.

BODY WEIGHT DECREASED. The body weight of the members in the Anti-Coronary Club as a group decreased during their time on the Prudent Diet. To what extent overweight contributes to coronary heart disease has been much debated. However, life insurance statistics show that desirable body weight is positively associated with longevity. Considering height, body weight, and sex, "desirable body weight" is the range of weight at which the least risk to disease and shortened life span occurs.

THE RATE OF HEART ATTACKS WAS REDUCED BY MORE THAN ONE-HALF. Most important of all, the figures in the study showed that for members of the Anti-Coronary Club the incidence of heart attacks was reduced by more than one-half the expected rate.

3

Practical Applications of the Prudent Diet

If you wish to follow the Prudent Diet you may find it interesting and desirable to know exactly what you are eating now. Every change is built upon something already existing. Ask yourself these questions:
How adequate is your diet in essential nutrients?
Does your calorie intake meet the needs of your age and activity?
Do fats constitute a large part of your diet?
Are the *saturated fats* in your foods particularly high?
Are the *polyunsaturated fats* in your foods particularly low?

You may be surprised to find that you are consuming too much fat. Where does it come from? Most people who are interested in the Prudent Diet are nutrition-minded. You may already have made some changes in your diet. Perhaps you have cut down on fried foods, are eating chiefly broiled or roasted meats, shy away from fat-rich gravies, and use no butter on your bread. Possibly you have eliminated rich cakes and pies. But you may not realize that most of the everyday common foods are high in *hidden fats*, fats not readily seen (see the chart on hidden fats).

Practically all animal foods contain a very large proportion of fat. Take the frankfurter, for instance. Most of its calories come from fat, even though the label truthfully states "ALL BEEF," which many people think means "all protein." The average weight of a frankfurter is about 2 ounces. The total calories are about 100; the calories from protein are about 16; the calories from fat are about 80. Such luncheon meats as liverwurst, pastrami, and salami are of similar composition. We think of animal foods as sources primarily of protein, yet the fat calories are more than double the protein calories in eggs, most meats, whole milk, and such whole milk products as American cheese.

HIDDEN FAT IN SOME COMMON FOODS

FOOD	FAT AS PER CENT OF TOTAL CALORIES
Frankfurters	80
Hamburgers	64
American cheese	73
Cream cheese	91
Sour cream	88
Danish pastry	56

Cakes and pies also contribute to a high fat intake. Three fourths of their calories may be fat. Even pound cake, most cookies, and Danish pastry (considered "plain" cake by many) may derive half or more of their calories from fat. Butter and sweet cream are generally recognized high in fat, but many people fail to realize that so are sour cream and cream cheese.

All fats, whether of animal or vegetable origin, are composed of three basic types of fatty acids: saturated, polyunsaturated, and monounsaturated fatty acids. For simplification, these fatty acids are referred to in this book as fats.

Most meats, as well as eggs and dairy products, contain predominantly saturated fats, while fish, shellfish, most vegetable oils, and most vegetable products such as grains and nuts contain predominantly polyunsaturated fats (see lists below).

Saturated fats raise the cholesterol level of the blood, while polyunsaturated fats lower it. Monounsaturated fats neither raise nor lower it to any extent.

The cholesterol level can be lowered by diet in two ways. One can follow a diet extremely low in fats, the fat comprising about 15 to 20 percent of the total calories. Some populations in the Far East use such diets. Or, one can follow a diet in which about 30 percent of the total calories are fat, with polyunsaturated predominating over saturated fats. For a diet to be palatable to most people of Western civilizations, the second alternative seems preferable. The Prudent Diet is based on this pattern.

It cannot be overemphasized that the saturated fats must be reduced in order for the polyunsaturated fats to be effective.

The following lists divide foods into those containing predominantly saturated and polyunsaturated fats.

FATTY ACID COMPOSITION OF CERTAIN FOODS

PREDOMINANTLY SATURATED	PREDOMINANTLY POLYUNSATURATED
meats—beef, lamb, pork	fish and shellfish
egg yolk	liquid vegetable oils; safflower, corn, cottonseed, soybean, others
whole milk	
whole milk cheeses	
cream, sweet and sour	very special shortening ("V.S.S.")
cream substitutes	
ice cream	mayonnaise and salad dressings
butter	
margarines high in saturated fats	polyunsaturated margarines
hydrogenated shortenings	most nuts—almonds, pecans, walnuts

PRACTICAL APPLICATIONS OF THE PRUDENT DIET 15

PREDOMINANTLY SATURATED	PREDOMINANTLY POLYUNSATURATED
chocolate*	peanuts and peanut butter
coconut and coconut oil	whole grains
palm oil	products made with any
cashew nuts	of these foods
avocados	
products made with any of these foods	

The fat in poultry is about equally distributed between saturated and polyunsaturated fats.
Olives and olive oil contain predominantly mono-unsaturated fats. Remember that both animal and vegetable fats can be highly saturated.

As the following table shows, butter is a highly saturated fat. The saturated fats predominate over the polyunsaturated fats more than twenty times. The fat in all dairy products made from milk is of the same composition, but the range of fat content varies from low (cottage cheese) to high (butter).

The Prudent Diet, therefore, restricts the use of butter, whole milk, whole milk cheeses (most cheeses are high in saturated fats), ice cream, cream (sweet and sour), cream cheese, and all foods containing any of these.

Hydrogenated vegetable shortenings are also high in saturated fats. Because they do not get rancid and will keep indefinitely, they are widely used in home and restaurant cooking. These shortenings are predominantly used for deep-fat frying, in bakery goods, and in such commercially prepared foods as potato chips, snack foods, TV dinners, prepared frozen foods, cake and cookie mixes, and most crackers and cookies.

There is a wide choice of polyunsaturated vegetable oils. The least saturated are safflower, corn, soybean, and cottonseed oils. The chart shows that vegetable oils (with the exception of coconut oil, palm oil, and

---

* Cocoa and chocolate syrup from cocoa contribute an insignificant amount of cocoa butter.

16 THE PRUDENT DIET

olive oil) are high in unsaturated fats. They are necessary for a desirable ratio of polyunsaturated to saturated fats in your diet. Two to three tablespoons of vegetable oil (in salads, cooking, or baking) is recommended daily for adults. Vegetable oils are used exten-

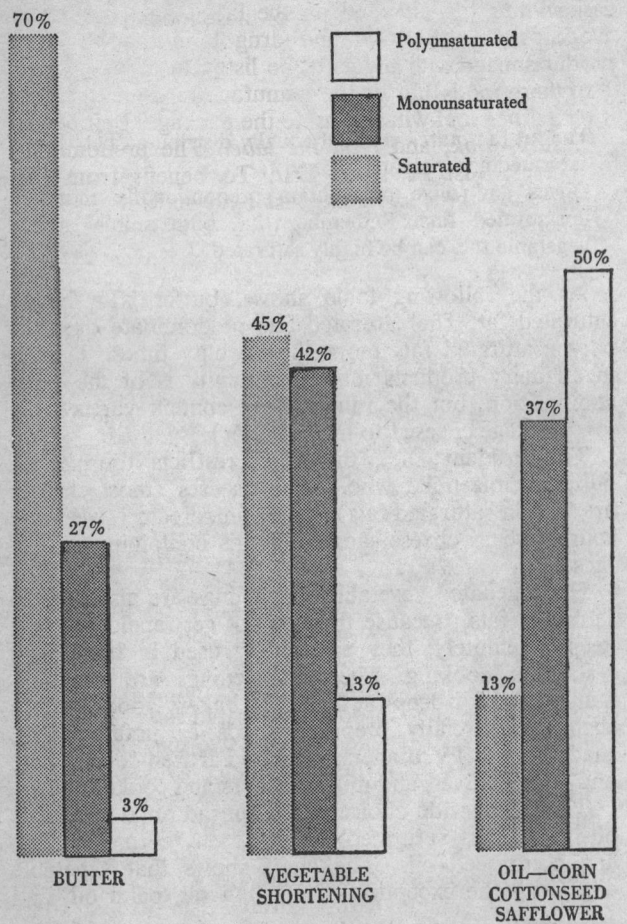

DISTRIBUTION OF FATTY ACIDS—FATS

sively in cooking in many countries known for superior cuisines.

Margarines are available in a wide range, from highly unsaturated to saturated types. Margarine should be selected for polyunsaturated fat content. The predominance of liquid vegetable oils over the hydrogenated portion will be indicated on the label, as required by the United States food and drug laws that make it mandatory for ingredients to be listed in order of their predominance—that is, the manufacturer is required to state on the label what is inside the package. Before you buy, *stop*, *look*, and *read the label*. The predominant ingredient must be listed *first*. To benefit from this information, the consumer must read and interpret the label correctly. The wife of an Anti-Coronary Club member reported that she stopped buying their favorite bread because butter was listed as an ingredient. When it was suggested that she read the label again, she found that butter was almost at the end of the list, denoting an insignificant amount; thus they could have the bread they preferred.

Margarines are not a substitute for vegetable oils. With few exceptions, vegetable oils contribute a larger amount of polyunsaturated fats to the diet than margarine does.

Since olive oil, predominantly a monounsaturated fat, and all other monounsaturated fats neither raise nor lower blood cholesterol, these are primarily a source of calories. If you wish to use olive oil for flavor, combine a small amount with a larger portion of a more highly unsaturated oil.

Most fish and shellfish are low in fat, but whatever fat is present is high in polyunsaturated fatty acids. The Prudent Diet recommends at least five meals of fish or shellfish a week. With the wide choice available, eating fish is a joy rather than a hardship to members of the Anti-Coronary Club. A survey shows that the most popular choices are flounder, halibut, herring, salmon, shellfish, sole, swordfish, and tuna.

Red meats are high in saturated fats, as the chart shows. These saturated fats comprise more than nine times the amount of polyunsaturated fats in these meats.

18 THE PRUDENT DIET

Because most Americans eat large amounts of red meat, these saturated fats contribute to their high blood cholesterol level.

To control blood cholesterol levels, we must eat less meat. The latest reports from the United States Department of Agriculture indicate that Americans consume about three pounds of these high-fat meats per week.

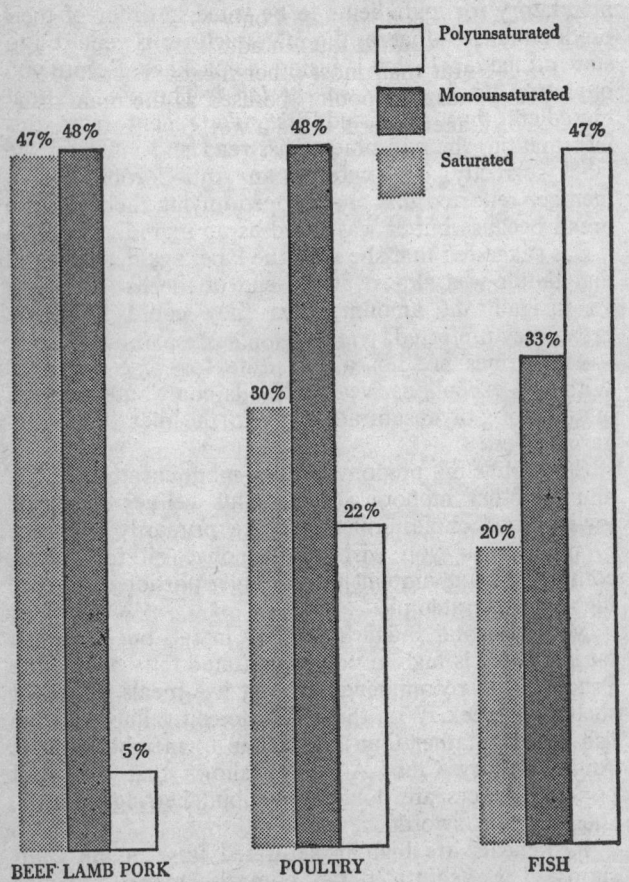

DISTRIBUTION OF FATTY ACIDS—PROTEIN FOODS

The Prudent Diet suggests one pound per week, but this amount of meat does not include veal and poultry. A serving of four ounces of cooked meat is recommended, which is an adequate serving for the athlete as well as the man behind the desk. Supplemented by potatoes, other vegetables, a salad, bread, and fruit, this will make a fully satisfactory meal.

Poultry has a more desirable composition of fats. The saturated fats predominate only to a minor extent over the polyunsaturated fats. In addition, poultry tends to be lower in fat than most other meats. The Prudent Diet recommends that poultry be used as the main dish for lunch or dinner several times a week.

THE NEED FOR PROTEIN

Many Americans have an exaggerated idea of their protein requirement. Just how much protein is needed? For the healthy adult, the National Research Council recommends about 1 gram of protein per kilogram of body weight. For an adult weighing 65 kilograms (about 156 pounds), 65 grams of protein daily would be satisfactory. This allowance includes approximately 50 percent above an amount estimated as sufficient for keeping body tissues in maintenance and repair. Considerations behind this wide margin are the individual variations in needs of normal persons and the variety of protein quality of their food. Protein requirements per kilogram of body weight are greater for children during periods of rapid growth and for pregnant and lactating women.

There are two kinds of protein foods: those from animal sources and those from vegetable sources. Not all protein foods are equivalent for growth and repair of body tissues. Those from animal sources (meat, eggs, fish, poultry, and milk) are individually the most efficient, but vegetable proteins (dried peas and beans, lentils, nuts, and such grain products as bread and cereals), when a variety are combined, can and do furnish a satisfactory source of protein.

A well-filled bread basket on the dinner table, a substantial lentil or split-pea soup will go a long way toward appeasing appetite and meeting protein requirements; also, these foods provide satisfaction when served with a small portion of animal food. This idea can be carried out as simply or as elegantly as you wish. Examples of such combinations are given in Part II.

Protein in the daily diet will be more than ample if it contains the amount of protein foods on the following list.

FOODS SUPPLYING PROTEIN DAILY FOR THE ADULT

FOOD	AMOUNT	PROTEIN (in grams) (average values)
meat	4 ounces (dinner)	28
fish or shellfish	3 ounces (lunch)	20
skim milk	2 cups (1 pint)	18
bread	4 slices	8
cereal	1 cup	4
Total for the day		78

Most diets will contain other sources of protein, such as vegetables, nuts, and cottage cheese. Protein over and above what the body needs for growth, repair, and maintenance is a source of calories only.

Experience with the Anti-Coronary Club has shown that men are usually perfectly contented with a modest portion of meat. Frequently it is a wife who must get used to the idea that by providing her husband with less meat than before, she is actually doing him a kindness.

IS IT HARD TO GET USED TO THE PRUDENT DIET? It is impossible to generalize about adjustment. The members of the Anti-Coronary study group who have interested wives seem to make the changes rapidly and without effort as have some others—bachelors and husbands who have always taken an active part in the kitchen. But there are also those who take many months to make all the desirable changes, and some who never keep to the diet effectively.

The majority of men in the study group enjoy eating fish and shellfish frequently, are satisfied with four eggs a week, get used to eating beef less frequently and in smaller portions, find that poultry can be cooked in many delicious ways, learn to enjoy veal, find polyunsaturated margarines no hardship, and like eating more bread and potatoes to meet their calorie requirements.

Many of these men, however, found it harder to get used to oil as a part of the daily diet (this is of major importance in order to achieve a desirable ratio of saturated to unsaturated fats), the use of oil to make foods taste better, eating enough green, leafy, or deep-yellow vegetables, establishing the habit of eating some citrus fruits daily, and consuming an adequate amount of skim milk.

Many popular foods are made with oil as a base—French, Italian, and Russian dressing, tartar sauce, and mayonnaise. Since eating a green salad each day is a good habit, this is a good way to add oil to the diet. Many other ways to use oil are included in Part II.

COMMON SENSE—THE MOST IMPORTANT INGREDIENT

What do most men who have adjusted well to this eating pattern have in common?

They understand the basic principles of the diet.
They recognize the wide food choices possible and make good use of the great flexibility that the diet offers.
They do not feel that they are dieting, but have made this new way of eating an enjoyable part of life.

No person leading a normal life can avoid occasionally eating foods considered undesirable on the Prudent

Diet. Even those who keep to it faithfully will sometimes deviate from the recommended pattern. Entertaining for business, socializing, and travel are among such occasions. But often it is possible to make wise selections—in a restaurant, for example. Even at someone's home, discretion can be used. Sometimes, of course, there is no choice. The wisest thing then is to accept the situation. An occasional lapse will not affect the benefits of the Prudent Diet.

While the Prudent Diet suggests avoiding, whenever possible, all the very fat meats (pastrami, salami, corned beef, and so on) and high-fat dairy products, common sense must guide you in setting the limits. There is a great difference between frequent consumption in large amounts and infrequent consumption in small amounts. A sliver of sausage on an hors d'oeuvre plate, or some grated cheese in a bowl of soup or a casserole hardly makes any difference. Several recipes in Part II contain some of these foods used with discretion.

4

The Mathematics of Reducing

*Make less thy body hence, and more thy grace.
Leave gormandizing. Know the grave doth gape
For thee thrice wider than for other men.*

SHAKESPEARE, Henry IV, Part Two,
Act V, Scene 5

Will the battle with obesity ever be won? Vast numbers of Americans are afflicted with excess body fat. Nearly everyone knows about its undesirable effects. Obesity is an important risk factor in heart attacks and strokes, peripheral vascular disease, diabetes, gallbladder disease, and a host of other ailments. While it is not fully understood just what role obesity plays in the development of disease, there is no doubt that it is a contributing factor to higher mortality rates.

Risks to health, however, are not the major concern to the obese person, as many studies have shown. None of the risks to health is as disturbing as the ungainly appearance; the double chin, "spare tire," and clothes that have become too tight. The obese person's self-esteem suffers. He or she easily falls prey to the "magic" of reducing diets. Innumerable fad diets have swamped the country. Each new one, no matter how absurd, has been accepted with enthusiasm by many persons desperately seeking a solution to their problem.

Americans spend untold millions yearly on "aids" to weight reduction, many of which are useless and even dangerous. There are diet pills (appetite curbers, tranquilizers, and stimulants), water pills (diuretics), hormones, and other medications, many of which are unscrupulously dispensed. Enormous industries thrive on the production of these and on the manufacture of equipment to get rid of undesired pounds. The promise of beauty and weight loss without restricting calories is a powerful incentive.

How is it possible, you may ask, for intelligent, educated people to be persuaded that if they eat enough of certain foods their body fat will melt away? In *The Hidden Persuaders*, Vance Packard suggests that women will buy promise and they will buy hope. Promise and hope may create a beautiful daydream, but it will contribute very little to success in weight control, where facing reality is the first important step.

Promoters of fad diets may use subtle means to imply that their diet plans stem from authentic, reputable sources. This may account for their tremendous following. Most diets are soon abandoned. Lost weight is promptly regained, and sometimes excess pounds are added. This seesawing of weight is considered by the medical profession to be more detrimental to health than being obese.

To most people the words "diet food" suggest few or no calories. However, the meaning of "diet food" is totally unspecific. A slice of "diet bread" furnishing only 50 calories compared to the usual 65 to 70 calories may just be sliced thinner than regular bread. "Diet ice cream" may be prepared with a sugar substitute that may be used by the body like sugar. Such ice creams contain about the same amount of fat as regular ice cream; therefore they have about the same number of calories. "Diet margarine" has a higher water content than other margarines. Just how much margarine do you eat daily? Surely not enough to save many calories. The "no-butter," "no-cholesterol," "no-animal fat" cream substitutes may contain saturated coconut or palm oil or hydrogenated fat just as undesirable as the cream that they replace. There is, of course, a need for commercial foods prepared without sugar, without salt, and without fat, for patients on various therapeutic diets. Properly labeled foods and better consumer education are the answer to misinformation.

Vitamins cannot make up for a faulty diet. The American public goes out in a big way for vitamins from the bottle. Many people with careless food habits derive false assurance from the fact that they are taking vitamins. Therapeutic or supplementary vitamins are valuable agents in the treatment and prevention of deficiency diseases but are strictly a physician's province.

A dietary study completed in 1968 by the United States Department of Agriculture indicates that nutrient deficiencies are common in this land of plenty. There has been a decline in the consumption of some foods essential to good health—milk, vegetables, and fruits. All income levels are affected. Obviously, since Americans as a nation have been getting fatter and fatter, we must be getting an abundance of calories from other sources. Consumption studies over the last fifty years provide the answers:

We have steadily increased our consumption of beef.
We eat more fat in baked goods—cakes, cookies, pastries, mixes, frozen prepared foods (not only high in fat but often of questionable nutrient content), and and astronomical amount of snack foods.
We consume formidable amounts of sugar, mostly in the form of candy, ice cream, and soft drinks.

However, many people today have become concerned about the quality of food. It will take the combined efforts of experts in nutrition, agriculture departments, and other governmental agencies, as well as business and the lay public, to work toward improvement in food and better health for all.

CAUSES OF OBESITY

Most obesity is caused by overeating; pathology accounts for only a few cases. A great deal of research has gone into learning why people overeat, and many possible reasons have been advanced. Eating is one of

America's greatest pleasures. An affluent society such as ours offers many inducements not always in keeping with our welfare. Certainly the unlimited supply of tempting foods available to almost everyone and widely advertised in all media contributes to the obesity problem.

Some of the causes attributed to obesity are: Food may be a solace in times of frustration, loneliness, and boredom. It may be used as a means to relieve tension, until eating has become a conditioned reflex action to any stress. Family eating patterns, often passed from one generation to the next, may be responsible.

Socio-economic levels may contribute—the higher the economic level, the lower the incidence of obesity.

Obese adolescents do not seem to eat so much more, but they are far less active than normal-weight children of their age group.

Obesity is a problem of all age groups. The fat baby almost certainly becomes the fat adolescent and the fat adult. To change a firmly established pattern of overeating becomes a lifelong struggle. Prevention should be the answer.

A person may lose, gain, or maintain his weight while following the Prudent Diet, depending on the kinds of foods and the amount he eats. This diet is ideally suited to weight reduction, for it includes all of the basic essentials of good nutrition, it emphasizes a well-balanced diet, it restricts the foods with high-fat and therefore high-calorie content (some meats, dairy products, and pastry), it encourages the use of low-fat protein foods (fish and shellfish, lean meats, cottage cheese, skim milk), it recommends the use of a wide variety of vegetables, and it suggests that fruits be the preferred dessert.

HOW TO ESTIMATE WEIGHT LOSS

Every weight loss is the result of a calorie deficit. When you eat fewer calories than you need to maintain your present weight, you create a calorie deficit. In every pound of body fat, about 3,500 calories are stored. To lose 1 pound of body weight, you must eat 3,500 calories fewer than are required to maintain your present weight.

For example: suppose you want to lose 10 pounds in 10 weeks. At present you consume 2,000 calories daily. When you reduce your calories intake by 500 calories a day, in 1 week you will have a calorie deficit of 3,500 calories. This is equivalent to the loss of 1 pound a week. By eating only 1,500 calories a day instead of the accustomed 2,000, over the 10-week period you will have created a calorie deficit of ten times 3,500 calories, or 35,000 calories.

This in essence is the principle of weight reduction.

ARE THERE ANY "FATTENING" FOODS?

All foods except water provide calories. Excess calories, regardless of origin, are stored as body fat. Therefore, foods cannot be called either fattening or non-fattening; but foods differ in the number of calories they

DIFFERENCES IN CALORIES BY WEIGHT

¼ pound beef (edible portion)	290 (average)
¼ pound chicken (edible portion)	220 (average)
¼ pound fish (edible portion)	160 (average)
8 ounces whole milk	160
8 ounces skim milk	90
1 tablespoon butter or margarine	100
1 tablespoon vegetable oil	125
1 ounce cream cheese	105
1 ounce cottage cheese	30
1 average slice pound cake (2 ounces or about 60 grams)	250
1 average slice bread (about 23 grams)	60
¼ pound fruit (edible portion)	85 (average)
¼ pound vegetables (edible portion)	25 (average)

DESIRABLE WEIGHTS
(Metropolitan Life Insurance Company)

Weight in Pounds According to Frame (In Indoor Clothing)

Men of Ages 25 and Over

HEIGHT (with shoes on, 1-inch heels) Feet	Inches	FRAME SMALL	MEDIUM	LARGE
5	2	112—120	118—129	126—141
5	3	115—123	121—133	129—144
5	4	118—126	124—136	132—148
5	5	121—129	127—139	135—152
5	6	124—133	130—143	138—156
5	7	128—137	134—147	142—161
5	8	132—141	138—152	147—166
5	9	136—145	142—156	151—170
5	10	140—150	146—160	155—174
5	11	144—154	150—165	159—179
6	0	148—158	154—170	164—184
6	1	152—162	158—175	168—189
6	2	156—167	162—180	173—194
6	3	160—171	167—185	178—199
6	4	164—175	172—190	182—204

Women of Ages 25 and Over
(For girls between 18 and 25, subtract 1 pound for each year under 25.)

HEIGHT (with shoes on, 1-inch heels) Feet	Inches	FRAME SMALL	MEDIUM	LARGE
4	10	92— 98	96—107	104—119
4	11	94—101	98—110	106—122
5	0	96—104	101—113	109—125
5	1	99—107	104—116	112—128
5	2	102—110	107—119	115—131
5	3	105—113	110—122	118—134
5	4	108—116	113—126	121—138
5	5	111—119	116—130	125—142
5	6	114—123	120—135	129—146
5	7	118—127	124—139	133—150
5	8	122—131	128—143	137—154
5	9	126—135	132—147	141—158
5	10	130—140	136—151	145—163
5	11	134—144	140—155	149—168
6	0	138—148	144—159	153—173

provide for a given weight. Highest in calories for their weight are fat-rich foods; next come concentrated carbohydrate foods (sugars and starches); lowest in calories for their weight are foods high in water such as most vegetables.

CALORIE NEEDS FOR OLDER PERSONS

Next to growth and activity, age has the greatest influence on calorie needs. From the time adulthood is reached, there is a steady decrease in calorie requirements to maintain desirable weight. If you do not eat less as you get older, you will gain weight.

Your nutritional needs, however, do not decline as you advance in age. An adequate intake of protein, minerals, and vitamins is necessary to maintain health and vigor. This means that as age increases, the calorie intake has to be budgeted more carefully, since there is less room for nonessentials. Check the Desirable Weights chart for the approximate weight for your sex and height. See chart Daily Calorie Allowances for Adults, which indicates decreasing calorie needs with advancing age for maintenance of weight.

DAILY CALORIE ALLOWANCES FOR ADULTS, ASSUMING LIGHT PHYSICAL ACTIVITY

Pounds	Calorie Allowance at Age		
	22	45	65
	MEN		
143	2650	2400	2200
154	2800	2600	2400
165	2950	2700	2500
	WOMEN		
110	1800	1650	1500
121	1950	1800	1650
132	2050	1900	1700

5

Food Groups for Key Nutrients

Nutritionists have developed food guides for help in planning adequate, nourishing meals. These guides may divide the foods into four, five, six or even seven groups. The information is basically the same since the grouping is determined by some essential nutrients that certain foods have in common. When detailed information is desired, the larger number of groups may be preferable. For use in a more general way, fewer groups will suffice.

Foods supplying one or more of these "KEY" nutrients are grouped together, offering choices within each group. Most foods contribute more than one nutrient and may be outstanding in several.

For a more thorough understanding of the functions of macro and micro-nutrients and their interrelationships, references are included in the bibliography.

1. FISH, MEAT, POULTRY, EGGS—*for Protein, Iron and B-vitamins*

   FISH AND SHELLFISH—*good sources of polyunsaturated fats*
   Choose any kind—fresh, canned, frozen, smoked and pickled.
   At least five times a week for any meal.

   MEATS—beef, lamb and pork.
   A maximum of 16 ounces per week.
   Serve 4-ounce portions of cooked meat.

FOOD GROUPS FOR KEY NUTRIENTS 31

  Veal—relatively lean (in addition to other meat).
  Poultry—all kinds—serve often.
  Liver, heart and kidney—excellent nutritive values—serve occasionally.
  Avoid, whenever possible, *very fat meats:* bacon, corned beef, pastrami, salami, sausage, others.

  EGGS—a good source of vitamin A.
  A maximum of 4 eggs per week for adults.
  4 to 7 eggs per week for children.

2. MILK AND DAIRY PRODUCTS—*for Calcium, Riboflavin, Protein*
  Skim or Low-fat Milk only for adults—1 pint daily. Any kind: fluid, nonfat dry, skimmed evaporated, buttermilk, yogurt.
  Whole Milk for Children—1 pint daily; any milk in excess of this should be skimmed or low-fat milk.
  Cottage, Pot and Farmer Cheese—low in fat and high in protein; use often.
  Whole Milk Cheeses (hard) such as cheddar, Swiss, munster and dessert-type cheeses—*not to exceed four ounces per week.*
  Avoid, whenever possible, *high-fat dairy products:* butter, sweet cream, sour cream, cream cheese, ice cream and foods containing them.

3. DARK GREEN, LEAFY AND DEEP YELLOW VEGETABLES—*for vitamin A*
  At least 3 to 4 servings per week.
  DARK GREEN, LEAFY: broccoli, chicory, collards, escarole, mustard greens, spinach, other greens—they are also good sources of vitamin C, iron and folacin (folic acid).
  DEEP YELLOW: carrots, pumpkin, sweet potatoes, winter squash.
  All vegetables contribute nutrients.
  Eat a variety of other vegetables daily, raw and cooked.
  Serve potatoes often.

4. FRUITS—*for vitamin C daily*
   Orange, orange juice, grapefruit juice, tomatoes, tomato juice, cantaloupe, strawberries, mangoes, papayas.
   Eat extra fruits daily besides one of the above.
   All fruits contribute nutrients.
   Fruits—*your best dessert.*

5. BREADS AND CEREALS *for B-vitamins, Iron, Calories*
   Eat whole grain or enriched bread or cereal at every meal.
   All breads and cereals contribute nutrients.
   Avoid, whenever possible, cakes, cookies, pastries —*high in saturated fats*.

6. VEGETABLE OILS, VERY SPECIAL SHORTENING (V.S.S.) AND MARGARINES *containing Polyunsaturated Fats*
   Vegetable oils: 2 tablespoons daily for adults. Use in salad dressings, cooking and baking.
   V.S.S. for fine cakes, cookies, pastries.
   Margarines for table spreads.
   Substitute vegetable oils and V.S.S. for other fats in food preparation.
   Avoid, whenever possible, butter, lard, hydrogenated cooking fats, margarines high in saturated fat, cream substitutes and foods containing them.

6
Summing Up

Dr. Norman Joliffe called the diet "prudent" because the word means sensible or wise. In brief, the Prudent Diet is a well-balanced diet, designed to promote positive health and to prolong the vigorous span of life.

The Prudent Diet recommends curtailing excessive intake of fat meats, high-fat dairy products, eggs, hydrogenated shortenings, and foods containing any of these ingredients; consuming more fish and shellfish; and substituting polyunsaturated vegetable oils and margarines for butter, lard, hydrogenated shortenings, and other saturated fats. The Prudent Diet advocates neither excessive use of nor complete omission of any one food.

The Prudent Diet fulfills all requirements for nutritional adequacy as recommended by the Food and Nutrition Board of the National Research Council.

PART TWO
The Prudent Diet in Practice

7

Planning Meals for Pleasure and Health

The advantages of the Prudent Diet are not only in reducing the risk of heart attacks and related diseases, but in helping you and your family feel younger, stronger, and more energetic. It can open up a whole new world of wonderful food. But its use demands an open mind, a spirit of adventure, a willingness to change food habits and notions rooted over a lifetime. It also involves a new approach to planning and preparing meals. In this part of the book we offer guidance when you set your feet on the new road.

THE PRUDENT DIET IS FOR THE WHOLE FAMILY

"I'd like a Prudent Diet for my father, he needs it," is a request we frequently get. But while father may need it most, the Prudent Diet is for all the family, including the children.

Good nutrition is a lifetime job. A woman who is well nourished has a better chance for a normal pregnancy and a healthy baby. The physical and mental health of a child, even before conception, is influenced by the nutritional state of his mother-to-be. The food he will eat is going to have a direct bearing on the way a child grows and develops. All through life we can protect our health by eating an adequate diet. The Prudent Diet may contribute to a longer life, but, perhaps more important, it increases the chances to live life more fully.

WHY BALANCE YOUR DIET?

Individual vitamins, minerals and essential amino acids (building blocks of protein) in food are responsible for specific vital functions. Fats and carbohydrates also play important roles. However, all nutrients depend on one another to perform their tasks; they participate in an intricate, interrelated system. Some nutrients provide the substances upon which others will act, and some are necessary to spark the reaction. Hence, a shortage of one essential dietary factor will impair the ability of others to function adequately. An overabundance of certain foodstuffs, such as saturated fat and refined carbohydrate (mainly sugar), may overtax the capacity of body mechanisms and interfere with various metabolic processes.

A well-balanced diet is one that provides all necessary nutrients in desirable amounts to keep the complex body machine functioning at its best potential. The theory behind such a diet is complicated; to follow it is simple.

The essential foods required for the Prudent Diet are listed in Chapter 5 in six groups. This list will guide you in creating meals that are varied and delicious in addition to being well balanced.

In simplified form, the requirements of the Prudent Diet are:

Daily: A high quality protein food with every meal
Milk and other dairy products
Vegetables high in vitamin A (three or four times a week)
Fruits for vitamin C
Whole grain or enriched breads and/or cereals
Vegetable oils high in polyunsaturated fat
See Food Groups for Key Nutrients.

In addition to the information given in Chapter 5,

here are some suggestions about using certain recommended foods.

Eggs

The Prudent Diet recommends not more than four eggs a week for adults and up to seven for children. Instead of always having an egg for breakfast, try having one two mornings a week, eating an egg-salad sandwich for lunch another day, and using the fourth in pancakes or a dessert. If you like a substantial breakfast, have a cottage-cheese omelet or increase a serving of scrambled eggs by adding an extra egg white. Since there is no fat in egg whites, they are not restricted on the Prudent Diet.

Milk

Everyone needs milk every day. Calcium-rich foods are important throughout one's lifetime for the development and maintenance of strong bones and teeth. Milk is our best source of calcium.

The daily recommendations are two cups (one pint) of whole milk for children and the same amount of skim milk or low-fat milk for adults. Young children frequently drink too much milk, crowding out other essential foods. Adolescent boys and young adult men also sometimes consume inordinate amounts of milk. Because of the high fat content of whole milk, it should be limited to one pint daily, even for children, with any additional milk in the form of skim milk or low-fat milk. Adults should avoid whole milk. Those who do not drink milk at mealtime should plan to take it regularly as a snack, with cereal, or as an ingredient of soup or dessert. Low-fat yogurt or buttermilk can be substituted for regular skim milk. All types of low-fat milks have approximately the same nutritive value. You can choose from fluid skim milk, evaporated skim milk, non-fat dry milk, buttermilk or yogurt.

Cheese

The low-fat cheeses—cottage, pot and farmer—are highly recommended. These are made from skim milk.

"Creamed" cottage cheese is also highly recommended; it too is made of skim milk to which whole milk or cream has been added in an amount so small that it does not count.

The cheese highest in fat is cream cheese, which is almost entirely fat. Dessert-type cheeses such as Camembert and "hard" cheeses like cheddar, Swiss, or Edam are also high in fat. Though some of these cheeses have skim milk listed as an ingredient, this does not mean that they are low in fat. If you like a "hard" cheese sandwich occasionally, it can be fitted into your diet, but the total amount of these cheeses should not exceed four ounces a week. Two ounces of high-fat cheese is an ample amount for a lunch or supper main dish. If your diet in general is low in foods containing saturated fats, a moderate amount of "hard" cheese has a place in your meals. Remember it is the total fat that matters.

Peanut Butter

A food that is high in vegetable protein, B vitamins, and unsaturated fat is peanut butter. "Less than 80 years ago, peanut butter was unknown. Today, it takes more than 500 million pounds yearly to satisfy American appetites. Ironically, it was created as a 'health food,' but it achieved its widespread popularity mainly because Americans like its flavor," wrote Morton E. Nitzburg, vice president of Peanut Associates, Inc., in "Peanut Butter ... and How It Spread" (*School Lunch Journal*, April 1967).

Among other interesting data this article cites a food industry survey which found peanut butter the No. 1 sandwich choice of children from 2 to 17 years of age.

Adults also like peanut butter. While primarily used as a sandwich spread, it is a good ingredient in cookies, breads, and other foods. Peanuts are usually regarded as nuts, but they belong in the category of mature dry legumes, along with beans, peas, and lentils—all good sources of vegetable protein.

MENUS TO VARY YOUR MEALS

"Fish for breakfast?"
"How about smoked salmon?"
"Oh, yes. But that's for Sunday!"

Habits can and do change. People can learn to enjoy different foods, even for breakfast. But not everybody is adventurous, especially early in the day.

Nevertheless, in adopting the Prudent Diet, you are making changes in your food habits. Why not take advantage of this fact to make your meals as interesting as possible? Whether you eat at home or in a restaurant, the recommended foods can be combined to make every meal of the day enjoyable as well as healthgiving. Use the menus in this chapter as a starting point; then put your own ingenuity to work at devising your own combinations.

Begin with breakfast. Even if the time allowed may be only a few minutes, you can concentrate on eye appeal, which is most important when appetites may not be at their height. Citrus fruit for breakfast is a good habit—but its serving need not be restricted to this time of day; it has a place in other meals. For breakfast there are pleasant alternatives—tomato juice, cantaloupe, strawberries, mangoes—all rich in vitamin C.

Luncheon choices are wide, whether the meal is eaten in a restaurant, at home, or from a lunch box. Entertaining and being entertained are a regular part of workaday business life. One can be a thoughtful host or a pleasant guest and still make prudent selections in an elegant restaurant or the corner coffee shop. Always plan to have a substantial lunch, wherever you eat; this will reduce the desire for between-meal snacks.

For the main meal, there are interesting and delectable ways to cook beef, veal, poultry, fish and shellfish; a variety of vegetables, likely to succeed with husband and children; and delicious desserts that also add their share of nutrients.

The same principles can be applied to "special" meals and those for important occasions.

42 THE PRUDENT DIET

Quick Daily Breakfasts

Orange juice, grapefruit juice, or tomato juice
One of these:
    ready-to-eat or cooked cereal with milk
    poached egg on toast
    cottage cheese or peanut butter, toast, marmalade

Special Breakfasts

Strawberries, Canadian bacon, scrambled egg, English muffin

Tomato juice, buttermilk pancakes,* maple syrup, applesauce

Cantaloupe, smoked salmon, thinly sliced onion, pumpernickel

Sliced tomatoes, herring in wine sauce, black olives, dark bread

Half grapefruit, creamed Finnan haddie* on toast, broiled tomatoes

Yogurt flavored with honey and coriander, fresh blueberries, Scandinavian bread wafers

Lunch at Home

Leftover vegetables with some fish, chicken or meat, combined to make an attractive salad

A small amount of cooked vegetable and some milk or broth—put into a blender to make a good bowl of soup

Cottage-cheese omelet* with stewed tomatoes

Ice-cold yogurt soup (Tarator*) for a hot day

A sandwich—see suggestions under The Lunch You Carry or Lunch in the Coffee Shop

The Lunch You Carry

If you take your lunch to the office or to school, the sandwich is your best bet. Vary the fillings and use different kinds of bread, vegetables, and fruits. Good choices are chicken, turkey, ham, hard-cooked egg, Swiss cheese, peanut butter with jelly, thinly sliced onion or green papper. Or take a small can of tuna,

---

An asterisk (*) indicates that the recipe is given in the following chapters; see index.

salmon, or sardines, a wedge of lemon, and some bread, not forgetting the can opener.

Carry vegetables that will stay crisp—cherry tomatoes, carrot sticks, celery, green pepper strips—and fruit that is ripe but firm—apple, pear, peach, banana, tangerine. A crisp homemade cookie also carries well.

Taking your lunch saves money and assures a well-planned meal.

SNACKS

Growing children and some adults need nourishing snacks between meals. Keep on hand: fresh and dried fruit, fruit juice, tomato juice, raw vegetables, skim or low-fat milk, buttermilk, yogurt, cottage cheese, peanut butter, nuts, peanuts, bread (an extra loaf in the freezer).

LUNCH IN THE COFFEE SHOP

APPETIZERS: tomato juice, fruit cup, raw vegetable salad

SOUPS: consomme, clam broth, vegetable soup, Manhattan clam chowder

SANDWICHES: chicken, turkey, ham, lean roast beef, tuna, salmon, sardine, sliced egg, American or Swiss cheese, peanut butter

SALADS: shrimp, hard-cooked egg, tuna, salmon, sardine, served with lettuce, tomatoes, mayonnaise; cottage cheese with fruit

DESSERTS: sherbet, Italian ice, gelatin, fruit

BEVERAGES coffee or tea, with milk if desired; skim milk, buttermilk, yogurt

FAMILY DINNERS WITH FLAIR

Pot roast*
Oven roast potatoes*
Green beans vinaigrette*
Fresh fruit salad

Lentil soup*
Shrimp salad on crisp greens

French bread*
Stewed apricots, homemade cookies

Roast chicken
Sweet potato and apple casserole*
Boston lettuce, French dressing
Fruit gelatin

London broil*
Baked potatoes
Tossed green salad
Orange sponge cake*

Chicken Teri-Yaki*
Sautéed broccoli*
Steamed rice
Sliced oranges

Lemon-broiled swordfish*
Tartar sauce*
Broiled tomatoes
Corn on the cob
Cantaloupe

Veal and chicken liver loaf*
Cauliflower with cream sauce
Watercress and beet salad*
Lemon sherbet*

SPECIAL DINNER MENUS

Fresh asparagus, Hollandaise*
Chinese braised chicken with mushrooms*
Steamed rice
Raw, tender spinach and Belgian endive with French Dressing*
Raspberry sherbet

Melon
Lamb and vegetables in casserole*
Romaine lettuce salad
Hot blueberry tarts*

PLANNING MEALS FOR PLEASURE AND HEALTH 45

SUMMERTIME SUPPER

Watercress and potato soup*
Cold poached salmon* with mayonnaise*
Avocado and tomato salad
Fresh fruit, Italian macaroons*

HOLIDAY BUFFETS

Caviar
Cucumber slices
Thin pumpernickel strips

Smoked turkey
Roast rump of veal
Cauliflower and peas,* mayonnaise*
Strawberry tart*

Stuffed cherry tomatoes*

Baked ham
Herbed potato casserole*
Salad of roasted peppers*

Frankfurt filbert torte*
Fruit bowl

To enjoy your own party, plan food that can be ready ahead of time—no last minute preparations for the hostess.

A salad of cooked vegetables will stand up well.

Raw vegetable garnishes can provide extra color and crispness.

Appoint a skilled hand to do the carving. (An electric knife helps to cut thin, attractive slices of meat and poultry.)

DINNER OR LUNCH IN A RESTAURANT

APPETIZERS

Melon, half grapefruit, fresh fruit cup, vegetable juices, fruit juices
Smoked salmon, sturgeon, caviar, oysters or clams on half shell

Herring in wine sauce, seafood cocktail
Artichokes, leeks vinaigrette, roasted peppers in oil, marinated eggplant
Radishes, scallions, olives

Soups

Consommé, clam broth, Manhattan clam chowder, bouillabaisse, gazpacho

Entrées

Fish or shellfish, broiled, baked, or poached, with tartar sauce or mayonnaise
Chicken, Cornish hen, squab, turkey, duckling, roasted or broiled
Roast veal, broiled fillet of beef, London broil
Roast leg of lamb, shish kebab
Fresh vegetables without sauce
Tossed green salad with French or Italian dressing

Desserts

Fresh berries, melon, fresh fruit salad, compote
Italian ices, sherbet, fruit gelatin
Sponge or angel food cake, almond macaroons
Liqueur or brandy

Beverages

Coffee, tea
Wine, beer, cocktails, liqueur

FOODS TO SKIP WHEN EATING OUT

Pâté, cream cheese, sour cream dips, spreads and toppings, sausage
Cream soups
Fried foods
Stuffings, casserole combinations, dishes made with cheeses and high in fat
Sauces and gravies
Biscuits, rich muffins, sweet rolls
Pies, pastry, cakes other than sponge or angel food
Puddings, ice cream, whipped cream, sweet and sour cream

8

Basic Information for the Prudent Diet

GREAT, YET INEXPENSIVE KICHEN HELPERS

Electric blenders, choppers, grinders, and mixers are nice to have. Studies show that owners don't use them as often as they might. Why? Who knows for sure? Based on our experience we guess that you, like us, prefer to handle small equipment that is easy to wash and easy to store. We are sure you will enjoy the great little kitchen helpers on this list.

THE STEAM-VENTED LID: the best dollar (or so) purchase you ever made; it is sold under several different names. After you try it, you will wonder how you ever did without it. We predict it will even accompany you on vacation when you plan to do your own cooking. These are some of the advantages in store for you:

Food will sauté in less time.

With less fat you get better browning and crisping.

Food will stay hot longer.

Prevents spattering stove, wall, and cook.

THE TIMER (minute minder): go about your business, it will call you when your chicken in the oven should be ready.

THE WIRE WHISK: for whipping up mayonnaise, Hollandaise and other sauces in a jiffy.

THE PEPPER MILL: freshly ground pepper, what a difference!

THE MOULI GRINDER: for nuts ground fine and fluffy without effort.

THE MOULI PARSLEY MINCER: fresh parsley is so good in many dishes—ready for you in minutes.

THE VEGETABLE PEELER: maybe you still peel potatoes with a knife. Break the habit and use the vegetable peeler; it is also good for scraping carrots, coring apples, scooping seeds from squash and shaving off thin lemon peel for drinks.

THE TWO-TINED FORK: there are still cooks who don't know what a big help a two-tined fork is.

THE SIX-PRONGED FORK: this odd-shaped fork does a good and fast job of mashing vegetables, especially for soup.

THE FRENCH VEGETABLE STEAMER BASKET: if you enjoy the taste of fresh vegetables and an easy way to prepare them.

INDIVIDUAL OVENWARE SERVING DISHES: Since Iva gave Martha a set of these, they have been working overtime. They are unsurpassed for baked fish, shellfish, and *au gratin* dishes. Food stays hot; it goes from oven to table.

A GOOD CORKSCREW: can save the day.

YOU SHOULD ALSO HAVE: a good knife sharpener; a serrated knife for bread—and one for tomatoes; a baster—also useful to withdraw fat-free liquids when making gravy and soups; a food mill; a lemon squeezer; accurate measuring spoons and cups; at least *one* measuring cup with a good pouring spout.

CHECK YOUR MEASURING KNOW-HOW

One cup in a recipe or food table means an 8-ounce fluid standard measuring cup. An ounce usually refers to a weight measure unless indicated that a fluid (volume) is meant.

EQUIVALENTS BY WEIGHT

1 pound (16 ounces)	—	453.6 grams
1 ounce	—	28.3 grams
3½ ounces	—	100.0 grams

BASIC INFORMATION FOR THE PRUDENT DIET

EQUIVALENTS BY VOLUME
(all measurements level)

1 quart	—	4 cups
1 cup	—	8 fluid ounces
	—	½ pint
	—	16 tablespoons
1 fluid ounce	—	2 tablespoons
1 tablespoon	—	3 teaspoons

HOW MUCH TO BUY

EQUIVALENTS BY WEIGHT
OF 1 CUP OF SOME COMMON FOODS
(easy to multiply or divide)

FOOD	CUP	OUNCES	GRAMS
Milk	1	8.6	244
Dry Milk Powder, varies with the type	1	2.4 to 3.7	68 to 104
Cottage Cheese	1	8.0	225
Hard Cheese, grated	1	4.0	112
Margarine, Butter (2 sticks)	1	8.0	224
V.S.S. (Very Special Shortening)	1	8.0	224
Oil	1	7.8	220
Peanut Butter	1	9.1	258
Flour, all-purpose, sifted	1	3.9	110
Starch, cornstarch, arrowroot, stirred before measuring	1	4.5	128
Rice, white, raw	1	6.8	191
Rice, wild, raw	1	5.8	163
Farina, raw	1	6.0	169
Cornmeal, dry	1	5.1	145
Barley, pearl, dry	1	7.2	203
Oatmeal, dry	1	2.8	80
Macaroni, dry (2" pieces)	1	3.0	86
Noodles, dry	1	2.6	73
Beans, dry seeds	1	6.8	190
Peas, dry seeds	1	7.1	200

FOOD	CUP	OUNCES	GRAMS
Chickpeas, dry whole seeds	1	7.4	210
Peanuts, roasted, shelled, medium halves	1	5.1	144
Almonds, shelled	1	5.0	142
Walnuts, shelled, halves	1	3.5	100
Walnuts, shelled, chopped	1	4.5	128
Dates, dried, pitted, cut	1	6.3	178
Apricot halves, dried	1	5.7	162
Prunes, dried with pits	1	5.8	165
Raisins, dried	1	5.7	160
Berries, fresh, average	1	4.9	140
Sugar, granulated	1	7.1	200
Sugar, brown, firmly packed	1	7.8	220
Sugar, powdered (confectioners), stirred before measuring	1	4.5	128
Honey	1	11.9	338
Molasses	1	11.5	325
Syrup	1	11.6	328
Cocoa, dry powder, stirred before measuring	1	4.0	112

WHAT TO KNOW ABOUT FRYING

Use vegetable oils rich in polyunsaturated fat for pan frying and deep frying; corn oil, cottonseed oil, and soy bean oil are all good.

Preserve the desirable qualities of the oil—avoid over-heating; never let it reach the smoking point.

Reheating changes oil to its disadvantage, therefore do not re-use it more than once.

Oil in which fish has been fried absorbs fish flavor; if used again, use it only for fish.

Frying increases the calories in food in direct relation to the amount of fat incorporated. Both type and surface area of food are factors in fat absorption. For instance, potatoes absorb much fat in frying and the more surface there is, as in potato chips, the more fat will be absorbed and the calories increased.

COMPARE CALORIE DIFFERENCES

100 grams (3½ ounces) potato, baked in skin   93 calories
100 grams (3½ ounces) French fried potatoes   274 calories
100 grams (3½ ounces) potato chips   568 calories

A heavy breading absorbs more fat than a light one.

The amount of fat absorbed in deep frying may be less than that absorbed in pan frying.

Fish or chicken, lightly floured or crumbed, does not use much fat when deep fried. Convince yourself: next time you fry a batch, measure oil before and remaining oil after frying. You may be surprised at the small quantity used.

Some foods are most delicious when fried well; enjoy them.

REGARDING RECIPES

Milk in recipes means *fat-free* or *low-fat milk*.

Margarine in recipes means *polyunsaturated* margarine.

When a choice of V.S.S. or margarine is offered, *V.S.S. is preferable*.

When safflower oil is suggested, it is because of its lightness and because it contributes no flavor of its own; this makes it very suitable for delicate cakes, cookies, and desserts.

Instant-blending flour does a special job when meat, fish, or other foods are dusted with flour before browning.

BAKING TIPS

We like unbleached flour for all of our baking.

Cakes containing fruit are apt to stick—grease pan and line with wax paper or use baking paper, in which case there is no need to grease the pan. Silicone-treated baking paper (parchment) is a boon. Cookies and cake will never stick.

Store every kind of cookie separately to keep soft ones soft and the crisp ones crisp. Put wax paper or plastic wrap between the layers. Store in a box or jar with a tight cover. Most of them will keep fresh for several weeks in the refrigerator.

VERY SPECIAL SHORTENING (V.S.S.)

Some of the favorite recipes in every cook's repertory —especially for delicate cakes, cookies, and pastries— depend on the creaming of fat, which cannot be achieved with oil. And margarines, we found, are not a satisfactory substitute.

Our attempts to get a fat for the Prudent Diet that would be high in polyunsaturated fat, cream readily, and be excellent in taste and texture resulted in our VERY SPECIAL SHORTENING (V.S.S.).

V.S.S. also proved to have other advantages. It gives that melt-in-the-mouth quality and fresh flavor to the baked product. It can be used in many different ways. V.S.S. will stay fresh for a long period of time when refrigerated and indefinitely when frozen. It is easy to handle and takes only minutes to prepare. Ingredients are readily available and inexpensive.

Substitute V.S.S. in direct proportion for solid shortening in any recipe.

1/2 pound (2 sticks) margarine, preferably unsalted

2/3 cup safflower oil
2 tablespoons cold water

1. Cream margarine well with an electric beater.
2. Very gradually beat in oil and water, alternately. Beat until thoroughly blended.
3. Place in a container, cover tightly, and refrigerate.

NOTE: This is a soft product when first made; it firms up slightly on standing. It is best to make it several days before you plan to use it.

YIELD: about 1-3/4 cups

PRUDENT YOGURT

For this yogurt less water is used in proportion to nonfat dry milk than when making fluid skim milk. This produces a more concentrated product.

nonfat dry milk, enough for 1 quart of milk
3 cups water only
1/4 cup commercial yogurt

1. Mix nonfat dry milk and water; slowly bring to the boiling point; then cool to lukewarm.
2. Thin out yogurt by adding about 1/2 cup of the lukewarm milk; stir well to make it smooth.
3. Add yogurt mixture to remaining milk and blend thoroughly.
4. Pour into serving-size cups; cover them with a towel.
5. Leave undisturbed for 5 to 6 hours, free from drafts and jolts.
6. Refrigerate after yogurt solidifies.
7. Save some yogurt to start a new batch. Occasionally start again with 1/4 cup commercial yogurt.

YIELD: about 3 cups

PRUDENT SOUR CREAM
A blender recipe

2 tablespoons lemon juice
3 tablespoons milk or buttermilk
1 cup (8 ounces) cottage cheese

1. Put lemon juice and milk in the blender.
2. While at low speed, gradually add cottage cheese. Change to high speed and blend for about 2 minutes.
3. Keep refrigerated in a covered jar.

If on standing "sour cream" becomes too thick thin it with milk or buttermilk to desired consistency.

YIELD: about 1-1/3 cups

9
Cocktailers and Hors d'Oeuvre

Smoked turkey, tiny mackerel in oil from Portugal, roasted peppers, Greek olives—all will delight your guests. In place of the usual party fare laden with saturated fat, you can serve your own flaky cocktail wafers, flavored with Roquefort cheese, curry, or peanut butter. The dough for these can be frozen, then wafers sliced and baked at your convenience; they are inexpensive, too.

In our experimenting, we have discovered some amazingly fine things to eat, adding interest to cocktailers—easy-to-eat finger foods to accompany a drink, and hors d'oeuvre to be served at the table as a first course.

COCKTAILERS
A descriptive word we lifted from Cocktailer Receipts

For the social hour before dinner—with sherry, cocktail, or apéritif—crisp sesame seed wafers, freshly roasted almonds Near East style, and stuffed cherry tomatoes may be sufficient. But when you invite a guest for cocktails, chances are you want a generous selection of both light and substantial accompaniments that are attractive, delicious, and unusual. You will find them in the following pages, from Chinese shrimp balls, onion quiche, and pizza to chilled cinnamon orange sections.

COCKTAILERS AND HORS D'OEUVRE

All your own favorite recipes can be adapted successfully to the Prudent Diet. When you use V.S.S., (Very Special Shortening, see page 52) you may discover that the quality of your homemade baking is better than ever. Spreads and dips made with yogurt and your own mayonnaise will have fresh appeal.

IN PLACE OF COMMERCIAL CRACKERS AND POTATO CHIPS USE:

Melba toast
Rye Crisp
Pretzels
Matzos
Italian bread sticks
Our own Special Cocktail Wafers

Fresh toast triangles
Crisp French bread
Scandinavian, rye, and whole wheat wafers

ALWAYS A GOOD CHOICE FOR CANAPES:

Smoked salmon   Anchovies   Smoked turkey
Smoked eel   Smoked whitefish Sardines
Caviar   Smoked cod liver

RAW VEGETABLES ADD FRESHNESS, FLAVOR, COLOR, AND CRISPNESS; THEY ALSO MAKE GOOD "DIPPERS"

Cauliflower buds   Thin slices of carrots, cucumbers,
Celery stalks   white and yellow turnip
Anise-flavored fennel

FRESH FRUITS:

Apple wedges   Cherries   Cinnamon Orange wedges
Melon balls   Kumquats   Fresh Pineapple cubes

HOT ROASTED CHESTNUTS

Very popular—serve with apértif wine. Allow 3 or 4 for a serving.

For good roasting, chestnuts must be fresh and of good quality. Rinse chestnuts, but do not dry. Cut a gash into the flat side of the shell. Put an asbestos plate on a burner of the stove. Place chestnuts on it and cover with a Pyrex bowl or heavy pan. Start roasting them at medium flame for about 5 minutes, then turn flame lower. Turn chestnuts after about 10 minutes and roast the other side for the same length of time.

ROASTED ALMONDS NEAR EAST

Preheat oven to 350°F. Put unblanched almonds on a baking sheet. Sprinkle with water and very lightly with salt. Roast for 15 to 25 minutes. The only way to tell if they are ready is to taste one.

SPREADS FOR CANAPES AND FILLINGS FOR PUFFS

Blend the following mixtures well. They may be made ahead of time. Flavors improve with "ripening." Store in the refrigerator.

CHEESE DILL AND CURRY SPREAD

- 1 cup pot or dry cottage cheese, sieved
- 2 tablespoons mayonnaise
- 1 tablespoon chopped fresh dill
- 1/4 teaspoon dry mustard
- 1/2 teaspoon curry powder

LIPTAUER CHEESE
From Czechoslovakia

- 1 cup pot or dry cottage cheese, sieved
- 4 tablespoons V. S. S. or margarine, creamed
- 1 inch anchovy paste
- 1 teaspoon grated onion
- 1 teaspoon paprika

ROQUEFORT WALNUT SPREAD

- 1 cup pot or dry cottage cheese, sieved
- 3 tablespoons Roquefort cheese, mashed well
- 4 tablespoons V. S. S. or margarine, creamed
- 1/4 teaspoon Worcestershire sauce
- 4 tablespoons chopped walnuts

HAM SPREAD

- 1-1/2 cups (about 1/2 pound) ham, baked or boiled, finely chopped
- 2 tablespoons relish or chopped gherkins
- 1 teaspoon dry mustard
- 2 to 3 tablespoons mayonnaise

CHICKEN OR TURKEY ALMOND SPREAD

- 1-1/2 cups cooked chicken, chopped
- 1/2 cup roasted almonds, chopped
- 1/2 cup chopped celery
- 1/2 teaspoon salt
- 3 to 4 tablespoons mayonnaise

CHICKEN WALNUT SPREAD

- 1-1/2 cups (approximately 1/2 pound) cooked chicken, chopped
- 1/2 cup chopped walnuts
- 1/2 teaspoon salt
- 2 tablespoons relish
- 2 to 3 tablespoons mayonnaise

TUNA OLIVE SPREAD

- 1 7-ounce can tuna, well mashed
- 1/2 cup stuffed olives, chopped
- 1 teaspoon grated onion
- few drops lemon juice
- 3 tablespoons mayonnaise

SHRIMP OR CRABMEAT SPREAD

- 1-1/2 cups boiled shrimp, or fresh or canned crabmeat, finely ground
- 2 tablespoons chopped gherkins
- salt, if needed
- 2 to 3 tablespoons mayonnaise
- a little chopped parsley

STUFFED CHERRY TOMATOES
Tasty, refreshing and decorative

1. Cut cherry tomatoes in half crosswise.
2. Press the halves gently to shake out the seeds. This is best done over the sink—it is easy to do.
3. Stuff the tomatoes with any of the preceding spreads or fillings, mounding slightly.

YOGURT DIP
From Greece

- 1 clove garlic, peeled
- 2 tablespoons chopped walnut meats
- 1 teaspoon oil
- 1 cup yogurt
- 2 tablespoons cucumber, peeled and finely cubed

1. Mash (finely) walnuts and garlic with oil in mortar or bowl.
2. Add yogurt and cucumber and chill.

CHICKEN LIVER PATÉ
A blender recipe

1/2 pound chicken livers	2 tablespoons sherry or brandy
1/3 cup margarine, softened	1/2 teaspoon salt
1/2 small onion, finely minced	1/2 teaspoon prepared mustard
	pinch of nutmeg
	pinch of allspice

1. In a small saucepan cover chicken livers with water, bring to a boil and simmer 7 to 10 minutes; drain.
2. Cut livers into pieces and put in blender together with other ingredients. Blend until smooth.
3. Chill. Serve with melba toast or fresh toast triangles.

FRESH HORSERADISH–PEANUT BUTTER SPREAD

1/3 cup freshly grated horseradish	1/2 cup peanut butter
1 tablespoon white vinegar	3 tablespoons skimmed evaporated milk
	salt and pepper

1. Mix horseradish with vinegar, combine with peanut butter and skimmed evaporated milk.
2. Beat until smooth. Season to taste with salt and pepper.

NOTE: Prepared horseradish can be used; drain off excess moisture, omit vinegar and proceed as above.

YIELD: about 1 cup

COCKTAIL WAFERS

V.S.S. makes a superior product but margarine may be used. Unsalted margarine is recommended. If you use salted margarine, omit salt from recipes.

PEANUT BUTTER CURRY WAFERS

- 1 cup sifted flour
- 1/2 teaspoon salt
- 1/2 teaspoon curry powder
- 1/2 cup V.S.S. or margarine (1 stick)
- 3 tablespoons peanut butter
- 3 tablespoons cottage cheese
- 1 egg yolk, 1 tablespoon water (to brush top)

1. Sift flour with salt and curry powder.
2. Cream V.S.S. with peanut butter and cottage cheese; combine lightly but thoroughly with flour mixture.
3. Form into a roll about 1-1/2 inches in diameter and wrap in foil or freezing paper. Chill several hours or until firm. This dough may be made ahead of time and kept in the freezer.
4. When ready to bake, preheat oven to 350°F. With a sharp knife, cut roll of dough into thin slices. Cut only a small portion at a time and keep remainder of roll chilled.
5. Place slices on an ungreased or baking paper-lined cookie sheet.
6. Brush slices with egg wash (egg yolk mixed with water). Sprinkle with your favorite seeds—caraway, celery, poppy, or dill.
7. Bake about 10 minutes or until lightly browned.

NOTE: These are good hot or cold. If kept tightly covered and cool, they will stay fresh several weeks. Wafers may be reheated before serving.

YIELD: about several dozen wafers

COCKTAILERS AND HORS D'OEUVRE 61

ANCHOVY WAFERS

1/2 cup pot cheese or dry cottage cheese
2 tablespoons good anchovy paste
1/2 cup V.S.S. or margarine (1 stick)
1 cup sifted flour
1 egg yolk, 1 tablespoon water (to brush top)
celery or poppy seeds

1. Mash pot cheese well with a fork; mix with anchovy paste.
2. Cream V.S.S. with pot cheese mixture.
3. Combine with flour lightly but thoroughly. Depending on moisture of cheese, some extra flour, 2 to 4 tablespoons, may be needed.
4. Form into a roll, about 1-1/2 inches in diameter; wrap in foil or freezing paper. Chill several hours or until firm.
5. For baking instructions follow Peanut Butter Curry Wafer recipe. Use celery or poppy seeds to sprinkle on top before baking.

YIELD: about several dozen wafers

ROQUEFORT CHEESE WAFERS

1 cup sifted flour
1/2 teaspoon salt
1/4 teaspoon pepper
3 tablespoons Roquefort cheese
3 drops Worcestershire sauce
3 tablespoons cottage cheese
1/2 cup V.S.S. or margarine (1 stick)
1 egg yolk, 1 tablespoon water (to brush top)
caraway seeds

1. Sift flour with salt and pepper.
2. Mash Roquefort cheese well with a fork; add Worcestershire sauce and cottage cheese, mixing well.
3. Cream V.S.S. with Roquefort and cottage cheese mixture; combine lightly but thoroughly with flour mixture.

4. Form into a roll about 1-1/2 inches in diameter; wrap in foil or freezing paper. Chill several hours or until firm. This dough may be made ahead of time and kept in the freezer.

5. For baking instructions follow Peanut Butter Curry Wafer recipe. Sprinkle caraway seeds on top before baking.

YIELD: about several dozen wafers

SESAME SEED WAFERS
Adapted from "Charleston Receipts"

1 cup sesame seeds
2 cups sifted flour
1 teaspoon salt
dash of cayenne
2/3 cup V.S.S. or margarine
5 to 6 tablespoons ice water

1. Brown sesame seeds lightly in a dry pan over low heat, stirring as they brown.

2. Sift together the flour, salt, and cayenne.

3. Cut fat into flour mixture until it resembles coarse cornmeal.

4. Add water, a spoonful at a time, until mixture is moistened enough to hold together. Add sesame seeds and work lightly with hands until smooth.

5. Shape into rolls about 2 inches in diameter. Wrap in foil or freezing paper and chill, preferably in the freezer, until firm or ready to use.

6. When ready to bake, preheat oven to 350°F.

7. With a sharp knife, cut rolls into thin slices and bake on ungreased or baking paper-lined baking sheet for 15 to 20 minutes or until lightly browned.

8. Sprinkle lightly with salt and cool on a rack.

NOTE: If placed in a tightly covered jar or box, and kept cool, wafers will keep fresh for several weeks. They can be reheated before serving and are also good cold.

YIELD: about several dozen wafers

SESAME BISCUITS

1/2 cup sesame seeds
2 cups sifted flour
1 teaspoon baking powder
1/2 teaspoon salt
1/4 cup (1/2 stick) margarine
1/4 cup safflower oil
1/4 cup cold milk
coarse salt

1. Toast sesame seeds until light brown in a pie pan in a 350°F. oven. Allow them to cool.
2. Sift flour with baking powder and salt. Cut margarine into flour mixture until it resembles coarse cornmeal. Mix in the sesame seeds.
3. Pour oil and milk into a cup; beat with a fork until thickened and creamy. Pour all at once over flour mixture.
4. Mix with a fork until dough forms a ball; divide in half to roll out in two batches; chill.
5. Roll out chilled pastry very thin (1/8 inch) between two sheets of wax paper. With pastry wheel or sharp knife cut into 1-1/2-inch squares. Arrange squares on an ungreased baking sheet and bake at 400°F. about 15 minutes.
6. While hot sprinkle very lightly with coarse salt.

COCKTAIL PUFFS

Delicious, attractive, versatile, easy and fun to make. They are equally good baked or fried. All of the spreads and fillings listed in this chapter are good to use in these little puffs. They also make a fine luncheon dish, served with creamed fish, shellfish, poultry, or mushrooms.

1/2 cup water
3 tablespoons oil (preferably safflower)
1/2 cup sifted flour
pinch of salt
2 eggs
1 tablespoon Parmesan cheese (optional)

1. In a small saucepan heat water and oil to the boiling point. Add flour and salt—all at once.
2. Cook, stirring, for a few minutes, until the mixture leaves the sides of the pan and balls together. Remove from stove.
3. Into the mixture beat one egg right away, incorporating it thoroughly, then add the second egg and mix well. Stir in the cheese. At this point, the mixture may be refrigerated until you wish to bake the puffs.
4. When ready to bake, preheat oven to 425°F.
5. With two teaspoons, shape small puffs. Place them 2 inches apart on an ungreased baking sheet or on baking sheet lined with baking paper.
6. Bake puffs for about 20 minutes. They will be golden brown, crisp and double in size. DO NOT open the oven door for the first 10 minutes to see how they are coming.
7. To make sure they are fully baked, open one puff before removing them from the oven to check if they need a few more minutes' baking time.
8. Slash puffs with a sharp knife and return them to the turned-off oven for about 10 minutes, to completely dry out. Leave the oven door ajar.

NOTE: The baked puffs may be reheated in a moderate oven. Fill just before serving.

Fried Puffs

When puffs are fried, they need plenty of room in the pan as they expand more than the baked puffs. See What to Know about Frying, Chapter 8.

Dessert Puffs

Use the same basic recipe, but omit cheese and in place of salt add 2 teaspoons of sugar. These puffs should be baked only (not fried). Use Bee Sting Cake vanilla cream filling and icing as for Swedish Tea Ring.

YIELD: about 36 tiny cream puffs

PIZZA

1 package dried yeast	Famous Pizza Filling (see following recipe)
1-2/3 cups lukewarm water	
3 tablespoons oil	1/2 cup grated Romano or Parmesan cheese
4 cups sifted flour	
1 teaspoon salt	

1. Dissolve yeast in lukewarm water; add oil.
2. Sift together flour and salt into a bowl. Add yeast mixture and combine well. Turn onto a floured board; knead until smooth.
3. Put dough into a bowl and cover with a towel. Let rise until double in bulk and light (about 2 hours). At this point, dough can be punched down, refrigerated for a day or two or frozen for future use.
4. Punch down and let rise again until light. Preheat oven to 400°F.
5. Oil 2 pizza pans. Punch down dough, roll, pat and fit into pans.
6. Spread Famous Pizza Filling on top. Do not allow to rise. Sprinkle filling with cheese.
7. Bake until crust is golden brown, 20 to 25 minutes. Serve hot.

YIELD: two 14-to-16-inch pizzas

FAMOUS PIZZA FILLING
Adapted from Mama Mia Cookbook

2 medium onions, sliced thin	1 6-ounce can tomato paste
1/4 cup oil	3 cups water
1 2-ounce can anchovy fillets	pepper to taste
	1 teaspoon oregano

1. Sauté onions in oil until lightly brown, stirring occasionally.
2. Add anchovies and oil from the can. Stir until

anchovies are reduced to a purée (takes just a few minutes).

3. Add tomato paste and water; stir until well blended. Add pepper and oregano.

4. Simmer uncovered until mixture is the consistency of a thick sauce, stirring occasionally. This will take about one hour.

ONION AND SMOKED SALMON QUICHE

CRUST

Use 1/3 recipe for the dough for Pizza (see page 65) or a regular one-crust pie recipe.

FILLING

- 1 pound onions, sliced thin
- 3 tablespoons oil
- 1/2 teaspoon salt freshly ground pepper
- 1 egg
- 2/3 cup yogurt (best when allowed to thicken somewhat on standing)
- 1/3 cup evaporated milk
- 2 ounces lox or Nova Scotia salmon cut into thin strips
- 2 tablespoons dry bread crumbs
- 4 tablespoons grated Romano or Parmesan cheese to sprinkle on top

1. Cook onions in oil over low heat until very soft, almost to a purée (do not brown). Partially cover the pan or use a steam-vented lid; stir occasionally. Allow 30 to 40 minutes for onions to get done. Add salt and pepper.

2. Preheat oven to 375°F.

3. Beat egg lightly. Combine with yogurt and evaporated milk; mix well.

4. Combine onions, smoked salmon strips, and egg mixture.

5. Oil an 8-inch pie pan. If you are using Pizza dough, punch down the risen dough, roll out, stretch

COCKTAILERS AND HORS D'OEUVRE

and pat to fit the pan, pushing the dough well into the corners (do not allow dough to rise). Or roll out pie crust and line pan.

6. Sprinkle crumbs on dough and pour in the filling. Sprinkle with grated cheese.
7. Bake for 50 to 60 minutes until crust is brown and filling is lightly browned on top.
8. Cut into small wedges and serve hot. This quiche may be reheated very successfully.

YIELD: one 8-inch quiche

HOT MEAT BALLS

- 1 pound lean beef, ground twice
- 1 teaspoon salt
- 2 teaspoons dry mustard
- 1 clove garlic, finely chopped
- 1 medium onion, grated
- dash of Worcestershire sauce
- 1/2 cup parsley, finely chopped
- oil for pan frying

1. Mix ingredients well but lightly. Roll into small balls the size of walnuts.
2. Brown quickly in hot oil. Cook to medium rareness or according to taste.
3. Serve hot with a good mustard.

YIELD: 2 to 3 dozen

PAN BAGNA
Mediterranean Hero

Good with beer or wine. Fine for the hungry young crowd.

- fresh crusty French bread
- garlic
- oil (part olive)
- lemon
- anchovies
- tomatoes, sliced thin
- salt
- mild onion, sliced thin
- green peppers, sliced thin
- stuffed or pitted olives, sliced

1. Cut the long French bread into serving-size portions and split lengthwise. Rub bottom crust of bread with a cut clove of garlic.
2. Drip oil lightly on the cut surface and sprinkle with lemon juice. Add anchovies, tomato slices and a bit of salt. Add onion, pepper and olive slices.
3. Cover with top half of bread and squeeze together.

CHINESE FRIED SHRIMP BALLS

- 1 pound raw shrimp, shelled, deveined, finely ground
- 2 tablespoons finely chopped scallions
- 1/3 cup finely chopped water chestnuts
- 1 teaspoon shredded ginger
- 2 tablespoons oil
- 1/2 teaspoon salt
- 1/4 teaspoon monosodium glutamate
- dash of pepper
- flour
- oil for deep frying
- soy sauce, mustard
- shredded white radish

1. Combine thoroughly shrimp, scallions, water chestnuts, ginger, the 2 tablespoons of oil, salt, monosodium glutamate, and pepper.
2. Pour some flour (about 1/4 cup) on a wax-paper-lined board. Pick up shrimp mixture by rounded teaspoonfuls, toss lightly in flour, and shape with fingers into balls.
3. Fry in hot oil (about 4 minutes) until golden brown, drain on absorbent paper.
4. Serve hot with soy sauce, mustard, and shredded radish.

MARINATED SWORDFISH CUBES

2 tablespoons oil
1/2 pound fresh swordfish, cut about 1/2 inch thick
pinch each of salt, oregano, rosemary or sweet basil
1/2 small bay leaf
2 peppercorns, and 2 whole allspice
juice of 1/2 lemon
paprika

1. Place 1 tablespoon of the oil into small broiling dish. Add swordfish and sprinkle lightly with salt, oregano, and rosemary or basil. Add bay leaf, peppercorns, and allspice. Add remaining oil and the lemon juice. Sprinkle freely with paprika.
2. Cover and refrigerate for several hours or overnight.
3. In a preheated broiler, broil for about 10 minutes until nicely browned.
4. Remove bayleaf, cool, cover again, and refrigerate in the juices for several hours or overnight.
5. At serving time, cut into 1/2-inch cubes with a sharp knife and arrange on crisp greens.

YIELD: about thirty 1/2 inch cubes

DOROTHY'S CHILLED ORANGE SECTIONS WITH CINNAMON
Grand for a buffet

4 oranges
1 teaspoon cinnamon
2 tablespoons brown sugar

1. Use very good eating oranges and leave peels on. Wash oranges well, cut each into halves lengthwise, then into 6 or 8 sections.
2. Mix cinnamon with sugar. Dip each piece into the sugar mixture and place in a glass serving bowl. Chill well before serving.

HORS D'OEUVRE

Present usage does not distinguish between cocktail accompaniments and hors d'oeuvre. However, we make a somewhat arbitrary distinction according to the function they serve. Our Cocktailers are planned to offer sufficiently diversified foods to satisfy small or big appetites, especially when dinner is a long time off. In choosing hors d'oeuvre we have kept in mind the original French meaning of the term—appetizers served at the table to introduce the main part of the meal. They are light, flavorful, interesting foods, meant to animate the appetite, not overwhelm it.

Popular hors d'oeuvre choices in areas of the world where they are a daily habit—France, Spain, Italy, Greece, the Near East—often consist of raw or cooked vegetables in the form of a salad. Fresh and attractively served radishes, scallions, and artichokes please the eye as well as the palate. Other excellent choices are some of the other world's first-course favorites: caviar, oysters, clams, shrimp, sardines with olives, and refreshing fruits. If adequate in protein, these hors d'oeuvre can also serve as main dishes for supper or luncheon.

ANCHOVY WITH TOMATOES
Adapted from Mama Mia Cookbook

4 medium-sized tomatoes
1 2-ounce can anchovy fillets
juice of 1 lemon
pinch of oregano (optional)
pepper

1. Select fully ripe but firm tomatoes. Wash and slice them into 1/4-inch slices.
2. Garnish each portion with 2 anchovy fillets.
3. Combine oil from the anchovies with lemon juice, pepper, and oregano; pour over tomatoes and anchovies.

YIELD: 4 portions

LEEKS VINAIGRETTE

Louis Diat, the great chef and author, tells us that in his childhood home in France leeks were always cooked in the soup and then served with salad dressing as hors d'oeuvre. Whatever your way of cooking them, you will find that leeks do something very good for the broth and the broth for the leeks.

- 8 medium-sized leeks
- 1 cup chicken broth or water, lightly salted
- 1/2 cup Vinaigrette Sauce*
- 1 tablespoon chopped parsley
- dash of fresh tarragon, chopped (if available)

1. Select fresh leeks. Trim off tough green leaves. Cut leeks in half lengthwise to be able to remove all sand; wash thoroughly.
2. Gently cook them in broth for 20 to 30 minutes. Remove from broth. Save broth for soup or sauce.
3. Mix Vinaigrette Sauce with the remaining ingredients and pour it over the leeks while they are still warm.
4. Serve slightly warm or chilled.

NOTE: Asparagus, green and wax beans are excellent prepared the same way.

MUSHROOMS A LA GRECQUE

- 1 pound small button mushrooms, or firm larger ones cut in half
- 1/2 teaspoon salt
- 1 clove garlic freshly ground pepper
- 1 bay leaf
- 1/2 teaspoon dried thyme
- 1/2 cup water
- 1/2 cup cider vinegar
- 1/3 cup lemon juice
- 1/2 cup oil

1. Trim and wash mushrooms. Put half of them into a saucepan.

2. Mix seasonings, water, vinegar, lemon juice and oil; pour over the mushrooms.

3. Bring to a boil, cover and simmer for 5 minutes or until tender; do not overcook. Remove mushrooms from liquid and place in a bowl or jar.

4. Add the remaining mushrooms to the cooking liquid and simmer as before. When cooked, remove and add to the first portion.

5. Simmer liquid to reduce it and concentrate flavor. Correct the seasoning and strain over the mushrooms.

6. When cold, cover and refrigerate. They will keep well for several days.

CHOPPED EGGPLANT

This is the kind of dish people become passionately attached to. They are unwilling to accept even a minor variation in the flavor they expect to find. For that reason we include the three popular versions.

CHOPPED EGGPLANT
Armenian style

| 1 eggplant (1-1/2 pounds) | 2 tablespoons oil |
| 1 clove garlic, mashed | salt and pepper to taste |

1. Broil eggplant until tender and skin is blackened on foil-lined broiler pan under a medium flame.

2. Turn it several times while cooking, which should take about 15 to 20 minutes.

3. When tender (soft to the touch), take from broiler and remove skin (this is easy).

4. Mash the pulp, add garlic, oil, salt, and pepper; mix well. Chill before serving.

NOTE: Rye or pumpernickel bread is preferred with this dish.

CHOPPED EGGPLANT
Rumanian style

1 tomato, peeled and chopped
1 green pepper, seeded and chopped (optional)
1 small onion, finely chopped
1 tablespoon lemon juice or vinegar
pinch of sugar (optional)

1. Broil, mash, and season eggplant as in previous recipe.
2. Combine with the above ingredients and stir to blend.

YIELD: 5 to 6 servings

CHOPPED EGGPLANT
Arabian style

Broil, mash and season eggplant as for Armenian Style. Then add 1/2 cup seasame tahini (seasame paste). Mix thoroughly. Chill before serving.

NOTE: Serve any style chopped eggplant on Romaine lettuce and garnish with black olives and tomato wedges.

CHARCOAL ROASTED CHOPPED EGGPLANT

For a very special Near East flavor, the next time you cook on the outdoor grill—after your meat, fish, or poultry is done—place an eggplant directly on the charcoal embers. For even roasting, turn with prongs occasionally. Cooking time will be about 20 minutes. When skin is blackened and eggplant tender, remove it to a board. Remove skin with a wet knife. Proceed as in any of the recipes for chopped eggplant.

PULSE AND THE BIBLE

"Prove thy servants, I beseech thee, ten days; and let them give us pulse to eat and water to drink. Then let our countenances be looked upon before thee, and the countenances of the youths that eat of the King's meat." Thus pleaded one of the noble youths "with knowledge and skill in all learning and wisdom." Deported from Judah to Babylon and to Nebuchadnezzar's court, after the fall of Jerusalem in 602 B. C., the youths were to receive special training for three years to stand prepared before their ruler. During this period they were to eat daily of the King's meat and to drink the King's wine.

The youth's request was granted. And at the end of the ten days "their countenances appeared fairer and fatter in flesh than all the children which did eat the portion of the King's meat. So the steward took away their meat and the wine which they should drink and gave them pulse." At the end of the training period they passed with a score ten times better than all the magicians and the enchanters in the King's realm.

Daniel I: 1–15.

CHICKPEA TAHINI
An Arabian recipe that is very popular outside the Arab world

In its homeland, chickpea tahini is eaten with *pita*, a flat hollow roll, which is used like an oversized dipper. A popular luncheon dish in Israel, chickpea tahini is served with a piece of herring, tomato, green pepper, and olives. It is on the menu in many restaurants.

- 1 cup dried chickpeas or 3 cups canned
- water to cover
- 1 tablespoon oil
- 1/2 teaspoon salt
- 1 clove garlic, mashed
- 1/2 cup tahini (sesame paste)
- 1 teaspoon olive oil per serving (optional)

COCKTAILERS AND HORS D'OEUVRE

1. Soak dried chickpeas 8 hours. Gently cook them until tender in water in which they have been soaked from 1-1/2 to 2 hours. Add more boiling water during cooking, as necessary. Add 1 tablespoon oil to help keep foam down.
2. When tender, put chickpeas through a food mill and add salt, garlic, and sesame paste; chill well.
3. Serve with a little olive oil on top of each serving and garnish with radishes and olives.

NOTE: After soaking, chickpeas can be peeled by rubbing them between the fingers. It is a bit awkward at first but will be fast and easy if you persist. This cuts cooking time down appreciably and the peas may not need to be puréed, just mashed.

YIELD: 6 to 8 servings

ROASTED PEPPER SALAD
From Bulgaria

A whole new world of food opened for Martha in the northeastern corner of Bulgaria on the Black Sea. Buying vegetables and fruits was an important daily task. There was an abundance of green and red peppers, purple eggplants, okra, mountains of watermelons and barrels filled with black, oily olives. The mere sight of them was wonderful. Peppers were roasted on top of the hot stove plate until their skins blackened and blistered. A tantalizing aroma penetrated the house. Martha's enthusiasm for peppers earned her the nickname "Cuska" (Pepper).

All of these new foods had an instant appeal, except for one—with the olives, it was not love on first bite. But olives, like marriage, they said—one has to get used to.

1. Wash and dry firm green peppers.
2. Preheat broiler. Cover broiler pan with aluminum foil. Broil peppers under medium flame, carefully turning them a few times, until the skin has blackened on all sides and until they are just tender. This will take about 10 minutes.

3. Place peppers in a bowl, cover tightly, and let stand 10 to 15 minutes. This step helps to loosen the skins.

4. Peel the blackened skins off gently with a paring knife dipped in water. Cut the peppers lengthwise and remove seeds.

5. Arrange peppers in a salad bowl and cover with a dressing of 1 tablespoon oil and 1 teaspoon vinegar for each pepper.

6. Add salt and pepper to taste. Add a clove of garlic, peeled and halved (optional). Cover and refrigerate.

NOTE: These peppers develop their flavor after standing 2 to 3 days.

CHOPPED LIVER

1/2 pound chicken livers (beef or calves' liver may be used)
2 tablespoons finely chopped onions
2 tablespoons oil
2 hard-cooked eggs
salt and pepper
pinch of cinnamon, allspice, marjoram, or poultry seasoning (optional)

1. Sauté chicken livers and onions in oil until lightly browned. Cook gently until livers are just done. Since livers have a bouncing, erratic behavior in the pan, put a lid on part way to protect yourself, or use a steam-vented lid throughout.

2. Remove any skin and membranes from livers. Mash or chop them.

3. Combine chopped liver and onion mixture, eggs, and seasonings, and mash all well with a fork.

4. If additional moisture is necessary, add a little broth or oil or some of each.

5. Serve on a bed of Romaine lettuce.

YIELD: 4 to 5 servings

BATTER-FRIED SHRIMP

1 pound raw shrimp
1/2 cup sifted flour
1 teaspoon baking powder
1/2 teaspoon salt
pinch of sugar
1 tablespoon oil
1 egg
1/2 cup beer or water
oil for frying
Tartar Sauce*

1. Shell and devein shrimp.
2. For batter, sift dry ingredients and stir in oil, egg, and beer or water; beat lightly. Allow to stand for 1 hour.
3. Dip shrimp in batter, one by one. Fry in hot oil until golden brown and drain on absorbent paper.
4. Serve with Tartar Sauce.

YIELD: 6 servings

BAKED STUFFED CLAMS

3 tablespoons oil
2 cloves garlic, mashed
1 tablespoon chopped onion
2 tablespoons chopped parsley
1/3 cup dry bread crumbs
pinch of oregano
pinch of salt
2 cups chopped clams, fresh steamed or canned (2 10-ounce cans)
2/3 cup clam liquid
2 tablespoons Parmesan cheese, grated
2 tablespoons dry bread crumbs

1. In hot oil gently sauté garlic, onion, parsley, bread crumbs, oregano, and salt until crumbs start to brown—not more than 2 to 3 minutes.
2. Add clams and clam liquid and mix well. Spoon into small, individual baking dishes. Sprinkle with cheese and crumbs.
3. Bake at 375°F. for about 25 minutes or until top is browned.

YIELD: 4 to 6 servings

GEFILLTE FISH

The word "gefillte" comes from the German word "gefüllt," meaning stuffed. That was the way gelfillte fish was made in Eastern European countries and probably still is in some areas. The fish skin was left intact, the flesh carefully removed, boned, chopped, seasoned and stuffed back into the fish skin, which was then sewn together. It was boiled or baked, and sometimes browned in the oven after boiling. This was a holiday dish *par excellence*. It took skill and time to prepare. Today, homemade gelfillte fish balls are happiness enough.

- 2 pounds whole fish (pike, whitefish, and carp are traditional but many other kinds may be used)
- 1 onion
- 1 egg
- 1 slice white bread, soaked in water and squeezed dry
- 1 teaspoon salt
- 1/2 teaspoon pepper
- 1/2 cup water or club soda (approximately)

FISH STOCK

- 1 onion, sliced
- 1 carrot, scraped and sliced
- 1 tablespoon salt
- 2 to 4 peppercorns
- 1 bay leaf (optional)

1. Clean, remove head and skin, and bone the fish. Reserve head and bones for stock.
2. Finely chop fish and onion in a chopping bowl or put through a food chopper, using the fine blade. Mash thoroughly afterward.
3. Add egg, bread, seasonings, and enough water to make a soft, light mixture. Form balls about the size of an egg.
4. In a pot just large enough to hold the fish, combine reserved bones and head and add vegetables and seasonings.
5. Add the fish balls, cover with cold water, bring to a boil, and simmer for about an hour.
6. Serve hot or cold, with horseradish—preferably

beet horseradish. When served cold, let fish balls cool in strained broth, which will jell.

YIELD: 6 to 8 portions

SCHMALTZ HERRING IN DILL SAUCE

- 2 fillets of schmaltz herring, cut into 1-inch slices
- 1/2 cup plain yogurt
- 3 tablespoons oil
- 1/4 cup vinegar
- 1/4 teaspoon sugar
- 2 tablespoons dry white wine (optional)
- 1 medium onion, sliced thin
- 6 peppercorns
- 2 bay leaves
- a few sprigs of fresh dill

1. Combine yogurt, oil, vinegar, sugar, and wine and mix well.
2. In a wide jar, arrange in alternating layers herring and onion slices. Distribute peppercorns, bay leaves, and dill among the layers.
3. Pour in the yogurt mixture. Gently, with a fork, tilt the layers so that yogurt mixture covers herring and other ingredients well.
4. Cover jar. Refrigerate for several days before serving.

TARAMASALATA

In Greece, cured red mullet roe is used for this dish, but salmon roe (red caviar) does very well.

- 4-ounce jar red caviar
- 1 small onion, grated
- 1 cup oil
- 4 slices white bread, soaked in water and squeezed dry
- juice of 2 lemons

1. Mash the caviar and be sure the thin membranes of the roe have burst.
2. Add onion, then add 1/2 of the oil, a little at a time, as one does when making mayonnaise.
3. Mix in the moistened bread, alternately with remaining oil and lemon juice.
4. Cover and chill. This will keep well for several days.
5. Serve on a bed of crisp greens, garnished with black olives.

NOTE: Taramasalata also makes a fine spread. Proceed as above but omit the bread.

10
Soups

A few onions, some of yesterday's bread, a piece of cheese to grate—and French onion soup was born. The cook's name is lost in antiquity, but the creation lives on, to the pleasure of countless lovers of good soup. Equally simple and delicious are watercress and potato, turnip and carrot, zucchini and rice soup—all borrowed from the French housewife. She has a way with soup—few ingredients, uncomplicated methods. A careful and thrifty shopper, she buys vegetables as the season brings them, for best flavor and low price.

Soup can be your vegetable, your main dish, or dinner in one. The dried legumes with their hearty flavor also provide good vegetable protein. A well-seasoned split pea, lentil, or bean soup is both nourishing and enticing.

When a soup combines substantial amounts of chicken, meat, or fish with vegetables, it becomes a complete meal. Examples are chicken pot au feu, Scotch broth, or clam chowder. Any one of these, served with crunchy bread and a bowl of fresh fruit for dessert, makes a dinner fit for your most cherished guests.

HOW TO MAKE GOOD SOUP

GOOD BROTHS help to make tasty soup. You don't have to make your own broth; there are many good canned broths and concentrates such as bouillon cubes, powders, and extracts.

To ENHANCE CHICKEN SOUP (your own as well as a commercial product), simmer it with a piece of fresh ginger, a clove of garlic, or both. Or add, just before serving, some dry white wine or a few drops of lemon juice.

BEEF BROTH MAY BE IMPROVED by a little dry sherry or Madeira, added when ready to serve.

NEVER WASTE ANY GOOD LEFTOVER BROTH. If you have no immediate use for it, freeze it. It will come in handy not only for soup but also for sauces, gravies, meat loaves, stews, and casseroles.

THICKEN SOUP with rice or pasta or by mashing some of the starchy vegetables in the soup, such as potatoes and dried legumes.

THE FOLLOWING WAYS TO THICKEN SOUPS ARE FOR SAUCES AS WELL:

A ROUX, cooking flour in fat as you would for white sauce

A PASTE, mixing flour or cornstarch with water and adding to the finished soup, boiling it just until the starch is cooked

"BEURRE MANIÉ," made by mixing margarine and flour; then added in small bits to the simmering soup and cooked just 2 minutes before serving.

MAYONNAISE, AIOLI, EGG YOLK will bind (thicken slightly, prevent solids from settling, hold together, make smooth and creamy). Soup is not allowed to boil after adding any of these.

BE LIGHT-HANDED WITH SEASONINGS. A food's flavor should not be overpowered. Clever seasoning can heighten flavor; with few exceptions, the amount of seasoning should be no more than to add a certain pleasant, elusive quality.

The quantity of a seasoning in recipes is frequently too little to be described in an actual amount. In English it is often called "a pinch," in Southern German dialect "a minute idea," and with French wit "a suspicion."

TCHAV
Sorrel or sour grass soup
Polish-Russian origin

1 pound sorrel
1 quart boiling water
1 teaspoon salt
2 eggs
pinch of pepper
yogurt or Prudent Sour Cream

1. Wash sorrel thoroughly and chop well; put in a saucepan. Add the boiling water and salt. Boil 5 minutes.
2. In a large bowl beat the eggs. Pour a small amount of the hot sorrel soup into the eggs, stirring until well mixed.
3. Slowly add the remainder of the soup; add pepper. Allow to cool.
4. Serve cold with yogurt or Prudent Sour Cream. This cold soup may also be served with hot boiled potatoes.

NOTE: Tchav can be made with half sorrel and half spinach, in which case a little lemon juice is added before serving.

YIELD: 4 to 6 servings

BORSCHT (Beet Soup)
Polish-Russian origin

1 bunch young beets, with greens
1-1/2 quarts of boiling water
salt
2 eggs, beaten
juice of 1 lemon
sugar to taste

1. Cut off greens and trim them. Wash beets and greens thoroughly. Boil beets in water for about 15 minutes or until they can be peeled.
2. Grate the peeled beets on a coarse grater or cut them very fine. Chop the greens.
3. Cover the beets and greens with the boiling

water and add salt. Simmer until beets are tender, about 15 minutes.

4. Beat eggs in a large bowl. Pour a small amount of the hot borscht into the eggs, stirring constantly to prevent curdling.

5. Slowly add this to the rest of the borscht, then add lemon juice and sugar.

6. Serve hot or cold with plain yogurt or Prudent Sour Cream and hot boiled potatoes if desired.

NOTE: Omit greens, if desired.

YIELD: 5 to 6 servings

CARROT SOUP

1 pound carrots, scraped	1 tablespoon oil
1 medium onion or 3 shallots	1/4 teaspoon sugar
	4 cups chicken broth
1 clove garlic	salt and pepper
1-1/2 medium potatoes	parsley or chives, chopped

1. Grate carrots on a coarse grater. Slice onion, garlic, and potatoes thinly.

2. Put oil and sugar in a saucepan and add vegetables. Cover and cook gently over a very low flame for about 10 minutes or until tender.

3. Add broth and simmer another 15 to 20 minutes.

4. Put vegetables in blender and blend about 1/2 minute, or put through a food mill to purée them.

5. Return puréed vegetables to the pot, reheat soup, and correct seasonings with salt and pepper.

6. Add parsley or chives.

NOTE: Hot croutons served separately are good with this soup.

YIELD: 4 to 5 servings

FRENCH ONION SOUP

- 3 tablespoons vegetable oil
- 2 large onions, sliced thin
- 4 cups of bouillon or stock
- salt and pepper
- toasted bread slices
- 2 tablespoons grated Parmesan cheese

1. Sauté onions in oil until golden. Add stock and simmer 1/2 hour. Season with salt and pepper.
2. Serve over small slices of toasted bread. Sprinkle with cheese just before serving.

YIELD: 4 servings

ZUCCHINI AND RICE SOUP

- 1 pound zucchini
- 1 medium onion, chopped
- 4 tablespoons oil
- 6 cups chicken broth or bouillon
- 1/2 cup rice, uncooked
- 1 egg yolk (optional)
- few drops of lemon juice
- salt and pepper
- parsley or chives, chopped

1. Wash zucchini but do not peel; chop it coarsely.
2. Sauté zucchini and onion in oil for a few minutes in a heavy soup pot.
3. Add broth and bring to a boil. Cook until zucchini are barely tender. Remove from broth and mash lightly with a large fork.
4. Add rice to broth and cook until just tender.
5. Return the mashed zucchini to the soup and simmer 5 to 10 minutes.
6. Mix egg yolk with a little of the hot soup and a few drops of lemon juice. Add to the soup but do not boil.
7. Correct seasoning and add parsley or chives. You may pass a pitcher of cold milk at the table for those who wish to add some to their soup.

YIELD: 5 to 6 servings

WHITE TURNIP AND POTATO SOUP

3 young white turnips (about 1 pound), pared and sliced
3 medium potatoes, pared and thinly sliced
5 cups chicken broth or bouillon
2 tablespoons margarine
1 cup milk
salt and pepper to taste
2 to 4 tablespoons undiluted skimmed evaporated milk

1. Place vegetables, broth, and margarine in a saucepan. Bring to boil and cook until vegetables are tender, about 10 minutes.
2. Mash vegetables with a large fork or put through a sieve or food mill. Return them to saucepan.
3. Add milk and reheat soup. Correct seasonings with salt and pepper.
4. Just before serving add skimmed evaporated milk, for a richer consistency, flavor, and color.

YIELD: 6 servings

WATERCRESS AND POTATO SOUP

1 bunch watercress, washed and coarsely chopped
2 tablespoons oil
3 cups bouillon or broth
1 medium onion, chopped
3 medium potatoes, sliced
1 tablespoon margarine
1 tablespoon flour
1 cup hot milk
salt, pepper, nutmeg
1/4 cup skimmed evaporated milk, undiluted (optional)

1. In 1 tablespoon of the oil, cook watercress until wilted. Add 1/2 cup of the bouillon; bring to boil and simmer 5 minutes. Set aside.
2. In remaining oil in a large saucepan, sauté onion until transparent.

3. Add potatoes and remaining bouillon; cook until potatoes are tender.

4. Put watercress and potatoes through a food mill, or use a blender or just mash them. Return to pot and reheat soup to boiling.

5. Blend margarine with flour; add in small bits to the boiling soup, stirring to blend. Boil 2 minutes; add the hot milk. Do not allow to boil.

6. Correct seasoning with salt, pepper, and nutmeg. Add evaporated milk, for extra creaminess.

NOTE: For more pronounced flavor use two bunches of watercress.

YIELD: 4 to 6 servings

ROMAINE LETTUCE AND FRESH PEA SOUP

- 1 head tender Romaine lettuce (about 1 pound), cleaned and shredded
- 1 medium onion, chopped
- 3 tablespoons oil
- 6 cups chicken broth or bouillon
- pinch of curry
- salt and pepper to taste
- 2 tablespoons margarine
- 2 tablespoons flour
- 3/4 cup fresh, young, shelled peas (about 3/4 pound in pod)
- 1/2 cup water (approximately) to cook peas
- pinch of sugar
- pinch of salt

1. In a large pot sauté Romaine lettuce and onion in the oil. Cook gently, stirring with a large fork for even cooking, until lettuce is wilted and just barely tender, about 5 minutes.

2. Chop vegetables finely by hand or blend for a few seconds. Do not over-blend.

3. Return vegetables to the pot, add bouillon and seasonings, and bring to boil.

4. Blend margarine with flour and add in small bits to the boiling soup, stirring to blend. Boil for 2 minutes.

5. Put the peas in a small pot. Pour boiling water over them, just enough to cover. Add sugar and salt, and cook until peas are just tender.

6. Add peas and liquid to soup.

NOTE: Tender escarole or zucchini is a delicious alternative for the Romaine lettuce.

YIELD: 6 servings

CREAM OF MUSHROOM SOUP

- 1/2 cup Duxelles (see following recipe)
- 2 tablespoons margarine
- 2 tablespoons flour
- 4 cups chicken broth
- 1/4 cup skimmed evaporated milk
- salt and pepper to taste
- few drops lemon juice

1. Heat margarine in a saucepan, add duxelles and simmer for a few minutes.

2. Add flour and cook, while stirring, until light brown. This step is very important to bring out the very special flavor and texture of the soup.

3. Add chicken broth, stirring to blend. Bring to a boil and simmer for 15 to 20 minutes.

4. Add milk and reheat but do not boil.

5. Correct seasoning with salt and pepper and add lemon juice.

YIELD: 4 servings

DUXELLES
(Mushroom Concentrate)

When there is a good buy on mushrooms (they do not have to be of prime quality, the result will be just as good) make duxelles. It will add something extra special to meat sauces, stuffings for poultry and vegetables; makes a wonderful base for mushroom sauce or mushroom soup. Duxelles keeps well in the refrigerator.

1 pound mushrooms
4 tablespoons oil
1 small onion, chopped
1 teaspoon lemon juice
1 teaspoon salt
pepper

1. Clean mushrooms and chop them finely.
2. In a wide-bottomed saucepan, heat the oil and add mushrooms, onion, and lemon juice.
3. Cook, while stirring, until all moisture has cooked away, then add salt and pepper to taste.

CREAM OF SPINACH SOUP

1/2 pound fresh spinach or 1/2 package (10 ounces) frozen
1 small onion, chopped
2 tablespoons oil
2 tablespoons flour
3-1/2 cups chicken broth
1/2 cup skimmed evaporated milk
salt and pepper to taste
pinch of nutmeg

1. Trim and wash the spinach. Warm water helps remove sand.
2. Cook 3 to 5 minutes in the water that clings to the leaves. When frozen spinach is used, cook it as directed on package.
3. Finely chop the spinach or purée in a food mill or blender.
4. Sauté onion in oil until transparent in a medium saucepan. Stir in flour and cook until dry and bubbly.
5. Add chicken broth and bring to a boil, while stirring.
6. Simmer for about 10 minutes, add puréed spinach and simmer 5 minutes more.
7. Slowly add the milk and heat again but do not boil. Add seasonings and let stand a few moments to blend flavors before serving.

YIELD: 4 servings

Three Favorite Soups From Southern Germany

FLAEDCHEN SOUP

4 cups bouillon or broth, hot	1 to 2 tablespoons chopped parsley or chives

FLAEDCHEN

1/4 cup flour	1 egg
1/2 cup milk	1/4 teaspoon salt

1. Mix flour and milk until smooth. Add egg and salt and mix well.
2. Heat a crêpe pan or skillet well and oil lightly. Put about 3 tablespoons batter in the hot pan, then tilt pan so that a thin pancake results.
3. Over a low flame, bake the *flaedchen* to a golden brown on one side. With a spatula, carefully turn and brown on the other side. Proceed until all batter is used, stacking the pancakes on a plate.
4. Roll the stack of pancakes together like a jelly roll. Cut them crosswise into thin strips.
5. Put a portion of the flaedchen into each soup bowl and pour the hot broth over the strips.
6. Garnish with chopped parsley or chives.

YIELD: 4 servings

OATMEAL SOUP

In Martha's childhood this simple soup was always served to anyone who had a tummy upset. Nobody, to this day, ever doubted this soup's soothing properties. But its hearty flavor and creamy consistency made it an all-time favorite under any circumstances.

1/2 cup rolled oats
2 cups water
3 cups bouillon or chicken broth
1 tablespoon margarine
1/2 cup diced cooked chicken (optional)
salt and pepper to taste

1. Combine oats and water; bring to boil. Add broth and margarine; simmer for about 30 minutes.
2. Add chicken and correct seasoning with salt and pepper.

NOTE: Sometimes this soup was made with stock from veal shanks with some of the diced meat added to the soup before serving.

YIELD: 4 servings

FRESH PEA AND DUMPLING SOUP

Dumplings (recipe below)
1 pound fresh young peas, shelled (do not substitute frozen or canned)
1/4 head Romaine or Boston lettuce, finely chopped
1/4 cup parsley, finely chopped
6 cups chicken broth

1. Prepare dumpling batter according to the following recipe and refrigerate.
2. Combine peas, lettuce, parsley, and chicken broth in a large saucepan. Cook briskly until peas are tender.
3. Drop dumpling batter from a teaspoon into the simmering broth.
4. Cook from 5 to 8 minutes in the partially covered saucepan. The dumplings will expand and be light and feathery.

DUMPLINGS

2 tablespoons V.S.S. or margarine
1 egg
pinch of salt
pinch of nutmeg
3 to 4 tablespoons flour

Cream the fat until light and fluffy, then add egg and continue creaming well. Add seasonings. Add flour and mix thoroughly. Consistency will be a soft batter.

YIELD: 5 to 6 servings

Two Fine Cold Soups

TARATOR
From Bulgaria

- 1 quart plain yogurt, chilled
- 1/2 cup ice water
- 1/4 cup oil (some olive)
- 1 fresh cucumber, peeled, finely diced
- 1/4 cup walnut meats, chopped or broken
- 1 clove garlic, finely chopped
- salt to taste
- 1 tablespoon parsley, finely chopped (optional)

Mix ingredients just before serving. Some prefer to serve a tablespoon of oil separately on each bowl.

YIELD: 4 servings

GAZPACHO

- 1 pound ripe tomatoes
- 1/2 small cucumber, partially peeled (leave a little of the peel on)
- 1/4 green pepper, seeded
- 1/2 small onion
- 1 clove garlic
- 2 or 3 cups ice water
- salt
- 6 tablespoons oil (some olive)
- 2 tablespoons vinegar

1. Cut tomatoes into small pieces.
2. Coarsely chop cucumber, pepper, onion, and garlic and put into the blender with 1 cup of the water; blend no more than 10 seconds.

3. Add tomatoes, salt, oil and vinegar; blend 5 seconds more. This part of the recipe can be made ahead of time and chilled until ready to serve.

4. At serving time add the remaining ice water and correct seasoning. Hot croutons are very good served with this soup.

YIELD: 4 servings

ABOUT DRIED LEGUMES

One cup of dried legumes will yield from 2 to 3 cups cooked. Dried beans and whole dried peas must be soaked. Split peas and lentils may be cooked without soaking, but we prefer to soak these also. Cook dried legumes in the water in which they have been soaked. If you are in a hurry, cover legumes with cold water, bring to a boil, boil 2 minutes, then soak for 1 hour (they can be soaked longer, if more convenient).

To the cooking water, add 1 tablespoon of oil for each cup of legumes. The oil will help to keep the foam down during cooking.

Cook legumes gently with only occasional stirring; rapid boiling and frequent stirring cause the skins to break.

SPLIT PEA SOUP

Joy of Cooking was Martha's first American cook book and remained one of her favorite ones to turn to. It was given to her by her uncle Max Schott, a friend and neighbor of the author of *Joy of Cooking*, Mrs. Irma Rombauer, of whom he was very fond.

Born in a small town in Germany, Max lost his parents when he was four years old and was brought up in an institution. At seventeen, he came to the United States, where he found his element—freedom to pursue his own ideas. To his high-spirited and dynamic nature, every obstacle—of which there were many—presented a challenge. He developed the Climax Molybdenum Company, a far-reaching mining enterprise. Endowed with vision, he had unshakable faith in the importance of molybdenum. Time has proved him right. Molybdenum has even played an important part in the Apollo space program.

Uncle Max loved split pea soup and enjoyed reminiscing about the steamship captain who shared his predilection. On a crossing to Europe, Uncle Max listened with interest to the captain's account of his responsibilities, which included inspecting the food service. "Tomorrow," the captain said with a happy smile, "a special pleasure is waiting for me in third class—split-pea soup."

- 1 cup split peas
- 3 cups water
- 3 tablespoons oil
- 1 medium onion, chopped
- 1/2 cup chopped celery with leaves
- 1 medium carrot, scraped, cut into small cubes
- 2 tablespoons chopped parsley
- 3 cups bouillon or stock
- 1/4 teaspoon curry
- pinch of turmeric (optional)
- salt and pepper
- 1 tablespoon margarine
- 1 tablespoon flour
- croutons (see following recipe)

1. Bring to a boil the split peas, water, and 1 tablespoon of the oil. Boil for 2 minutes; set aside for 1 hour, or longer if more convenient.

2. In remaining 2 tablespoons of oil in a large soup pot sauté onion, celery, carrot, and parsley for 5 minutes.

3. Add split peas and water in which they were cooked to the sautéed vegetables. Add bouillon, curry, and turmeric.

4. Bring to a boil and simmer for about 1 hour or until peas are tender. Purée soup if desired. Correct seasoning with salt and pepper.

5. Blend margarine with flour and add small bits to the boiling soup, while stirring; boil 2 minutes.

6. Serve hot with croutons.

NOTE: Try Mrs. Rombauer's suggestion of fish stock (especially good is a fine shrimp stock).

YIELD: 6 servings

CROUTONS

2 tablespoons margarine

2 slices day-old bread, cut into small cubes

Heat margarine and slowly fry bread cubes to a golden brown; be careful—they brown quickly. At serving time sprinkle them on the soup while sizzling hot.

SOUTH GERMAN LENTIL SOUP

1 cup lentils
3 cups water
1 tablespoon oil
3 cups bouillon or stock
1 bay leaf
1 small onion, stuck with 2 cloves
1 clove garlic, mashed
1 medium potato, peeled, cut into small cubes
1 to 2 tablespoons vinegar (optional)
salt to taste
1 tablespoon margarine
1 tablespoon flour
2 frankfurters (optional)

1. Bring to boil lentils, water, and oil. Boil for 2 minutes; set aside for 1 hour (or longer if more convenient).
2. Add bouillon, bay leaf, onion, and garlic and cook gently for 30 to 40 minutes or until lentils are tender. Remove onion and bay leaf.
3. Add potato cubes and cook about 15 minutes or until tender.
4. Add vinegar and correct seasoning.
5. Blend margarine with flour and add in small bits to the boiling soup, while stirring. Boil for 2 minutes.
6. Heat frankfurters in a small amount of water. Slice them and add to soup just before serving.

YIELD: 6 servings

A Variation of SOUTH GERMAN LENTIL SOUP

1 cup lentils	1 stalk celery, chopped
3 cups water	1 carrot, scraped, cut
1 tablespoon oil	into small cubes
3 cups bouillon or stock	1 tablespoon chopped parsley
1 bay leaf	1 tablespoon tomato paste
1 clove garlic, mashed	pinch of thyme
2 tablespoons oil	salt
1 medium onion, chopped	1 tablespoon margarine
	1 tablespoon flour

1. Bring to boil lentils, water, and the 1 tablespoon of oil. Boil for 2 minutes; set aside for 1 hour (or longer if more convenient).
2. Add bouillon, bay leaf, and garlic; cook gently for 30 to 40 minutes or until lentils are tender; remove bay leaf.
3. In the 2 tablespoons of oil, sauté onion, celery, carrot, and parsley for 5 minutes.
4. Add sautéed vegetables and tomato paste to the soup and cook until vegetables are tender, about 20 minutes.
5. Add thyme, correct seasoning.
6. Blend margarine with flour and add in small bits to the boiling soup, while stirring. Boil for 2 minutes.

YIELD: 6 servings

PINK BEAN OR RED KIDNEY BEAN SOUP
With cinnamon—Near East style

1 cup beans	3 cups bouillon or stock
3 cups water	1/4 to 1/2 teaspoon cinnamon
3 tablespoons oil	salt and pepper
1 medium onion, chopped	1 tablespoon margarine
1 clove garlic, mashed	1 tablespoon flour

1. Bring to boil beans, water, and 1 tablespoon of the oil. Boil for 2 minutes; set aside for 1 hour (or longer if more convenient).
2. In remaining 2 tablespoons of oil sauté onion until transparent.
3. Combine beans and the water in which they were cooked with sautéed onion, garlic, and bouillon. Gently cook until beans are tender, about 1-1/2 hours.
4. Purée beans, leaving some whole for contrast.
5. Reheat and bring to boil. Add cinnamon and correct seasoning.
6. Blend margarine with flour and add in small bits to the boiling soup, while stirring. Boil for 2 minutes.

YIELD: 6 servings

BLACK BEAN SOUP

1 cup beans	1 tablespoon margarine
3 cups water	1 tablespoon flour
3 tablespoons oil	2 tablespoons dry sherry
1 medium onion, chopped	1 hard cooked egg, chopped (optional)
1 clove garlic, mashed pinch of dry mustard	6 very thin slices of lemon
3 cups bouillon or stock	
salt and pepper to taste	

1. Bring to boil beans, water, and 1 tablespoon of the oil. Boil for 2 minutes; set aside for 1 hour (or longer if more convenient).
2. In remaining 2 tablespoons of oil, sauté onion until transparent.
3. Combine beans and the water in which they have been cooked with onion, garlic, mustard, and bouillon. Gently cook until beans are tender, 2 to 3 hours.
4. Purée beans, leaving some whole for contrast.
5. Reheat soup and correct seasoning.
6. Blend margarine with flour and add in small bits

to the boiling soup, while stirring. Boil for 2 minutes. Add sherry.

7. Garnish each bowl of soup with chopped egg and a slice of lemon.

NOTE: Purées of beans are delicious served on boiled white rice. Black bean puree is especially attractive on saffron flavored rice.

YIELD: 6 servings

EEL SOUP
From Holland

1 pound eel, skinned, cut into 1-inch pieces	1/2 bay leaf
	1/2 teaspoon vinegar
	3 tablespoons margarine
1 quart water	
2 teaspoons salt	3 tablespoons flour
2 slices onion	1 egg yolk
2 slices lemon	1 tablespoon chopped parsley
4 peppercorns	

1. Bring to boil water, salt, onion, lemon, peppercorns, bay leaf, and vinegar.
2. Add eel; bring to boil. Simmer for about 20 minutes. Remove eel and reserve; strain broth.
3. Heat margarine in a saucepan and add flour. Cook, while stirring, until dry and bubbly.
4. Gradually add broth, bring to boil, stirring constantly. Boil for 5 minutes; correct seasoning.
5. Add eel and reheat.
6. Mix egg yolk with a little of the hot soup; add to the rest of the soup. Heat, but do not boil.
7. Sprinkle with parsley before serving.

YIELD: 4 servings

BOUILLABAISSE "MANHATTAN"

You can make good bouillabaisse only with strictly fresh fish.

1 pound each eel, skinned, red snapper, whiting
1 medium lobster (other fish may be used)
1 small onion, finely chopped
1 leek, white portion, finely chopped
2 cloves garlic, mashed
1 tablespoon tomato paste
2 ripe tomatoes, peeled, seeded, and mashed lightly
2 sprigs parsley, crushed
1 bay leaf
pinch of thyme
pinch of saffron, crushed
salt and pepper
1/4 cup oil (some olive)
1-1/2 quarts boiling water

1. Have fish dealer clean and cut fish and lobster into serving pieces.
2. Put fish, vegetables, seasonings, and oil into a large bowl.
3. Mix all well and marinate for several hours in the refrigerator. This step is very important for the exceptional flavor of this dish.
4. Twenty minutes before serving, put eel and lobster (the more firmly fleshed fish) in a big pot. Pour the boiling water over the fish and boil rapidly, uncovered, for about 10 minutes.
5. Add the rest of the fish, vegetables, and seasonings. If necessary, add more boiling water, just enough to cover fish.
6. Bring to boil again, simmer 10 to 15 minutes until fish is done. The delicately fleshed fish such as snapper and whiting should be cooked gently.
7. Serve over small pieces of toasted bread. Sprinkle with parsley.

YIELD: 6 servings

SALT CODFISH SOUP
Mediterranean

- 1 medium onion, chopped
- 4 tablespoons oil (some olive)
- 1 leek, white part, chopped
- 1 clove garlic, mashed
- 1 ripe tomato, peeled, chopped, or 1/2 cup canned tomatoes
- 2 medium potatoes, peeled, halved, cut into 1/4-inch slices
- 3 cups water
- 1/2 bay leaf
- 1 pound salt codfish, soaked for 12 hours, cut into 3-inch pieces
- pinch of thyme
- pinch of saffron
- 1/2 cup dry white wine (optional)
- small slices of toasted bread lightly rubbed with a cut clove of garlic
- 1 tablespoon chopped parsley

1. Lightly brown onion in oil in a medium saucepan.
2. Add leek, garlic, and tomato; sauté 5 minutes.
3. Add potatoes and water; cook until potatoes are tender, 20 to 30 minutes.
4. Add bay leaf, fish, thyme, saffron, and wine; simmer about 20 minutes.
5. Serve over toasted bread slices. Sprinkle with parsley.

YIELD: 4 to 5 servings

BOURRIDE
"White Bouillabaisse"

1 pound each haddock, red snapper, and whiting (other fish may be used)	1 quart (about) boiling water
4 tablespoons oil (part olive)	2 sprigs parsley, crushed
1 small onion, chopped	1 bay leaf
1 leek, white portion, chopped	pinch of thyme
1 clove garlic, crushed	salt and pepper
1 cup dry white wine	4 tablespoons Aioli (page 249)
	1 tablespoon chopped parsley
	small slices of toasted bread

1. Have fish dealer clean and cut fish into serving pieces.
2. Sauté lightly in oil (do not brown) onion, leek, and garlic. Add fish, wine, boiling water (just enough to cover fish), parsley, bay leaf, thyme, salt and pepper.
3. Bring to boil. Uncovered, boil vigorously for 5 minutes. Simmer for another 5 to 8 minutes, until fish is done.
4. In a small bowl mix aioli with a few tablespoons of the hot broth. Add mixture to the soup.
5. Into each soup dish place two slices of toasted bread. Serve soup and fish over it. Sprinkle with parsley. If you wish, remove fish to a hot platter and serve broth and fish separately.

YIELD: 6 servings

FRESH STEAMED CLAMS

One dozen large or 2 dozen small clams will yield approximately 1 cup of chopped clams.

Let clams stand in cold water for about an hour. Scrub and rinse them well to remove sand.

Place clams in a large pot with 1/2 inch water in the

bottom. Cover tightly and cook until clam shells are steamed open.

Remove clams from shells. Strain broth and reserve.

MANHATTAN CLAM CHOWDER

- 2 medium onions, chopped
- 3 tablespoons oil
- 1 medium green pepper, chopped
- 2 medium potatoes, diced
- 2 cups canned tomatoes
- 1 stalk celery, diced
- 1 cup water
- 1 teaspoon salt
- pinch of pepper
- pinch of thyme
- 1 cup Fresh Steamed Clams, chopped (see above), or 1 can (10 ounces) chopped clams
- 1/2 cup clam liquor
- 1 tablespoon chopped parsley

1. Lightly brown onions in oil in a large saucepan.
2. Add other vegetables, water, and seasonings. Cook gently until vegetables are tender and flavors completely blended, about 1 hour.
3. Add clams and clam liquor; then just heat through. Sprinkle with parsley before serving.

YIELD: 4 servings

CREAM OF CLAM SOUP

- 1/2 small onion, chopped
- 2 tablespoons oil
- pinch of curry powder
- 1 cup Fresh Steamed Clams, chopped (see above), or 1 can (10 ounces) chopped clams
- 2 tablespoons flour
- 3 cups chicken broth
- 1/2 cup clam liquor
- salt and pepper
- 1/4 cup skimmed evaporated milk
- 1 tablespoon chopped parsley

1. In a medium saucepan sauté onion in oil until transparent.
2. Add curry powder and flour and cook until dry and bubbly, while stirring.
3. Add chicken broth, stirring constantly; bring to boil. Simmer 5 minutes.
4. Add clams and clam liquor; heat well but do not boil. Correct seasoning with salt and pepper.
5. Add evaporated milk. Sprinkle with parsley before serving.

YIELD: 4 servings

NEW ENGLAND FISH CHOWDER

2 cups water
1-1/2 teaspoons salt
1 pound fish (cod, halibut, or whiting)
1/4 cup chopped onion
2 tablespoons oil
1 cup diced raw potatoes
pepper
1 tablespoon margarine
1 tablespoon flour
2 cups milk
1/4 cup skimmed evaporated milk (optional)
chopped parsley or paprika

1. Bring water and salt to boil. Add fish and simmer 15 to 20 minutes (do not boil).
2. In a large saucepan cook onions in oil until transparent.
3. Add potatoes and fish stock. Boil 15 minutes or until potatoes are tender; add pepper.
4. Blend margarine and flour and add in small bits to the boiling soup; boil for 2 minutes while stirring gently.
5. Remove all bones and skin from fish, and flake. Add fish to soup and heat, but do not boil.
6. Heat milk and add to the soup. Add skimmed evaporated milk for extra creaminess.
7. Sprinkle with parsley or paprika before serving.

YIELD: 4 to 5 servings

CHICKEN POT AU FEU
Chicken and Soup

- 3- to 4-pound chicken, cut into quarters
- salt
- 1 tablespoon lemon juice
- boiling water
- 1 clove garlic
- 1 slice fresh ginger (optional)
- 1 chicken bouillon cube
- 2 leeks (white part) split in half, lengthwise, and sand carefully removed
- 2 carrots, scraped, split in half lengthwise
- 2 young white turnips, peeled and cut in half

1. Rub a little salt and the lemon juice into chicken and refrigerate for one hour or longer.
2. Put chicken into a pot just large enough to hold it; pour boiling water over it to cover.
3. Add garlic, ginger, and bouillon cube; bring to boil and simmer, covered, until done, about 1-1/2 hours.
4. In a separate pot, during the last half hour of cooking time, cook the vegetables gently in some of the chicken broth, partially covered, until just tender.
5. Serve the broth clear or with rice, pastina, or fine noodles.
6. Serve the chicken with the vegetables.

NOTE: If some of the chicken and broth are left, cool the chicken in the broth, which, when chilled, will form a light golden gel. Serve the chicken cold with horseradish, chutney, watermelon pickle, or parsley mayonnaise.

YIELD: 5 to 6 servings

LAMB BROTH

2 lamb shanks, trimmed
1 tablespoon salt
1 clove garlic
1 onion, cut into a few pieces
1 stalk celery, cut into a few pieces
2 quarts water

1. Rub salt into meat and let stand in the refrigerator 1 hour or longer. This improves the flavor of meat.
2. Bring to a boil meat, vegetables, and water. Reduce heat and simmer until meat is tender, 1-1/2 to 2 hours.
3. Strain broth and remove all fat.
4. Remove meat from shanks and dice.

SCOTCH BROTH

Make the Lamb Broth first. See recipe above.

2 cups water
1/2 cup pearl barley
1 tablespoon oil
2 medium carrots, diced
2 medium white turnips, diced
2 medium potatoes, diced (optional)
2 quarts Lamb Broth
diced lamb from cooked shanks
salt and pepper
1 teaspoon chopped parsley

1. Bring to a boil the water, barley, and oil. The oil helps to keep foam down. Simmer 1 hour or until barley is tender.
2. Add vegetables and Lamb Broth. Cook until vegetables are done, about 15 minutes.
3. Add diced lamb and salt and pepper to taste. Sprinkle with parsley and serve hot.

YIELD: 6 to 8 servings

VARIATIONS OF SCOTCH BROTH

1. Before adding the vegetables to the barley, sauté them in 2 tablespoons oil for a few minutes. This gives a richer taste. If you like this soup thickened, mix 1 tablespoon margarine with 1 tablespoon flour, then, during the last few minutes of cooking, add this bit by bit to the boiling soup, stirring to blend.

2. Use beef in place of lamb and proceed in the same way.

3. Use chicken or turkey in place of lamb. Rub salt lightly into the poultry and sprinkle with lemon juice; let stand for 1 hour or longer, then proceed in same way. If available, add a piece of fresh ginger to the broth.

4. Use giblets in place of lamb and proceed in the same way, then season broth with dry white wine.

11

Fish and Shellfish

Fish is a food of major importance in the Prudent Diet. It is high in good-quality protein, rich in minerals and vitamins, and the fat it contains is highly unsaturated. Substituting fish for some of your meat means a reduction in saturated fat and an increase in polyunsaturated fat in your diet. The Prudent Diet recommends at least five fish meals a week, for dinner, lunch, or breakfast.

A great variety of fish is available to New Yorkers and people in the states near either seacoast. About 200 kinds of fresh fish from lakes, streams, and the ocean come to the New York markets for wholesale and retail trade. Many of them are available in local fish stores. Smoked, pickled, dried, frozen and canned fish are found in many grocery and food specialty stores throughout the country. In whatever form it comes to your table, fish offers the same valuable nutrients, but the flavor of fresh fish is incomparable.

Almost everyone loves fresh fish—witness the many popular seafood restaurants. Yet there are few homes where it is served frequently; and the variety chosen is as limited as are the ways of preparation. If you learn to broil, bake, fry, steam, braise, and poach fish, you will discover how easy it is to achieve delectable results. Every kind of fish has a distinct flavor and texture, and different methods are better for some types than for others.

Montaigne, the great French writer, said, "*Je suis friand de poisson, et fais mes jours gras des maigres et mes fêtes des jours de jeûne.*" (I am so fond of fish I make Shrovetide, Lent, and my feast days fast days).

ABOUT FISH AND SHELLFISH

Use both your nose and eyes, when buying fresh fish. All fresh-caught fish have a pleasant smell; salt-water fish have an "oceany" fragrance. Flesh will be firm and elastic, gills pink or red, eyes bulging and bright. With experience, you will recognize the appearance of fresh fish.

No fish market near by? Find a good market, even if it is not close to your home. If in one trip you buy fish for more than one meal, you will save time. Plan broiled flounder, for instance, for the day of purchase and boiled shrimp for a future meal. For best flavor cook all fish on the day you buy it.

Your fish dealer will scale and clean the fish for you and also bone and cut it, if you ask him. He will tell you which fish are in season and plentiful and even advise you on preparing fish unfamiliar to you.

"Fish is cooked to develop flavor, not to make it tender. Fish flesh is naturally tender. *Overcooking* dries and toughens fish," quoting from "Fish 'n' Tips" by The Fishery Council of New York. We add that *undercooking* must also be avoided. Fish must be cooked until the flesh has lost its translucency and flakes when touched with a fork. When done, flesh will separate from the bone—not adhere to it.

Fish to be sautéed, broiled, or fried, including batter-fried, should be well dried with paper toweling and dusted with flour (unless the recipe indicates otherwise). "Instant blending" flour does an especially good job for this.

Many fine dishes can be made from canned, dried, frozen, pickled, and smoked fish. These are popular in salads, sandwiches, casseroles, and as hors d'oeuvre. Many cooks favor canned salmon or tuna and frozen fillets, not thinking of the great abundance of other choices, such as sardines in oil or mustard or tomato sauce, smoked mackerel, whitefish, sturgeon, kippered and pickled herring, and many others, The variety of fish for your table is unlimited.

TIME AND TEMPERATURE CHARTS
FOR PREPARING FISH DISHES

BROILING FISH FILLETS

Name of Fish	Thickness of Fillets Vary from	Baste During Broiling	Broiling Time
Bluefish	1/4 to 3/4 in.	Once	6 min.
Carp	1/4 to 1 1/4 in.	Once	8–10 min.
Cisco (Lake Herring)	1/4 to 1/2 in.	Once	5–7 min.
Cod	1/2 to 1 in.	Twice	8–10 min.
Flounder	1/4 to 1/2 in.	Once	5–7 min.
Fluke	1/4 to 2/3 in.	Twice	5–8 min.
Haddock	1/3 to 2/3 in.	Twice	5–8 min.
Hake	1/4 to 1/2 in.	Twice	6–8 min.
Mackerel	1/4 to 1 1/4 in.	Once	6–8 min.
Mullet	1/4 to 3/4 in.	Twice	6–8 min.
Pike	1/4 to 2/3 in.	Once	6–8 min.
Pollock	1/2 to 1 in.	Twice	6–8 min.
Porgy	1/4 to 5/8 in.	Twice	6 min.
Sea Bass	1/4 to 1/2 in.	Twice	5 min.
Sole-Lemon	1/4 to 3/4 in.	Twice	5–8 min.
Sole-Gray	1/4 inch usual thickness	Once	5 min.
Weakfish	1/4 to 3/4 in.	Twice	6 min.
Whitefish	1/4 to 3/4 in.	Once	6–8 min.
Whiting	1/4 to 3/4 in.	Twice	5 min.

110 THE PRUDENT DIET

BAKING FISH

Name of Fish	Thickness	Baking Time Head On	Baking Time Head Off
SMALL FISH:			
Bluefish	1½ in.	1½ min. per oz.	2 min. per oz.
Butterfish	½ in.	3 min. per oz.	
Croaker	1½ in.	1½ min. per oz.	2 min. per oz.
Flounder	1 in.	2 min. per oz.	
Herring	1 in.	1½ min. per oz.	2 min. per oz.
Mackerel	2½ in.	2 min. per oz.	1 min. per oz.
Pike	2¼ in.	1¼ min. per oz.	1 min. per oz.
Porgy	2 in.	1 min. per oz.	1¼ min. per oz.
Sea Bass	1½ in.	1⅔ min. per oz.	2 min. per oz.
Mullet	2 in.	1½ min. per oz.	2 min. per oz.
Weakfish	1½ in.	1⅔ min. per oz.	2 min. per oz.
Whiting	2 in.	1¼ min. per oz.	1½ min. per oz.
LARGE FISH or PIECES:			
Carp	2½ in.	12 min. per lb.	16 min. per lb.
Cod	2¾ in.	9 min. per lb.	12 min. per lb.
Florida Mackerel	2½ in.	17 min. per lb.	19 min. per lb.
Haddock	3¼ in.	10 min. per lb.	14 min. per lb.
Halibut	2¾ in.		11 min. per lb.
Salmon	2¼ in.		11 min. per lb.
Spotted Sea Trout	3½ in.	14 min. per lb.	15 min. per lb.
Striped Bass	2½ in.	12 min. per lb.	16 min. per lb.
Whitefish	1½ in.	15 min. per lb.	16 min. per lb.

From "FISH 'n' TIPS" Fishery Council, New York, N.Y. 10038

BROILING FISH STEAKS

Type of Steak	Thickness	Time On 1st Side	Time On 2nd Side	Extra Bastings
Cod	½ in.	3 min.	5 min.	1
	1 in.	5 min.	5 min.	1
Salmon	½ in.	3 min.	3 min.	.....
	1 in.	3 min.	5 min.	.....
Swordfish	½ in.	3 min.	3 min.	.....
	1 in.	3 min.	5 min.	.....
Fresh Tuna	½ in.	3 min.	3 min.	.....
	1 in.	4 min.	5 min.	.....
Halibut	½ in.	3 min.	3 min.	1
	1 in.	4 min.	5 min.	1
Striped Bass	½ in.	3 min.	3 min.	1
	1 in.	4 min.	4 min.	1

FISH AND SHELLFISH

BROILING WHOLE DRESSED FISH

Name of Fish	Distance From Source of Heat	Time On 1st Side	Time On 2nd Side
Bluefish	3 in.	4 min.	5 min.
Butterfish	3 in.	4 min.	5 min.
Carp (up to 3 lbs.)	6 in.	12 min.	14 min.
Cisco (Lake Herring)	6 in.	4 min.	5 min.
Croaker	6 in.	5 min.	8 min.
Flounder	3 in.	10 min.	White Side up—don't turn
Fluke	3 in.	8 min.	White Side up—don't turn
Mackerel	6 in.	3 min.	5 min.
Mullet	6 in.	5 min.	9 min.
Pike	6 in.	5 min.	8 min.
Porgy	3 in.	3 min.	6 min.
Sea Bass	6 in.	5 min.	6 min.
Swellfish Tails	3 in.	5 min.	6 min.
Weakfish	6 in.	3 min.	5 min.
Whitefish	6 in.	5 min.	8 min.
Whiting	6 in.	4 min.	5 min.

BROILING SPLIT FISH

Name of Fish	Distance From Source of Heat	Thickness of Fish	Broiling Time
Bluefish	3 in.	3/4 in.	8 min.
Bonito Mackerel	3 in.	1/2 to 1 1/2 in.	10 min.
Croaker	2 in.	3/4 in.	8 min.
*Carp	6 in.	1/2 to 1 1/2 in.	12–14 min.
Cisco (Lake Herring)	3 in.	1/4 to 1 in.	9–11 min.
Hake	3 in.	1 in.	6–8 min.
Mackerel	2 in.	3/4 to 1 in.	8–10 min.
Mullet	3 in.	1/4 to 1 in.	10–12 min.
Porgy	3 in.	1/2 to 1 in.	6–8 min.
*Pike	3 in.	1/4 to 1 1/4 in.	8–10 min.
Sea Bass	3 in.	1/2 to 1 in.	6–8 min.
Weakfish	2 in.	1/2 to 3/4 in.	6–8 min.
Whitefish	3 in.	1/2 to 1 1/2 in.	10–12 min.
Whiting	3 in.	1/4 to 1/2 in.	6–8 min.

---

* Carp and Pike should be basted twice during the broiling period instead of the single basting recommended for the other varieties.

BROILED FISH

When you broil fish, is it dry? Is the juice in the pan instead of the fish? Your fish will be juicy if you remember that the juice will flow in the opposite direction to the source of heat.

To Prepare Fish for Broiling:

Dry on paper toweling and dust with flour. Season with salt and pepper; brush with oil.

Basting with more oil or margarine during cooking may be necessary.

For extra good flavor, squeeze lemon juice liberally on fish 1/2 hour before broiling.

To Broil Fish:

Preheat broiler (unless indicated otherwise by your range manufacturer).

Preheat a heavy pan or griddle in the oven or on top of stove.

Place prepared fish on lightly oiled aluminum foil boat; transfer fish on foil to hot griddle and into broiler.

Fish will cook from above (broiler) and below (hot griddle) at the same time and the juice will stay in the fish.

Do not turn the following fish during broiling: fillets, split fish, whole flounder, fish steaks less than 3/4 to 1 inch thick.

Broil thin fish such as fillets very near flame to brown quickly.

Broil split fish skin side down.

Broil whole flounder white side up.

Fish steaks and whole fish thicker than 1 inch should be turned after 3 or 4 minutes.

FRIED FISH

Cut fish into serving pieces and pat dry.

For all pan-frying, use the steam-vented lid; this will avoid the "fried-fish smell"; fish will cook faster, be crisp and juicy, stay hot longer.

FISH AND SHELLFISH

PAN-FRIED FISH

Breading: Dip fish into flour seasoned with salt and pepper; shake off excess flour.

Dip fish into egg beaten with milk or water: 1 egg or 2 egg whites to 2 tablespoons milk for 1-1/2 pounds of fish.

Roll in fine bread crumbs.

Pan-frying the fish: In a skillet, heat 1/4 inch oil (oil should not reach smoking point).

Do not crowd fish in skillet—crowding prevents browning.

Cook until nicely browned on one side, turn and brown other side.

Blot off any excess oil. Serve on a hot platter.

DEEP-FRIED FISH

See What to Know about Frying, page 50.

THREE WAYS TO PREPARE FISH FOR DEEP-FRYING:
1. Bread fish as for pan-frying.
2. Dip fish into skimmed evaporated milk seasoned with salt and pepper; dust with fine bread crumbs or flour.
3. Very small fish, such as smelts, may be dipped into batter.

TO DEEP-FRY FISH

An automatic fryer or a heavy saucepan is equally satisfactory. The pan should be no more than 1/3 full of oil.

Either a wire basket or a slotted spoon is useful to lift out the pieces of fried fish.

1. Heat oil (do not let it smoke); it is ready for frying when a 1-inch cube of bread browns in about 40 seconds or when oil reaches about 370°F.
2. Place fish in hot oil; do not crowd the pan. Cook until golden brown, 3 to 5 minutes. Drain on absorbent

paper and season to taste. Deep-frying does not absorb more oil (and may use less) than pan-frying.

3. Serve with tartar sauce.

POACHED FISH

This is one of the easiest and best ways to cook fish, delicious also when served cold. Use salmon, halibut, cod, whitefish, pike, eel or other fish.

1-1/2 pounds fish	1 tablespoon lemon juice
1-1/2 teaspoons salt	
2 cups water	1 teaspoon vinegar
4 peppercorns	1 small onion sliced
1 bay leaf	

1. Cut fish into serving pieces. Rub salt lightly into fish.
2. Pour water and remaining ingredients into a saucepan just the right size to hold fish; bring to a boil.
3. Place fish in stock (stock must cover fish) and bring again to boiling point, cover lightly—steam must be able to escape.
4. Simmer fish (do not boil) until it flakes when touched with a fork and has lost its translucency—about 15 minutes.
5. Serve mustard sauce with cod; Hollandaise with salmon and halibut; homemade mayonnaise and parsley mayonnaise with salmon, eel, pike, and whitefish; lemon "butter" with all of these fish.

NOTE: To serve cold, remove fish to a serving dish, strain stock over it, and chill. Serve with mayonnaise.

YIELD: 4 servings

BAKED FISH WITH TOMATOES

Use cod, haddock, carp, mackerel or other fish.

  2 pounds fish (fillets or steaks)
  2 medium-sized onions, sliced
  6 tablespoons oil
  2-1/2 cups canned tomatoes, drained
  1 clove garlic, crushed
  1/2 teaspoon paprika
  salt to taste
  juice of 1/2 lemon
  chopped parsley
  lemon slices

1. Sauté onions until golden brown in 4 tablespoons of the oil.
2. Add tomatoes, garlic, paprika, salt, lemon juice, and remaining 2 tablespoons of oil. Simmer about 20 minutes.
3. Preheat oven to 400°F.
4. Place fish in a baking dish and cover with the sauce. Bake approximately 30 minutes.
5. Before serving, garnish with chopped parsley and lemon slices.

YIELD: 4 servings

BRAISED FISH

This is a good way to cook a large fish such as striped bass, salmon, pike, whitefish, or carp.

  3- to 4-pound whole fish
  2 tablespoons margarine
  1/2 medium onion, sliced
  2 to 3 sliced mushrooms (optional)
  2 sprigs parsley
  1 bay leaf
  4 peppercorns
  pinch of thyme
  2/3 cup dry white wine
  lemon slices

1. Preheat oven to 375°F. Sprinkle inside of fish with salt and lemon juice.
2. In a pan just the right size to hold fish, put margarine, onion, mushrooms, parsley, bay leaf, peppercorns, and thyme.
3. Place fish on vegetables. Pour wine over fish. Cover pan lightly with aluminum foil.
4. Cook 40 to 50 minutes, depending upon size of fish. Baste with liquid in pan several times during cooking.
5. Garnish with lemon slices. Serve with parsley potatoes.

YIELD: 6 to 8 servings

STEAMED FISH

Steamed fish is delicately flavored and moist. Use halibut, cod, whiting, sea bass, perch, and others.

1-1/2 pounds fish steak or fillet *or* 2 pounds whole fish	salt and pepper to taste

1. Pour about 2 inches of water into a large pot that has a cover. Place a rack (or bowl) at least 3 inches high in the pot to support the platter of fish.
2. Lightly oil a heat-proof platter, put fish on platter. Transfer platter to rack (water must not touch the fish). Bring water to boil and cover pot.
3. Gently steam until fish has lost its translucency, 15 to 30 minutes, depending on thickness. Replenish water if it should boil away.
4. Season fish with salt and pepper and serve on platter on which it was steamed. Serve with lemon or mustard "butter" or Hollandaise sauce.

YIELD: 4 servings

RUSSIAN FISH STEW
With a French touch

Use halibut, flounder, cod, scrod, whitefish, pike or other fish.

1-1/2 pounds fish	4 small onions
1 teaspoon salt	1 cup clam juice
juice of half a lemon	1 cup water
	1 bay leaf
2 medium carrots, cut into strips	4 peppercorns
	1/4 cup Aioli or Hollandaise Sauce
2 medium potatoes, halved	

1. Cut fish into serving pieces. Do not remove skin. Sprinkle fish with salt and lemon juice. Refrigerate until ready to use.

2. Put vegetables, clam juice, water, bay leaf, and peppercorns into a pot wide enough to hold fish in a single layer. Cook vegetables until tender, about 20 minutes.

3. Place fish, skin side down, on top of vegetables and cover the pot. The fish will cook in the steam. Cook 5 to 15 minutes, depending upon thickness of fish.

4. Thin the Aioli or Hollandaise with a little of the hot broth and serve separately with the fish stew or combine Aioli or Hollandaise with a little of the broth and blend with the remaining fish broth (do not boil).

YIELD: 4 servings

BAKED FISH WITH MUSSELS

The French call it a Spanish recipe. Use whole red snapper, striped bass or other whole fish, or a large piece of fish.

- 1 pint mussels, cleaned
- 2 tablespoons oil
- 1/2 medium onion, chopped
- 1/2 clove garlic, mashed
- 2 ripe tomatoes, peeled and seeded, or 1 cup canned tomatoes, drained
- 2 tablespoons chopped parsley
- pinch of saffron
- salt and pepper to taste
- 2 to 3 pounds whole fish
- 3 ounces dry white wine
- lemon wedges

1. Steam mussels open with a little water in a covered pot. Remove them from their shells and reserve.
2. In the oil, sauté onion and garlic for 2 minutes (do not brown), then add tomatoes, parsley, saffron, salt, and pepper. Simmer for a few minutes.
3. Preheat oven to 375°F. On a baking pan, place a large enough sheet of aluminum foil to envelop the whole fish.
4. Sprinkle inside of fish with salt, pepper, and lemon juice. Place fish on the foil and surround with tomato mixture and mussels. Pour wine over the fish. Bring foil up on all sides to cover fish well and twist foil to close it tightly.
5. Bake for 45 to 60 minutes, depending on size of fish.
6. Serve with lemon wedges.

NOTE: This dish is also very good made without the mussels.

YIELD: 4 to 6 servings

SCANDINAVIAN FISH PUDDING

A blender recipe. Use haddock, cod or halibut

1 medium onion, coarsely cut	1/2 cup skimmed evaporated milk
1-1/4 pounds raw fish, cubed (skinned and boned)	1/4 cup water
	1 teaspoon lemon juice
1 tablespoon cornstarch	1 egg
1 tablespoon water	1/4 teaspoon pepper
	pinch of nutmeg
	1 teaspoon salt
	1/3 cup oil

1. Preheat oven to 350°F.
2. Cover onion with water in a small saucepan, bring to boil, and cook for a few minutes; drain and rinse with cold water (to remove strong onion flavor).
3. Mix cornstarch and the 1 tablespoon water to a smooth paste. Mix evaporated milk with the 1/4 cup water; combine with cornstarch paste.
4. In the blender, put lemon juice, egg, pepper, nutmeg, and salt. Cover and blend a few seconds.
5. Remove cover; pour oil into center in a slow, steady stream while blender is in slow motion. Gradually add milk mixture; blend a few seconds. Pour half the blender mixture into a jar and set aside.
6. To the remaining mixture in the blender add half the fish and half the onion. Cover container and blend 30 seconds; stop and stir down with a spatula. Cover and blend until smooth (about 30 seconds). Pour into a mixing bowl.
7. Repeat with remaining milk mixture, fish, and onion.
8. Combine the blended mixtures and pour into a greased casserole. Bake in a shallow pan of water about 40 minutes, or until a knife comes out clean when inserted halfway between center and edge of casserole.
9. Serve pudding hot with Hollandaise or mushroom sauce.

NOTE: This pudding is delicious cold as well as hot. Serve cold pudding with mayonnaise thinned with a little yogurt or buttermilk and flavored with dill, parsley, or horseradish.

YIELD: 4 servings

STEAMED FISH CANTONESE

1-1/2 pounds whole fish (sea bass or pompano, preferably with head and tail on)
1 clove garlic, crushed
1/2 teaspoon sugar
1 teaspoon shredded ginger root
3 tablespoons oil
1 tablespoon sherry
1 tablespoon soy sauce
2 scallions, chopped

1. Place fish on a foil boat made of heavy aluminum foil. Mix garlic, sugar, ginger, 1 tablespoon of the oil, sherry, and soy sauce and spread on fish.
2. Place a rack in a large pot and a heatproof platter on the rack. Pour about 2 inches of water into the pot (water is not to touch the fish). Put the fish in foil on the platter.
3. Bring water to a boil, cover pot, and steam fish about 30 minutes. Replenish water if it should boil away.
4. Mix scallions with remaining 2 tablespoons of oil and pour over fish at serving time.
5. Serve fish with interesting green vegetables such as mustard or dandelion greens, broccoli, or spinach.

NOTE: Red snapper, porgy, flounder and most fish may be steamed successfully in this way.

YIELD: 2 servings

BAKED WHOLE STRIPED BASS

3 to 4 pounds striped bass
thin lemon slices
tomato halves (optional)

1. Preheat oven to 350°F.
2. Sprinkle inside of fish with salt and pepper. Place in a baking pan lined with oiled heavy aluminum foil. Brush fish with oil and dust with a little flour. Sprinkle with paprika.
3. Make cuts with a sharp knife 2 inches apart across the fish and insert lemon slices. If room in the baking pan permits, bake tomato halves alongside of fish.
4. Bake from 35 to 45 minutes depending upon thickness of fish.
5. Serve with Lemon Butter (page 259).

NOTE: Potatoes may be baked with the fish, but should be started 20 minutes before the fish is put into the oven. No meal could be easier or better.

YIELD: 6 to 8 servings

BAKED SPLIT STRIPED BASS

1. Preheat oven to 425°F.
2. Split fish (3 to 4 pounds) and place it skin down in a pan lined with oiled foil.
3. Sprinkle with salt and pepper and about 2 tablespoons of lemon juice. Brush with oil, dust with flour, and sprinkle with paprika.
4. Bake 20 to 30 minutes.
5. Serve with lemon or parsley "butter."

NOTE: Red snapper, whitefish and large sections of salmon or mackerel may also be baked in this way.

LEMON BROILED BLOWFISH

Blowfish is also good deep fried, like scallops.

1 pound blowfish
1/4 cup oil
juice of 1 lemon
salt and pepper to taste
1 tablespoon flour
paprika to taste
1 tablespoon margarine

1. Preheat broiler; also heat a shallow pan, lined with aluminum foil.
2. Roll fish in oil and place on foil in the hot pan. Mix lemon juice, salt, and pepper and pour over fish. Mix flour with paprika and sprinkle it over fish, then dot with margarine.
3. Broil about 3 inches from flame for 5 to 7 minutes. Do not turn fish.
4. When you serve it, make sure that each portion gets a little of the good juice.

YIELD: 3 servings

ELEANOR'S DELICIOUS FRESH CODFISH CAKES

1 pound fresh codfish	2 medium potatoes, cubed
1 cup water	1 tablespoon margarine
1 teaspoon salt	
1/2 medium onion, cut into a few slices	1/2 teaspoon baking powder
	1 egg, beaten lightly
	pepper
	fine bread crumbs

1. Combine the water, salt, and onion in a saucepan and bring to a boil. Add the fish (water should cover fish) and simmer about 15 minutes or until fish is done.
2. Remove fish from stock; skin, bone, and flake the fish.
3. Remove onion from stock, add potatoes, and cook until tender; drain.
4. Mash potatoes, mix with margarine, and stir until creamy. Add baking powder, egg, and pepper to taste. Add fish and mix well.
5. Shape into cakes (handle carefully—mixture is soft) and roll in crumbs. Refrigerate cakes until ready to fry; these cakes can be prepared several hours ahead of time.
6. Pan-fry in oil to a golden brown on both sides.
7. Serve with garlic-flavored mayonnaise (Aioli) or tartar sauce.

YIELD: 4 servings

FRESHENING DRIED SALT CODFISH

Prepare (freshen) all salt cod as follows before using.

1. Soak fish in cold water about 6 hours, changing the water once.
2. Drain and cover fish with fresh water. Bring to the boiling point, simmer (do not boil) from 5 to 10 minutes. Cover and let stand for one-half hour.

PURÉE OF SALT COD
Brandade de Morue

- 1 pound dried salt cod
- 1 clove garlic, mashed
- 3/4 cup oil (some olive)
- 1 cup skimmed evaporated milk
- 2 tablespoons lemon juice
- nutmeg and black pepper

1. Follow directions for preparing salt codfish (see previous recipe).
2. Remove skin and bones and cut fish into small pieces. Run fish and garlic through the fine knife of a food chopper. Then, with a wooden spoon, mash into a fine paste (this is not hard to do).
3. Heat oil and milk separately until warm (not hot).
4. Put a little of the oil in a saucepan and add the fish. Over a very low flame, heat the fish, incorporating, little by little, the oil and milk alternately, while stirring. Beat all well to a light fluffy purée.
5. Season with lemon juice, nutmeg, and freshly ground pepper.
6. Serve with crisp toast, fried croutons, or crusty French bread.

YIELD: 4 servings

SALT CODFISH AND SPINACH
Mediterranean

1/2 small onion, chopped	1/2 clove garlic, mashed
2 tablespoons oil	1 cup milk
1 tablespoon flour	salt, pepper, and nutmeg
1 pound fresh spinach, cooked and chopped	1 pound dried codfish, freshened

1. In a saucepan sauté onion in oil until transparent.
2. Add flour and cook, while stirring, until dry and bubbly. Add spinach and garlic and simmer a few minutes. Gradually stir in milk; heat to a boil. Season lightly with salt, pepper, and nutmeg. Set aside.
3. Pat fish dry with paper toweling. Remove skin and bones. Cut fish into serving pieces; dush with flour. In a skillet heat a small amount of oil and sauté fish until golden.
4. Place fish in a casserole. Spoon creamed spinach over it. Heat through in a 325°F. oven, about 15 minutes.

NOTE: You may substitute one 10-ounce package frozen chopped spinach, cooked, for the fresh spinach.

YIELD: 4 servings

VARIATION OF SALT CODFISH AND SPINACH
This is popular in north and central France.

1. Prepare creamed spinach as in preceding recipe.
2. Flake the freshened codfish, removing skin and bones. Gently combine fish with creamed spinach and spoon into a baking dish. Sprinkle with 2 tablespoons bread crumbs and dot with 2 tablespoons margarine.
3. Heat through and brown in a 400°F. oven, about 10 minutes.

CANNED SARDINES AND SPINACH
A tasty, inexpensive main dish

1. Prepare creamed spinach as for Salt Codfish and Spinach, using 1/2 cup of milk only (see above).
2. Spoon creamed spinach into individual shallow baking dishes. Arrange sardines over spinach and sprinkle with a few drops of lemon juice and some grated cheese.
3. Broil until heated through and lightly browned on top.

BROILED CANNED SARDINES

Broil sardines, sprinkled with a few drops of lemon juice, on a foil-lined pie tin, until crisp. Serve on toast with tomato wedges and black olives.

YIELD: 4 small servings

EEL IN ASPIC

1-1/2 pounds eel, skinned and cut into two-inch pieces
salt and pepper to taste
1 clove garlic, crushed
1 onion, sliced
1 bay leaf
1 cup water
1/2 cup dry white wine
1 tablespoon lemon juice

1. Season eel with salt and pepper.
2. Place all other ingredients in a saucepan and bring to a boil. Add eel, cover pan lightly, and simmer 15 to 20 minutes.
3. Transfer eel to a bowl and strain the liquid over it. Cool and place in refrigerator. The liquid will jell when well chilled.
4. Serve with parsley mayonnaise.

YIELD: 4 servings

FINNAN HADDIE IN CREAM SAUCE

1-1/2 pounds smoked haddock (finnan haddie)	1 teaspoon grated onion
3 tablespoons oil	1/2 teaspoon salt
2 tablespoons flour	pepper
1-1/2 cups milk	few drops Worcestershire sauce

1. Cover fish with cold water, bring to a boil, and simmer 15 minutes. Drain and cool, then flake fish, removing skin and bones.
2. Heat oil, stir in the flour, and cook until dry and bubbly. Gradually add milk and onion, stirring constantly. Boil for a few minutes. Add seasonings and gently add the fish.
3. Serve hot over toast, with rice, or with baked or boiled potatoes. The creamed fish can also be placed in a casserole, sprinkled with some grated cheese and browned under the broiler.

YIELD: 4 servings

BROILED HALIBUT

1-1/2 pounds halibut steak (about 3/4 inch thick)	1/2 onion, sliced
	1/4 cup lemon juice
	salt and paprika
2 tablespoons oil	1 tablespoon margarine

1. Preheat broiler.
2. Heat a heavy pan for broiling and line it with foil if desired. Brush surface of pan or foil with part of the oil.
3. When pan is hot, add halibut and cover with onion slices. Pour lemon juice over fish, dot with bits of margarine, and add remaining oil. Sprinkle with salt and paprika.
4. Broil for 8 to 10 minutes, depending upon thickness of fish. If fish is more than one inch thick, turn once, after 3 minutes, and finish broiling.

NOTE: When broiling a thick piece of fish, do not add onion and paprika until after the fish has been turned.

YIELD: 4 servings

HALIBUT BAKED IN SHERRY

1-1/2 pounds halibut steak	1 tablespoon lemon juice
2 tablespoons oil	1/4 cup dry sherry
1/2 teaspoon salt	1 teaspoon chopped parsley

1. Preheat oven to 350°F.
2. Use part of the oil to brush the bottom of a shallow baking dish. Place halibut in dish and sprinkle with salt. Combine remaining oil, lemon juice, and sherry; brush fish with mixture.
3. Bake about 30 minutes or until fish flakes. During baking baste fish with remaining wine mixture.
4. Sprinkle with parsley 5 minutes before removing from oven.

YIELD: 3 to 4 servings

MACKEREL FILLETS IN WINE SAUCE

1-1/2 pounds mackerel fillets, cut in serving pieces	strip of lemon peel
	pinch of tarragon
1/2 cup dry white wine	3 or 4 peppercorns
	small bay leaf
1/2 cup water	1/2 teaspoon prepared mustard
1 teaspoon salt	
1 onion, sliced	1 teaspoon chopped parsley

1. Simmer wine, water, salt, onion, lemon peel, tarragon, peppercorns, and bay leaf about 5 minutes, then strain.
2. In the strained broth, bring fillets to a boil and

simmer about 10 minutes. When cool enough to handle, take fish out of broth and remove skin and bones (handle carefully). Arrange fillets in a single layer in a shallow dish.

3. Season broth with mustard and parsley and pour over fish, then chill well.

NOTE: It is easier to cook fish in two portions in the same broth; cook half the fish and remove from broth, then cook the other half. Using this method, less broth will be needed and fish will have a superior flavor.

This also makes a fine hors d'oeuvre.

YIELD: 4 servings

FILLETS OF MACKEREL or BONED SHAD ESCABECHE (Marinated)

2 pounds fish, cut in serving pieces (leave on fish)

juice of 1 lemon or 1 lime

MARINADE

1 cup thinly sliced onions
1 green pepper, seeded, thinly sliced
1/2 cup thinly sliced carrots
1/2 cup thinly sliced celery

6 cloves garlic (left whole)
1/2 cup oil
2 teaspoons salt
2 bay leaves
10 peppercorns
1/2 teaspoon thyme
1 cup water
1/2 cup vinegar

FOR FRYING

2 teaspoons salt
1/2 teaspoon chili powder
flour for dredging

GARNISHES

chopped parsley
black olives
lemon or lime wedges

1. Sprinkle fish with lemon or lime juice and let stand about 20 minutes.

2. To make the marinade, cook vegetables in oil

until onions are transparent; do not brown. Add seasonings, water, and vinegar. Cover and cook gently about 20 minutes.

3. Pat fish dry with paper toweling; handle carefully. Sprinkle with salt and chili powder. Dip fish in flour and shake off excess.

4. In hot oil, fry a few pieces at a time, 2 to 3 minutes on each side. Place fried pieces in a single layer on a platter.

5. When all fish is fried, pour the hot marinade over the fish, making sure that each piece gets its share of vegetables.

6. Cool fish, cover loosely with waxed paper, then refrigerate at least 24 hours before serving.

7. At serving time, sprinkle with parsley, garnish with olives and lemon or lime wedges. Serve with crisp French bread.

YIELD: 8 servings for main dish
16 for hors d'oeuvre

BROILED SALMON

1. Select the tail end or a section of whole fish, split, rather than a salmon steak, as the fish will then be juicier.

2. Sprinkle fish liberally with lemon juice 1/2 hour before broiling.

3. Place fish skin side down on heavy aluminum foil (well oiled) and place on the preheated griddle or pan. Sprinkle fish with salt and pepper; dust lightly with flour. Dot with bits of margarine.

4. Broil 8 to 10 minutes.

SALMON BAKED IN WINE

1 pound fresh salmon (steak or fillet)
salt and pepper
1/3 cup dry white wine or dry sherry
2 tablespoons oil
juice of 1/2 lemon

1. Preheat oven to 400°F.
2. Place salmon in a baking pan and sprinkle with salt and pepper. Combine remaining ingredients and pour over fish.
3. Bake 15 to 20 minutes or until fish flakes easily when tested with a fork.

YIELD: 3 servings

SALMON PATTIES

The juice of a one-pound can of salmon is needed to make these patties, even though only one half of the fish in the can is used. This juice has a fine flavor and provides the needed liquid, or most of it (about 1/3 cup). Use the remaining salmon for salad or sandwiches.

- 1 can (1 pound) salmon
- 10 saltines, crumbled
- 1 egg
- 1 tablespoon finely chopped onion
- 1 tablespoon finely chopped green pepper
- black pepper to taste
- lemon wedges

1. Drain salmon, reserving the juice.
2. Combine 1/2 the salmon, the reserved juice, saltines, egg, onion, green pepper, and pepper to taste. Blend lightly. This mixture should be quite moist; if more liquid is needed, add 1 or 2 tablespoons milk.
3. Heat a little oil in a heavy skillet (do not overheat). Using a tablespoon, drop mixture into the hot oil and flatten patties out a bit. Brown on both sides.
4. Serve with lemon wedges.

YIELD: 2 servings

FILLETS OF SOLE WITH MUSHROOMS
Bonne Femme

- 1 pound fish fillets
- 2 tablespoons margarine
- 1 small onion, finely chopped
- 1/4 pound mushrooms, thinly sliced
- 1 teaspoon chopped parsley
- 1 tablespoon lemon juice
- salt and pepper to taste
- 1/2 cup dry white wine
- 2 teaspoons flour

1. Preheat oven to 325°F.
2. Place fillets in a baking pan which has been greased with 1 tablespoon of the margarine. You may wish to cut them into serving pieces for easier handling. Sprinkle fillets with onion, mushrooms, parsley, lemon juice, salt, and pepper. Pour wine over fish.
3. Bake 15 minutes or until fish has lost its translucency. Transfer fish to a hot serving platter.
4. In a small pot, heat remaining 1 tablespoon of margarine, add flour and cook, stirring, until dry and bubbly. Add liquid and vegetables from pan in which fish was cooked. Bring to a boil and cook 1 minute, until thickened.
5. Pour sauce over fish and serve hot.

YIELD: 4 servings

LEMON BROILED SWORDFISH

- juice of 1 lemon
- 2 tablespoons oil
- salt and pepper
- 1-1/2 pounds swordfish steak (about 3/4 inch thick)
- paprika

1. Mix lemon juice, oil, salt and pepper; pour over fish and let stand about 1/2 hour.
2. Preheat broiler and griddle or pan. Place fish on well-oiled aluminum foil boat.
3. Pour any remaining lemon juice mixture over fish

and sprinkle with paprika; then transfer to hot griddle in broiler.

4. Broil for about 8 to 10 minutes; do not overcook it. There is no need to turn fish unless it is thicker than 3/4 inch.

YIELD: 4 servings

TURKISH BROILED SWORDFISH ON SPITS

- 2 pounds swordfish (about 1 inch thick)
- 1 tablespoon lemon juice
- 1 tablespoon oil
- 1 tablespoon grated onion
- 1 teaspoon paprika
- salt to taste
- 10 small bay leaves
- chopped parsley
- lemon wedges

1. Cut fish into 1-inch cubes; place in a mixing bowl.

2. Combine lemon juice, oil, onion, paprika, and salt. Mix this thoroughly with fish. Add two of the bay leaves and refrigerate mixture for 2 to 3 hours.

3. When ready to cook, place fish on spits with an occasional bay leaf in between the pieces.

4. Broil on all sides, either over outdoor grill or in broiler, about 3 inches from flame.

5. Sprinkle with chopped parsley and serve with lemon wedges.

YIELD: 6 servings

SOY-SAUCE BROILED SWORDFISH
Very simple, delicious, and unusual

- juice of 1 lemon
- 2 tablespoons soy sauce
- 1 tablespoon oil
- 1-1/2 pounds swordfish (about 3/4 inch thick)

1. Mix lemon juice, soy sauce, and oil; brush this mixture on fish.
2. Broil as in preceding recipe for Lemon Broiled Swordfish.
3. Baste during broiling with leftover soy sauce mixture.

YIELD: 4 servings

SAUTÉED SHAD ROE

1. Dip shad roe in skimmed evaporated milk, seasoned lightly with salt. Drain and dust with flour.
2. In a skillet heat 1 tablespoon oil for one shad roe. Brown slowly on both sides while partially covered. Cook 10 to 15 minutes.
3. Serve sprinkled with parsley and garnished with lemon wedges. Tartar sauce or lemon "butter" are delicious with shad roe.

FRIED SCALLOPS

1 pound bay or sea scallops
1/3 cup skimmed evaporated milk
salt and pepper to taste
fine bread crumbs (toasted crumbs make a browner crust)
oil for deep frying

1. Wipe scallops with damp paper toweling to remove any bits of shell.
2. Mix milk with salt and pepper. Dip scallops into seasoned milk and roll them in bread crumbs. Fry in deep hot oil 3 to 4 minutes or until lightly browned.
3. Serve with lemon wedges, mayonnaise, or tartar sauce.

YIELD: 4 servings

BROILED SCALLOPS

1 pound sea scallops
1/4 cup oil
Seasoned Bread Crumbs (see following recipe)

1. Preheat broiler and griddle or heavy pan.
2. Wipe scallops with damp paper toweling to remove bits of shell. Dip scallops into oil, then roll them in seasoned crumbs.
3. Place scallops on oiled heavy aluminum foil and transfer foil to hot griddle. Broil quickly, turning once.
4. Serve with lemon wedges, mayonnaise, or tartar sauce.

YIELD: 4 servings

SEASONED BREAD CRUMBS

1 cup fine bread crumbs
1 teaspoon salt
1/4 teaspoon freshly ground black pepper
1/4 teaspoon oregano
2 tablespoons grated Parmesan cheese

Mix all ingredients well and store in covered jar in the refrigerator.

CURRIED SCALLOPS

1 pound scallops
1 tablespoon curry powder
2 tablespoons flour
1/2 teaspoon salt
2 or 3 tablespoons oil
1 clove garlic, crushed
3 tablespoons dry white wine or vermouth
chopped parsley

1. If scallops are large cut them in half. Dry them well.
2. In a paper bag mix curry powder, flour, and salt; toss scallops in mixture.

3. Heat oil in a skillet; add scallops and toss around quickly to brown on all sides. Do not crowd—if necessary, cook in two batches.

4. Add garlic to skillet and sauté one minute (do not brown). Add wine and cook just long enough to heat through.

5. Serve on boiled rice. Sprinkle with parsley before serving.

YIELD: 4 servings

COQUILLES SAINT JACQUES AU GRATIN

- 1 cup water
- 1 cup dry white wine
- 1 teaspoon salt
- 4 peppercorns
- 1 bay leaf
- 1 tablespoon lemon juice
- 1 pound scallops
- 1/2 pound shrimp
- 1 tablespoon finely chopped shallot or onion
- 2 to 3 mushrooms, chopped
- 2 tablespoons oil
- 2 tablespoons flour
- 2 teaspoons chopped parsley
- 2 tablespoons fine bread crumbs
- 2 tablespoons margarine
- 2 tablespoons grated cheese (optional)

1. Combine water, wine, salt, peppercorns, bay leaf, and lemon juice in a saucepan and bring to a boil.

2. Add scallops, bring to a boil again, and simmer for 3 or 4 minutes, depending upon their size; remove scallops.

3. Cook shrimp in this same stock for 3 or 4 minutes, depending upon their size. Remove shrimp, shell, and devein them.

4. Strain stock and set aside; you should have 2 cups.

5. Sauté shallots and mushrooms in oil until lightly colored. Add flour and cook for about 2 minutes. Stir in reserved stock, bring to a boil, cook for a few minutes, and add parsley.

6. If scallops are large, cut them the size of bay scallops. Large shrimp may be cut into 2 or 3 pieces.

Gently mix scallops and shrimp with sauce and fill 6 large scallop shells or ramekins. Sprinkle with bread crumbs, dot with bits of margarine, and sprinkle with cheese.

7. Heat under broiler at 425°F. for a few minutes, until top is lightly browned.

YIELD: 6 servings

ABOUT PAELLA

There are many versions of paella, most of them more elaborate than this recipe, which we like for its simplicity. It is a most fortunate combination—chicken, shellfish, and saffron rice.

Paella is a great dish. No famous chef created it, but necessity, mother of invention, brought it to life. The Spanish coast and rivers abound in an endless variety of fish and shellfish. Rice was a staple food. Fish and rice were fine together and even better with chicken. And a little chicken could be made to go a long way. There was saffron to enhance the flavor and enchant the eye.

The French classic, bouillabaisse, had its origin in a similar way. Fish that found no buyer on market day had to be used by the fisherman's family—eventually resulting in a great dish.

Of course, dishes like paella, bouillabaisse, and some of the miracles of Chinese cookery did not just happen. Painstaking care of the ingredients, curiosity, and more than just a dash of daring and originality must have played their parts. Almost invariably a country's reputation for fine food originated in its humble kitchens.

PAELLA
From Spain

This dish derives its name from the special pan in which it is cooked.

2 dozen small clams (or mussels), cleaned	1 frying chicken, cut into 2-inch pieces
1/2 cup water	1/2 teaspoon salt
4 cups clam and chicken broth, mixed	2 cloves garlic, mashed
1/4 teaspoon saffron, crushed	1-1/2 cups rice, uncooked
1/4 cup oil (part olive)	1/2 cup shelled fresh peas, cooked
	1 pimiento, drained, cut into strips

1. Steam open 1 dozen of the clams in the water (reserve remaining clams, uncooked, in shells). Remove cooked clams; strain broth and reserve.
2. Mix chicken broth with clam broth to make 4 cups. Add saffron.
3. Preheat oven to 350°F.
4. In a large flameproof casserole, heat oil and brown chicken pieces until golden. Remove chicken from pan, sprinkle with salt, and set aside.
5. Add rice to the casserole and cook, while stirring, until translucent. Add garlic, cook one minute more. Heat broth and slowly add to rice. Boil briskly for 5 minutes, while stirring. Add chicken and bring to a boil again.
6. Transfer to the oven and bake uncovered 25 to 35 minutes. Add a little more broth, if necessary, to keep rice moist.
7. Combine steamed clams and peas with rice and chicken. Distribute uncooked clams over this mixture; cover with aluminum foil and bake 10 minutes or until clams open and are heated through; garnish with pimiento strips.

YIELD: 4 to 6 servings

HOW TO SHELL AND DEVEIN RAW SHRIMP

With scissors cut through the shrimp shell, on the back, from head to tail.

Slip off shell, being careful to keep the tail meat intact.

With a pointed knife, remove the vein running along the back.

STEAMED SHRIMP

- 1 pound shrimp
- 1 cup water
- 2 peppercorns
- 2 allspice berries
- 1/4 teaspoon dry mustard
- 1 bay leaf
- 1/2 lemon, cut in half

1. With scissors cut through shrimp shell, on the back, from head to tail. Leave shell on. With a pointed knife, remove the vein running along the back.
2. Place deveined shrimp in a strainer or steamer basket.
3. Put water and seasonings in a large pot and place strainer over the water (shrimp should not touch water). Bring water to a boil and cover pot.
4. Steam 3 to 5 minutes, depending on the size of shrimp. Remove shrimp, cool, and store, covered, in the refrigerator until ready to use.

YIELD: 3 servings

BOILED SHRIMP

Shrimp are simmered, not boiled.

- 1 pound shrimp
- 1 cup water
- 1 teaspoon salt
- 3 peppercorns
- 1 tablespoon lemon juice
- 1 teaspoon vinegar
- 1/2 bay leaf

1. With scissors cut through shrimp shell, on the back, from head to tail. Leave the shell on the shrimp.

With a pointed knife, remove the vein running along the back.

2. Bring water and seasonings to a boil in a saucepan just large enough to hold the shrimp.

3. Add shrimp and return to boil (stock must cover shrimp). Reduce heat and simmer, covered, for 3 to 5 minutes, depending on size of shrimp.

4. If shrimp are not to be used right away, cool them (leaving shells on) in the stock. Remove bay leaf and store shrimp in stock, well covered, in refrigerator.

YIELD: 3 servings

SHRIMP À L'INDIENNE (in Curry Sauce)

1. Prepare boiled or steamed shrimp as directed in the two previous recipes. Remove the shells.

2. Prepare Curry Sauce (page 255) using shrimp stock as part of the liquid.

3. Combine sauce and shrimp and heat gently but thoroughly.

4. Serve with boiled rice.

YIELD: 3 servings

SHRIMP AND CRAB MEAT AU GRATIN

- 1 pound boiled shrimp, shelled and deveined
- 1 can (7-1/2 ounces) crab meat
- 2 tablespoons oil
- 3 tablespoons margarine
- 1 small onion, chopped
- pinch of curry powder
- 3 tablespoons flour
- 1 cup shrimp stock
- 1-1/4 cups chicken broth
- 1/4 cup skimmed evaporated milk
- 1 teaspoon lemon juice
- salt to taste
- 3 tablespoons grated Parmesan cheese
- cayenne

1. Follow recipe for Boiled Shrimp; strain stock and reserve. If shrimp are large, cut them in half.
2. Carefully remove cartilage from crab meat, leaving pieces intact as much as possible.
3. In a saucepan heat oil and 2 tablespoons of the margarine and sauté onion until transparent. Add curry powder and flour and cook, while stirring, until mixture is dry and bubbly.
4. Gradually add shrimp stock and chicken broth, bring to boil, and cook until thickened and smooth, stirring throughout. Add evaporated milk and lemon juice; correct seasoning.
5. Preheat oven to 350°F.
6. Spoon a layer of sauce into 4 individual baking dishes or in a 1-1/2-quart casserole. Arrange shrimp and crab over sauce.
7. Distribute remaining sauce over shellfish mixture. Sprinkle with cheese, very lightly dust with cayenne, and dot with remaining tablespoon of margarine.
8. Bake until heated through and lightly browned on top, about 20 minutes.

YIELD: 4 servings

HEDI'S BAKED SHRIMP

1 pound raw shrimp, shelled and deveined	1/2 cup Seasoned Bread Crumbs
1 tablespoon oil	1 teaspoon chopped parsley
1/2 clove garlic, mashed	

1. Preheat oven to 350°F.
2. Pour oil over shrimp and toss until all are well coated.
3. Mix garlic with seasoned crumbs and parsley. Roll shrimp in crumbs or shake in a paper bag.
4. Bake shrimp in a shallow pan for about 10 minutes. If more browning is desired, place under the broiler for 1 to 2 minutes.

YIELD: 3 to 4 servings

SHRIMP WITH GREEN PEPPERS AND TOMATOES

2-1/2 tablespoons cornstarch	1 teaspoon sliced fresh ginger or 1/2 teaspoon powdered ginger
2-1/2 tablespoons soy sauce	
1/4 cup water	
1 pound green peppers, seeded	1 clove garlic, crushed
1 pound fresh ripe tomatoes or 2 cups canned tomatoes	1-1/2 pounds raw shrimp, shelled and deveined
	1-1/4 cups stock (beef or chicken)
4 tablespoons oil salt and pepper to taste	4 scallions, cut in 1-inch pieces

1. Mix cornstarch and soy sauce with water and set aside. Cut each pepper diagonally into about 8 pieces and parboil 5 minutes. Cut tomatoes into wedges, 6 to 8 for each tomato.

2. Place oil, salt, pepper, ginger, and garlic in a hot skillet. Add shrimp and sauté for 3 minutes. Add green peppers and stock, mix well, and cook gently for about 8 minutes.

3. Add cornstarch mixture, tomatoes, and scallions. Cook, stirring carefully so that the tomatoes won't break up, until the juice thickens smoothly.

YIELD: 4 servings

SHRIMP À LA BELLE CRÉOLE

- 1/4 cup oil
- 1/2 cup sliced green pepper
- 1-1/4 cups finely sliced onion
- 1/2 cup diced celery
- 1/4 cup chopped celery leaves
- 2 tablespoons chopped parsley
- 2 cups canned tomatoes
- 1/4 cup seedless raisins
- 1/4 cup chili sauce
- 2 ounces blanched, toasted almonds, finely chopped (about 1/3 cup)
- 1/4 teaspoon each of thyme, curry, salt, pepper, cayenne
- 1 bay leaf
- 1-1/4 pounds cooked shrimp, shelled and deveined

1. Heat oil in a heavy skillet. Add green pepper, onion, celery, and celery leaves and cook over low heat until onions are transparent but not browned.
2. Add all remaining ingredients except the shrimp and simmer gently for about 1 hour, stirring occasionally to prevent sticking.
3. Remove bay leaf and add shrimp, then heat through.
4. Serve over boiled rice.

NOTE: Raw shrimp, shelled and deveined, may be used. Simmer them with the sauce for the last 5 to 10 minutes of cooking.

YIELD: 4 servings

CHINESE SHRIMP BALLS

- 2 pounds raw shrimp
- 1/3 cup finely chopped celery
- 3 tablespoons cornstarch
- 2 eggs
- 1/3 cup finely chopped scallions
- 1 teaspoon salt
- dash of pepper
- 1 teaspoon monosodium glutamate
- 1-1/2 teaspoons shredded ginger

1. Shell and devein shrimp, then chop or grind them finely and place in a mixing bowl. Add all remaining ingredients and mix well.
2. Fill a medium-sized saucepan half full of water and bring to a boil. With a teaspoon, form balls of the shrimp mixture and drop into the boiling water. When balls float to surface, remove and cool.

NOTE: Use these shrimp balls in combination with vegetables. See the following recipe for Shrimp Balls with Broccoli.

YIELD: 6 servings

SHRIMP BALLS WITH BROCCOLI

- 1 recipe Shrimp Balls (see preceding recipe)
- 1 pound (1/2 bunch) broccoli, cleaned and cut into 2-inch pieces
- 2 tablespoons cornstarch
- 4 tablespoons water
- 1/4 teaspoon monosodium glutamate
- 1 teaspoon sugar
- 2 tablespoons soy sauce
- 2 tablespoons oil
- 1 teaspoon fresh ginger, finely chopped
- salt and pepper to taste
- 2 cups stock (use broth in which shrimp balls were cooked, or chicken broth)

1. Mix cornstarch with water, monosodium glutamate, sugar, and soy sauce, and set aside.
2. In a large pan, heat oil with ginger, salt, and pepper. Add Shrimp Balls and broccoli and sauté for a few minutes. Add stock, cover, and simmer about 10 minutes until broccoli is just tender but crisp.
3. Stir cornstarch mixture well before adding it to the shrimp-broccoli mixture. Cook, while stirring, until sauce has thickened and is clear.

YIELD: 5 to 6 servings

LEMON BROILED SHRIMP

1 pound medium shrimp, shelled and deveined
2 tablespoons oil
juice of 1 lemon
salt and paprika
1 tablespoon margarine

1. Preheat broiler and a heavy pan or griddle.
2. Place shrimp on a foil boat which has been brushed with oil. Pour lemon juice over shrimp. Sprinkle with salt and paprika. Dot with margarine and add remaining oil.
3. Place foil boat on hot pan or griddle in broiler. Broil 8 to 10 minutes depending upon size of shrimp (do not overcook).

YIELD: 3 servings

MARINATED SCAMPI (SHRIMP)

1 clove garlic, mashed
1 teaspoon salt
1/2 teaspoon dry mustard
1/4 teaspoon pepper
2 tablespoons chopped parsley
1 tablespoon lemon juice
1/4 cup oil
1 pound large raw shrimp, shelled and deveined

1. Combine all ingredients except shrimp in a bowl.
2. Add shrimp and marinate for 1 to 2 hours before broiling.
3. Broil (in marinade) about 4 inches from flame for 4 to 6 minutes. Serve with boiled rice.

YIELD: 3 servings

SHRIMP CANTONESE STYLE

1-1/2 tablespoons cornstarch
1 teaspoon sugar
2 tablespoons soy sauce
1/4 cup water
3 tablespoons oil
1 teaspoon sliced fresh ginger
salt and pepper to taste
1 clove garlic, crushed
1-1/2 pounds raw shrimp, shelled and deveined
1 cup chicken stock
1 egg, beaten
2 finely chopped scallions

1. Mix cornstarch, sugar, and soy sauce with water and set aside.
2. Place oil, salt, pepper, ginger, and garlic in a large heated skillet. Add shrimp and sauté 3 minutes. Add stock, cover, bring to the boiling point, and simmer 5 minutes.
3. Add cornstarch mixture, mix thoroughly, and cook, while stirring, until the juice thickens smoothly. Stir in beaten egg and scallions. Turn off heat immediately so that the mixture will not boil.
4. Serve with boiled rice.

NOTE: You may not use fresh ginger often, but for the authentic flavor of some Oriental foods such as shrimp dishes from China or Indian Chutney it is indispensable. If you like to have it fresh to use at any time, freeze it. Peel, chop, or grate it. Wrap it in plastic or foil in teaspoon or tablespoon portions. It will keep a long time.

YIELD: 4 servings

SHRIMP TAHITI

- 2 tablespoons oil
- 4 scallions, sliced
- 2 tablespoons soy sauce
- 1/2 teaspoon turmeric
- 1/4 teaspoon ground cardamom
- 1 teaspoon salt
- 1/4 teaspoon Tabasco sauce
- 1 cup clam juice
- 1 teaspoon cornstarch
- 1 tablespoon water
- 1 pound raw shrimp, shelled and deveined

1. Sauté scallions in oil for 2 minutes. Add soy sauce, turmeric, cardamom, salt, Tabasco, and clam juice. Cook over low heat for about 10 minutes.
2. Mix cornstarch with water and stir into the hot mixture. Cook until thickened, about 1 minute. Add shrimp, cover, and cook gently for about 5 minutes.
3. Serve with boiled rice.

YIELD: 3 servings

ITALIAN SHRIMP BUONGUSTO

- 1 pound raw shrimp, shelled and deveined
- flour for dredging
- 1/4 cup oil
- 2 tablespoons dry white wine
- salt and pepper to taste
- 1 tablespoon chopped parsley
- 1 scallion, chopped
- lemon juice
- 1 teaspoon tomato paste, diluted with 2 tablespoons water

1. Roll shrimp in flour and brown in hot oil in a heavy skillet. Add wine and cook until wine has evaporated.
2. In a small dish mix diluted tomato paste, seasonings, parsley, and scallion. Pour over shrimp and simmer a few minutes. Add lemon juice and serve hot.

YIELD: 4 servings

STEAMED SQUID

A delicious fish with a hearty flavor.

1-1/2 pounds small squid, cleaned	1 clove garlic, mashed
1 medium onion, chopped	1 teaspoon salt pepper
3 tablespoons oil	1 tablespoon lemon juice
1/4 cup dry white wine or dry vermouth	1 tablespoon chopped parsley

1. Cut body of squid into 1/2-inch rings and tentacles into small pieces.
2. Sauté onion in oil until transparent. Add wine, squid, garlic, and remaining ingredients.
3. Cook over high heat, stirring, for a few minutes. Cover and simmer until tender, 30 to 50 minutes.

NOTE: A fresh tomato, peeled and cut into pieces or 1/4 cup tomato sauce may be added along with wine and seasonings.

YIELD: 4 servings

SCALLOPED CLAMS

2 cups steamed fresh clams, chopped	1/4 teaspoon salt
	1/2 teaspoon poultry seasoning
3/4 cup crumbled saltines	1/4 teaspoon salt pinch of pepper
1 cup thin White Sauce (page 253)	1/3 cup bread crumbs
	2 tablespoons margarine

1. Preheat oven to 375°F.
2. Season white sauce with salt, poultry seasoning, and pepper.
3. In a greased 1-1/2-quart casserole, arrange clams and saltine crumbs in layers. Pour sauce over, sprinkle with bread crumbs, and dot with margarine.

4. Bake about 25 minutes or until top is browned.

YIELD: 4 servings

JOHN'S GREEN PEPPERS STUFFED WITH CRAB MEAT

- 4 medium-sized green peppers
- 1/2 pound fresh crab meat (or one 7-ounce can)
- 1 tablespoon chopped onion
- 2 tablespoons oil
- 1/2 teaspoon curry powder
- 1/4 teaspoon salt
- dash cayenne
- 2 eggs, slightly beaten
- 2 tablespoons lemon juice
- 1 cup cooked rice
- 1/2 cup fine bread crumbs
- 2 tablespoons margarine

1. Preheat oven to 400°F.
2. Cut peppers in half lengthwise and remove seeds. Parboil in salted water 2 to 3 minutes, then drain.
3. Flake and remove shell and cartilage from crab meat.
4. Sauté onion in oil until transparent, but do not brown. Add curry powder, salt, cayenne, eggs, and lemon juice. Fold in rice and crab meat.
5. Fill pepper shells with crab mixture. Sprinkle with crumbs and dot with margarine.
6. Bake about 15 minutes, or until heated through and tops are browned.

YIELD: 4 servings

CRAB MEAT LASAGNA CALIFORNIA STYLE

- 6 ounces wide noodles
- 1/2 pound fresh cooked or 1 7-ounce can crab meat
- 1-1/2 cups cottage cheese
- 1/4 teaspoon salt
- pepper to taste
- 1 cup tomato sauce, canned or homemade
- 1/2 cup grated Parmesan cheese

1. Cook noodles in salted water and drain well. Remove bits of shell and cartilage from crab meat.
2. Combine egg with cottage cheese and season with salt and pepper.
3. In a shallow, greased baking dish, alternate layers of noodles, sauce, crab meat, cottage cheese mixture, and Parmesan cheese. Repeat layers.
4. Bake at 375°F. for about 30 minutes.

YIELD: 4 servings

TUNA FISH CASSEROLE WITH NOODLES

2 cups canned tuna (about 13 ounces)
3 tablespoons oil (part oil from tuna can)
1/2 medium onion, chopped
2 tablespoons flour
pinch of curry powder
1 teaspoon salt
pepper
2 cups milk
2 tablespoons chopped parsley
2 cups noodles, cooked
1/2 cup fine bread crumbs
2 tablespoons grated cheese
2 tablespoons margarine

1. Drain tuna, reserving the oil, and flake it.
2. Heat oil and sauté onion in it until transparent. Add flour, curry powder, salt, and pepper and stir until well blended. Cook until dry and bubbly.
3. Add milk gradually, while stirring, and cook until thick and smooth. Add parsley.
4. Arrange tuna and noodles in layers in a 2-quart oiled casserole. Pour sauce over it, sprinkle with bread crumbs and cheese, then dot with margarine.
5. Bake at 375°F. until heated through and browned on top, about 30 minutes.

YIELD: 6 servings

12
Poultry

Of course there are other birds for our table besides chicken, but none so popular. It seems to take a special occasion to warrant a roast duckling. While turkey is more available and less expensive than it used to be, it is not as versatile as chicken and somehow remains mostly a tradition for holidays and large family gatherings. All poultry is low in saturated fat, and therefore much recommended in the Prudent Diet. Luckily, it is one of the best bargains today.

Most families have their favorite ways with chicken. Different countries have their national chicken dish, such as Hungary's paprika chicken and Spain's saffron-flavored *arroz con pollo,* combinations so good they have become part of the international menu.

The ways with chicken are endless. It pays to add a few good recipes to your repertory now and then. Try sautéed, breaded chicken breasts; they take only minutes to prepare. Serve them with creamed spinach for a delicious meal. A combination sure to please is braised chicken with mushrooms, sherry, soy sauce and garlic —Chinese style. Sometimes serve your bird with Turkish rice, raisin and pignolia stuffing or a French-bread stuffing, seasoned with summer savory. If all these pleasures were not enough, this useful bird makes good soups, sandwiches and fine salads.

Squeeze fresh lemon juice on chicken before cooking; it makes a difference! The French have been doing it for ages.

LEMON FRIED CHICKEN

1 frying chicken, cut into serving pieces	1/2 teaspoon salt
	pinch of pepper
1/4 cup lemon juice	1/4 teaspoon thyme
1/4 cup oil	flour
	1/4 cup oil for frying

1. Place chicken pieces in a bowl just large enough to hold them.
2. Combine lemon juice, oil, salt, pepper, and thyme to make a marinade. Pour over chicken; be sure all chicken parts are marinated.
3. Let chicken remain in marinade for 1 hour in the refrigerator.
4. Preheat oven to 350°F.
5. Drain chicken and dust with flour. Heat oil in a heavy skillet. Place chicken in hot oil and fry until golden on all sides.
6. Transfer to a baking dish and finish cooking in the oven for about 30 minutes or until tender.

YIELD: 4 servings

BAKED CORN-CRISPED CHICKEN

1 frying chicken (about 2-1/2 pounds), disjointed	pinch monosodium glutamate
	1/2 teaspoon salt
1/2 cup corn flake crumbs	1 teaspoon curry powder
	1/3 cup skimmed evaporated milk

1. Preheat oven to 350°F.
2. Line a shallow baking pan with foil. Brush foil with oil.
3. Combine crumbs and seasonings. Dip chicken parts into evaporated milk and then roll in crumb mixture.
4. Place chicken parts on foil; do not crowd.

5. Bake in the oven for about 1 hour or until chicken is tender.

YIELD: 4 servings

HEDI'S JUICY ROAST CHICKEN

1 roasting chicken (about 3 pounds), split in half
salt and pepper
1 large onion, cut into thick slices
1/3 cup chicken broth

1. Preheat oven to 420°F. Sprinkle chicken with salt and pepper.
2. Place onion slices in a shallow baking pan. Put chicken on top of the onion, skin side up.
3. Roast at 420°F. for about 1/2 hour or until brown. Baste with 1/2 the chicken broth.
4. Reduce heat to 350°F. and continue roasting until tender, about 30 minutes. While roasting, baste 2 or 3 times with the remaining chicken broth and pan juices.

YIELD: 4 to 6 servings

CRUMB-BAKED CHICKEN

1 broiler (about 2-1/2 pounds), disjointed
1 teaspoon salt
1 cup fine bread crumbs
2 tablespoons grated Parmesan cheese
2 tablespoons chopped parsley
pinch of salt
pinch of cayenne pepper
1 clove garlic, chopped
6 tablespoons oil

1. Preheat oven to 350°F.
2. Sprinkle chicken pieces with the 1 teaspoon of salt.
3. Mix crumbs, cheese, parsley, salt, cayenne, garlic, and 4 tablespoons oil.

4. Put the remaining 2 tablespoons of oil in a shallow bowl. Dip each piece of chicken lightly in the oil, then dip into the crumb mixture, coating evenly.

5. Line a shallow baking dish with foil; oil the foil well. Add coated chicken pieces; do not crowd them.

6. Bake about 1 hour or until chicken is tender.

YIELD: 4 servings

CHICKEN TERI YAKI

1 broiler (about 2-1/2 pounds), disjointed
1/3 cup soy sauce
1/4 cup dry white wine or lemon juice
1 tablespoon sugar
1 teaspoon shredded ginger or 1/2 teaspoon ground ginger
1 clove garlic, mashed

1. Combine soy sauce, wine, sugar, ginger, and garlic. Marinate chicken in this mixture for 1 to 2 hours before baking.

2. Preheat oven to 325°F.

3. Place chicken pieces in a shallow baking dish; do not crowd.

4. Bake chicken for about 1 hour or until tender, basting 2 or 3 times with marinade during baking.

YIELD: 4 servings

MARINATED CHICKEN BREASTS

2 whole chicken breasts, cut in half
3 tablespoons oil
1/4 cup dry white wine or juice of 1 lemon
salt and pepper
flour
1/2 celery stalk, cut in a few pieces
1 thick slice of onion
2 rings of green pepper

1. Marinate chicken breasts with 1 tablespoon of the oil and the lemon juice or wine for several hours, in the refrigerator.

2. Remove chicken from refrigerator 3/4 to 1 hour before cooking to allow it to come to room temperature.

3. When ready to cook, drain and reserve the marinade. Pat chicken breasts dry with paper toweling. Sprinkle chicken with salt and pepper and dust with flour.

4. Put the remaining 2 tablespoons of oil into a heavy skillet, heat oil, add chicken breasts, and brown on both sides.

5. Reduce heat; add vegetables and reserved marinade. Cover pan partially or use steam-vented lid. Cook over *very low* heat until tender, about 1/2 an hour.

6. Watch and turn occasionally to prevent chicken from becoming too brown. If more liquid is needed, add a little broth or water.

7. Serve with hot French bread.

YIELD: 4 servings

BREAST OF CHICKEN MILANESE

breast of one chicken (2 halves)
flour
1 egg white or 1/2 egg
salt
pinch of ground ginger
3 tablespoons fine bread crumbs
1 tablespoon grated Parmesan cheese
2 tablespoons oil

1. Skin chicken breast; halve it and remove bones.

2. Pound the halves to flatten slightly. Dust them with flour.

3. Mix egg with salt and ginger. Dip breast halves into this mixture.

4. Combine crumbs with cheese and coat chicken with mixture. Let stand for 5 to 10 minutes, and then crust will adhere better.

5. Heat oil in frying pan and brown chicken about 5 minutes on each side.

NOTE: Creamed spinach and sautéed mushrooms are especially good served with this dish.

YIELD: 2 servings

CHINESE BRAISED CHICKEN

1 frying chicken	2 tablespoons dry sherry
2 cloves garlic, mashed	2 tablespoons soy sauce
3 tablespoons oil	
1/2 pound mushroom caps	1/2 teaspoon monosodium glutamate

1. Have the butcher chop chicken into approximately 2-inch pieces.
2. Brown chicken and garlic lightly in oil. Add mushroom caps, cover, and cook for 5 minutes.
3. Add sherry and cook until almost entirely absorbed. Add soy sauce and monosodium glutamate.
4. Cover and cook gently until chicken is tender, 20 to 30 minutes.

YIELD: 4 servings

CHICKEN AND HAM ROLLS-UPS

breasts of 2 fryer-broiler chickens	1 clove garlic, peeled, left whole
4 slices of boiled ham	1/4 pound mushrooms, sliced
12 capers	1/4 cup chicken broth
salt and pepper	1 tablespoon dry sherry
1 tablespoon flour	
2 tablespoons oil	

1. Split chicken breasts and remove skin and bones; flatten halves slightly.
2. Place a slice of ham on each portion, trimmed to fit the chicken. Put 3 capers on each slice of ham. Roll up the breasts and tie them with string.
3. Sprinkle the roll-ups with salt and pepper; dust with flour.
4. Heat the oil and garlic in a skillet large enough to hold chicken, mushrooms, and liquid. Add roll-ups

and brown lightly. Remove garlic; add mushrooms and broth.

5. Cover and cook over *very low* heat or transfer to a baking dish and bake covered, in a preheated 300°F. oven for about 20 minutes or until breast meat is tender.

6. Remove strings and place roll-ups in a hot serving dish.

7. Add sherry to the mushrooms; bring to boil and pour mushrooms and sauce over roll-ups. Serve with creamed spinach.

YIELD: 4 servings

CHICKEN WITH GARLIC

A courageous person must have invented this tasty dish. It does not have what you might consider a pungent "garlicky" flavor.

- 1 broiler (about 2-1/2 pounds), disjointed
- 1 tablespoon lemon juice
- salt and pepper
- 1 tablespoon flour
- 4 tablespoons oil (part olive)
- 2 garlic heads (about 20 to 30 cloves), peeled
- pinch of thyme
- 1/2 bay leaf
- 2 tablespoons dry white wine, brandy or vermouth
- chopped parsley

1. Rub lemon juice into each piece of chicken and season with salt and pepper; dush with flour.

2. In a pan with a cover, heat the oil and brown chicken pieces in it.

3. Add the garlic cloves and toss them around a bit but *do not brown*. Add thyme, bay leaf, and wine and cover the pan.

4. Cook over *very low* heat or in a preheated 300°F. oven for 30 to 40 minutes or until tender. Baste with the pan juices once or twice during cooking.

5. Before serving, remove bay leaf, correct seasoning, and sprinkle with parsley. Serve with a tossed salad and French bread.

YIELD: 4 servings

BASIC SAUTÉED CHICKEN

1 chicken (about 2-1/2 pounds), disjointed	salt and pepper flour
1 tablespoon lemon juice	2 tablespoons oil 1 tablespoon margarine chicken broth

1. Rub lemon juice into the chicken pieces. Sprinkle them with salt and pepper. Dust with flour, shaking off excess.
2. In a large shallow pan, heat oil and margarine. Sauté chicken pieces to brown, then partially cover pan.
3. Cook chicken at medium heat until tender, about 25 to 35 minutes.
4. If necessary, add a little chicken broth while cooking.

YIELD: 4 servings

CHICKEN WITH CURRY

4 tablespoons oil	1 tablespoon flour
1 chicken (about 2-1/2 pounds), disjointed	1 teaspoon curry powder
salt	1/4 cup dry white wine
2 medium onions, chopped	1/2 cup chicken broth

1. Heat the oil in a large, heavy, shallow pan.
2. Arrange the chicken pieces in the pan, sprinkle with salt, and brown chicken until golden. Remove chicken from pan and keep hot.

3. In the same pan, sauté onions until golden. Sprinkle with flour and curry powder, stir well, and cook about 2 minutes.

4. Add wine and broth, while stirring, and cook until smooth.

5. Return chicken to pan and partially cover or use steam-vented lid. Gently simmer another 15 to 20 minutes or until chicken is tender.

YIELD: 4 servings

CHICKEN FLAMBÉ WITH MUSHROOMS

- 1 broiler (about 2-1/2 pounds), disjointed
- 1 tablespoon lemon juice
- 1 teaspoon salt
- pinch of ground ginger
- pinch of pepper
- 3 tablespoons oil
- 3 tablespoons brandy
- 2 medium onions, sliced thin
- 1/2 pound mushrooms, sliced

1. Sprinkle chicken pieces with lemon juice, 1/2 teaspoon of the salt, ginger, and pepper.

2. Heat oil in a heavy pan, add chicken pieces, and sauté to a golden color.

3. To flame the chicken, warm a small metal pitcher or a very small saucepan. Pour brandy into pitcher or pan and place over very low heat. It will take only a minute to warm the brandy. Light brandy, pour it over the hot chicken pieces, and let the flames burn out.

4. Remove chicken pieces and keep warm.

5. In the pan in which chicken was browned, sauté onions and mushrooms until tender. Sprinkle with remaining salt. Return chicken to pan and spoon vegetables over it.

6. Cover pan and simmer chicken over very low heat 30 to 35 minutes or until chicken is tender, or cook in a preheated 300°F. oven, if desired, for 30 to 35 minutes.

YIELD: 4 servings

SAUTÉED CHICKEN WITH MUSHROOMS

- 1 chicken (about 2-1/2 pounds), disjointed
- 1 tablespoon lemon juice
- salt and pepper
- 2 tablespoons oil
- 1 medium onion, chopped, or 1 clove garlic, crushed
- 1/4 pound mushrooms, sliced
- 1 tablespoon flour
- pinch of cayenne
- 3 ounces dry white wine
- 1 tablespoon chopped parsley

1. Rub chicken pieces with lemon juice and sprinkle with salt and pepper.
2. Heat the oil in a large, heavy, shallow pan. Sauté chicken pieces to a light brown color.
3. Add onion (or garlic) and mushrooms and cook about 5 minutes or until onion and mushrooms are limp.
4. Sprinkle flour and cayenne pepper over chicken and vegetables and stir until flour is well absorbed. While stirring, add wine and bring to a boil; cook until smooth. If extra liquid should be necessary, add a little water or broth.
5. Cover pan partially or use steam-vented lid and simmer 20 to 30 minutes or until chicken is done.
6. Sprinkle with parsley before serving.

YIELD: 4 servings

BROILED CHICKEN FROM SOUTHERN ITALY

- 1 chicken, about 2-1/2 pounds, quartered
- 1 clove garlic, cut in half
- salt and pepper
- juice of 1 lemon
- 1/2 teaspoon oregano
- 3 tablespoons oil

1. Rub chicken with garlic and sprinkle with salt and pepper.

2. Mix lemon juice with oregano.

3. Place chicken pieces in a bowl and sprinkle each piece with lemon juice mixture. Cover bowl and refrigerate several hours.

4. To broil, remove chicken from lemon juice mixture and brush with oil. Broil 30 to 40 minutes. Baste several times with lemon juice mixture and any remaining oil.

YIELD: 4 servings

BARBECUED CHICKEN
Japanese style

1 chicken, about 2-1/2 pounds, halved	lemon juice
1/3 cup soy sauce	1/4 cup tomato ketchup
2 tablespoons dry white wine	2 tablespoons oil
	1/2 teaspoon rosemary or poultry seasoning

1. Place chicken halves in a dish.

2. Combine the remaining ingredients and pour over chicken. Marinate chicken for 1 to 2 hours before cooking.

3. Barbecue on outdoor grill or in oven broiler until tender, about 15 minutes on each side.

4. Baste with marinade 2 or 3 times during cooking.

YIELD: 4 servings

FAVORITE CHICKEN FRICASSEE

1 young chicken (about 3 pounds), disjointed	2 slices fresh ginger
1 teaspoon salt	2 cups chicken broth
1 tablespoon lemon juice	2 tablespoons oil
1 clove garlic	1 tablespoon chopped onion
	pinch of curry powder
	2 tablespoons flour

1. Sprinkle chicken with salt and lemon juice. Refrigerate for 1 or more hours before cooking.
2. Place the chicken in a pot just the right size to hold it. Add the garlic and ginger.
3. In a small pot, heat the broth and pour over chicken.
4. Bring the chicken and broth to the boiling point and simmer about 1-1/2 hours or until chicken is tender.
5. Remove chicken pieces and put them in a heated deep serving dish; keep hot. Strain and remove grease from stock and reserve for sauce. Measure out 2 cups.
6. To make the sauce, heat oil, add onion and curry powder, and sauté for about 2 minutes; do not brown.
7. Add flour, and stir and cook until mixture is dry and bubbly.
8. Gradually, while stirring, add reserved chicken broth (from which the fat has been removed). Bring to a boil and cook until smooth and glossy, while stirring. Correct seasoning, if necessary.
9. Pour sauce over chicken to serve.

YIELD: 4 to 6 servings

CHICKEN WITH OLIVES PROVENÇAL

- 1 chicken (about 2-1/2 pounds), cut into pieces
- 1 clove garlic, cut in half
- 1/2 tablespoon lemon juice
- salt and pepper
- 3 tablespoons oil (part olive)
- 1/3 cup dry white wine
- 1 anchovy fillet, chopped
- 1 large ripe tomato, peeled, seeded, and chopped or 1/2 cup canned tomatoes
- pinch of thyme
- 1/2 cup green olives, pitted

1. Preheat oven to 300°F.
2. Rub chicken with garlic halves. Save garlic for use in sauce. Sprinkle chicken with lemon juice, salt, and pepper.
3. Put oil in a flameproof casserole; brown chicken in it until golden; cover and bake 30 to 40 minutes or until tender. Remove chicken and keep warm.
4. Mash reserved garlic and add to the casserole in which chicken was cooked. Add wine, anchovy, tomato, and thyme; cook down until sauce is slightly thickened.
5. In a saucepan, cover olives with water, bring to boil, and simmer for a few minutes (to remove excess salt); drain.
6. In the casserole, arrange chicken and olives on top of sauce. Heat through and serve.

YIELD: 4 servings

CHICKEN PAPRIKA
From Hungary

There are many versions of this national favorite. Remember that paprika, the outstanding seasoning, is readily burned; this would ruin the dish.

1 chicken (about 2-1/2 pounds), disjointed	2 good-sized onions, sliced
salt and pepper	2 to 3 teaspoons paprika
2 tablespoons oil	1/2 tablespoon flour
2 tablespoons margarine	1/2 cup chicken broth

1. One or two hours before cooking, season chicken pieces with salt and pepper. When ready to bake chicken, preheat oven to 300°F.
2. On top of the stove, heat oil and margarine in a flameproof casserole. In it sauté onions until golden. Sprinkle paprika over onion and mix well.
3. Add chicken pieces to casserole and spoon onions over them. Sauté for a few minutes, until all is mixed and hot.

4. Cover and bake 45 to 60 minutes, depending upon size of pieces. Remove chicken and keep hot.

5. Mix flour with chicken broth and add to casserole. Bring to a boil on top of the stove, while stirring; simmer to cook down a little. Return chicken to casserole.

6. Pour sauce over it to serve. Noodles or rice go well with this dish.

NOTE: To keep paprika fresh and fragrant store it in the refrigerator.

YIELD: 4 servings

ARROZ CON POLLO
Chicken with rice

An easy-to-make, all-in-one main dish; equally good for the family meals or a buffet dinner.

- 1 chicken (about 2-1/2 pounds), disjointed
- 1/4 teaspoon saffron
- 2 tablespoons warm water
- 1 tablespoon lemon juice
- 1 tablespoon oil
- 1 teaspoon salt
- flour
- 1/4 cup oil
- 1 clove garlic, crushed
- 2 medium onions, chopped
- 1 pimiento, chopped
- 2 ripe tomatoes, peeled, chopped
- 1/2 teaspoon oregano
- 2 tablespoons chopped parsley
- 1 cup rice, uncooked
- pinch of cumin
- 1 teaspoon paprika
- 2 cups chicken broth

1. Place chicken pieces in a bowl for marinating.

2. Crush saffron; dissolve in warm water and combine with lemon juice, the tablespoon of oil, and salt.

3. Distribute saffron marinade well over all pieces of chicken and let stand about 1/2 hour.

4. Remove chicken pieces, saving any remaining marinade. Dust chicken pieces lightly with flour.

5. In a large skillet or flameproof casserole, heat

the 1/4 cup oil and brown chicken pieces in it; remove chicken and set aside.

6. To the skillet, add garlic, onions, pimiento, tomatoes, oregano, parsley, and any remaining marinade. Simmer, stirring occasionally, until onion is soft and mixture has cooked down.

7. Add rice and cook, while stirring, until rice is translucent; sprinkle with cumin and paprika.

8. Heat chicken broth and pour over rice; bring to boil.

9. Add chicken and bring to boil again. Cover and cook over very low heat until chicken is tender, about 45 minutes. Add a little more broth, if necessary, to keep moist.

YIELD: 4 servings

CHICKEN ESCABECHE

A South American recipe for preparing game birds, excellent too for chicken.

1 chicken (about 2-1/2 pounds), disjointed	6 peppercorns
	1/2 cup vinegar
	1/2 cup water
3 tablespoons oil	1 cup dry white wine
2 cloves garlic, peeled	1 tablespoon lemon juice
1 bay leaf	1 teaspoon salt
1 tablespoon capers	

1. Heat oil in a heavy skillet and brown chicken lightly.

2. Combine the remaining ingredients, for the marinade, in a saucepan and bring to a boil.

3. Place chicken pieces in a flameproof casserole and pour hot marinade over them.

4. Cover and simmer gently until chicken is tender, about 1 hour. Remove bay leaf.

5. Allow chicken to cool in the marinade, then refrigerate in marinade. Serve cold. This dish keeps well.

YIELD: 4 servings

ROAST DUCKLING BIGARADE

For a superior flavor get a strictly fresh-killed bird.

1 duckling, 4-1/2 to 5-1/2 pounds, ready for roasting	1 tablespoon vinegar
	1-1/2 cups duck or chicken broth (fat removed)
1 clove garlic, split	1/4 cup orange juice
salt	1 tablespoon lemon juice
ground ginger	
peel of one orange, white part removed	2 teaspoons cornstarch
	2 tablespoons water
1 tablespoon sugar	

1. Preheat oven to 350°F.
2. Remove as much fat as possible from duck. Rub entire duckling surface with garlic; sprinkle with salt and ginger.
3. Roast duckling 2-1/2 to 3 hours or until tender. Cover pan with aluminum foil for first hour of roasting, if desired. Remove fat as it accumulates. For easy removal, tilt pan and withdraw fat with a baster.
4. While duck is roasting prepare the sauce. Cut orange peel into thin strips, put them in a small saucepan and pour water over them. Bring to a boil, simmer a few minutes (this removes bitterness), and drain.
5. In a small skillet caramelize sugar to a rich medium brown (until it starts to foam). Add vinegar to dissolve sugar; combine with duck broth.
6. After duck is roasted, remove from pan and pour off all the fat. Add broth mixture to the roasting pan. Scrape down and cook off all the brown particles. Pour broth into a 1-cup measure. If much of the broth has cooked away, add more to make 1 cup liquid.
7. Combine broth, orange peel, orange juice, and lemon juice in a small saucepan. Mix cornstarch with water.
8. Bring sauce to a boil. Add cornstarch mixture, while stirring, and cook until slightly thickened and clear.

9. Serve some of the brown, transparent, flavor-rich (not sweet) sauce on each serving of duckling.

YIELD: 4 servings

ROAST DUCKLING WITH A CHINESE FLAVOR

No carving at serving time.

1. Roast duckling as directed in preceding recipe. Have duck roasted 1 to 2 hours before serving time.
2. When cool enough to handle, cut into serving pieces; remove any excess fat. Place pieces close together, skin side up, on an ovenproof platter.
3. One half hour before serving time, preheat oven to 350°F.
4. Mix 2 tablespoons soy sauce with 4 tablespoons dry sherry; spoon over duck.
5. Heat about 30 minutes, basting once or twice. Duck will be hot and crisp.

HOW TO BROIL THE TENDER SMALL TURKEY

1. Have butcher split a 5- to 6-pound turkey in half or quarters.
2. Rub turkey surfaces with a cut clove of garlic (optional). Liberally sprinkle with lemon juice. Let stand one hour or more in the refrigerator.
3. Preheat broiler. Line a shallow pan with heavy aluminum foil.
4. Season turkey with salt and pepper or powdered ginger, place it on the pan, skin side down. Brush surface lightly with oil or melted margarine.
5. Broil 9 to 10 inches away from heat; arrange distance so that turkey will start to brown in 15 to 20 minutes. Continue broiling until well browned, another 15 to 20 minutes.
6. Turn skin side up and broil until skin is brown and crisp, about 40 to 50 minutes.
7. Baste with mixture of lemon juice and chicken

broth 2 or 3 times during broiling on both sides. Total cooking time is about 1-1/2 hours.

NOTE: Young turkey makes a good fricassee. Follow recipe for Favorite Chicken Fricassee (page 160).

MATT'S POULTRY STUFFING

5 or 6 slices (1/4 pound) day-old, white French bread
1-1/2 teaspoons summer savory
1/2 teaspoon salt
4 tablespoons (1/2 stick) margarine, melted

1. Tear bread into small pieces or cut into 1/2-inch cubes.
2. Between your hands, crumble the dry summer savory, removing any sharp stems or pieces.
3. Combine bread with savory, salt, and margarine, and mix well.
4. Stuff chicken just before roasting.

YIELD: stuffing for a 3-pound chicken

SOUTH GERMAN BREAD STUFFING FOR POULTRY

1/4 pound French bread or 2 large rolls
1/3 cup oil
1 medium onion, chopped
2 tablespoons chopped parsley
2 eggs
1/2 teaspoon nutmeg
1 teaspoon salt
poultry seasoning to taste (optional)

1. Soak bread in water until soft, squeeze as dry as possible, and mash well with a wooden spoon.
2. Heat oil in a large frying pan and sauté onion until transparent.
3. Add bread and cook slowly to dry mixture out.

Little crusts will form on bottom; scrape these into the mixture occasionally.

4. Cook for about 20 minutes altogether until mixture is a homogeneous light brown. Put mixture into a bowl to cool.

5. Add parsley, eggs, nutmeg, salt, and poultry seasoning and mix thoroughly.

6. Stuffing will expand during cooking, so leave room when stuffing the bird. Any extra stuffing may be baked in a covered dish during the last hour of roasting. Or, use it to make small (walnut-sized) dumplings and serve them, simmered, in soup.

NOTE: Sautéed poultry liver, chopped, is a nice addition to this stuffing.

YIELD: stuffing for 3- to 5-pound bird

WHOLE WHEAT POULTRY STUFFING

- 5 or 6 slices (1/4 pound) day-old whole wheat bread
- 1-1/2 teaspoons summer savory
- 1/2 teaspoon salt
- 1 small carrot, finely chopped or shredded (about 1 heaping tablespoon)
- 2 tablespoons chopped celery, including a few leaves
- 1/4 small green pepper, chopped
- 4 tablespoons (1/2 stick) margarine, melted
- 1 small onion

1. Cut or tear bread into small pieces (about 1/2-inch cubes).

2. Between your hands, crumble the dry summer savory, removing any sharp stems or pieces.

3. Combine bread with savory, salt, and all the remaining ingredients except the onion; mix well.

4. Stuff chicken just before roasting. Insert the onion in the body cavity after the stuffing.

YIELD: stuffing for a 3-pound chicken

TURKISH POULTRY STUFFING

3 tablespoons oil	2 cups well-seasoned chicken broth, hot
1/2 cup pignolias	
1/2 cup raisins	1 chicken liver, sautéed in oil and chopped (optional)
1 cup rice	

1. Heat oil in a heavy saucepan, and sauté pignolias to a light brown. Watch carefully, as this takes just about a minute or two.
2. Add raisins, rice, and hot chicken broth. Cover and cook gently, about 20 minutes or until liquid is absorbed; cool.
3. While cooking, put a paper towel between pan and lid for 10 minutes to absorb excess moisture from rice.
4. With a large fork, gently stir liver into rice mixture.
5. Cool to room temperature before stuffing bird; rice will be fluffy and each grain separate. Stuff bird loosely.
6. Bake any extra stuffing in a covered dish for the last hour of roasting the bird.

NOTE: Italian rice, grown in the Po Valley, looks somewhat like brown rice. It cooks to a beautiful, creamy white nut-like grain, is delicious, and is very attractive in poultry stuffings and casserole dishes.

YIELD: stuffing for 3- to 5-pound bird

13

Lean Meats

MEATS IN YOUR MENUS

Today's pièce de résistance is pot roast, perhaps—tomorrow Wiener Schnitzel. There are so many good things to eat, it is hard to make a choice. Follow these simple recipes for an enticing variety of favorites; you'll find that you can make the fine, authentic dishes you believed to be the prerogative of professional chefs.

By alternating your main dishes between the fattier meats (beef, pork, and lamb) and veal, poultry, fish and shellfish and occasionally liver or kidneys, you not only have the pleasure of variety but also the assurance that meats high in saturated fats stay within recommended amounts.

Recipes in this chapter illustrate methods—how to pot-roast (braise is another word for it), what makes a fine light stew or a brown goulash, how to marinate meats. There are examples of delicious combinations of meats with fresh vegetables or dried legumes.

Choose vegetables and salads to bring out the best in your main dish. Jot down menus you have enjoyed so that you will remember them for repeat performances.

POT ROAST OF BEEF
Braised Beef

The secret of a tender, good pot roast is *not* to add water, wine, tomatoes or broth—this meat is to cook in its own juice. A flameproof heavy casserole, low temperature, and a sufficiently long cooking time are essential. Use round, rump or other lean beef.

3 pounds boneless beef (round or rump)	1 medium onion, sliced
	1 carrot, sliced
	paprika
1 tablespoon oil	1 jigger gin or vodka
salt and pepper	

1. Preheat oven to 275°F.
2. Heat oil in casserole and brown meat on all sides. As meat browns, sprinkle it with salt and pepper.
3. When meat is partially browned, add onion and carrot; sprinkle vegetables with paprika and brown them along with meat.
4. Pour liquor over meat. Cover casserole immediately and finish cooking in oven, turning meat once. Cooking time will be about 2-1/2 hours.
5. Make about 2 cups of gravy to serve with the above amount of meat (page 252).

NOTE: Italian Plums in Vinegar (see following recipe) are an excellent accompaniment to pot roast and to other beef dishes.

YIELD: 8 to 10 servings

ITALIAN PLUMS IN VINEGAR
An Alsatian recipe

4 pounds good, firm-ripe Italian plums (prunes)	2 sticks cinnamon, broken into a few pieces
2 cups red wine vinegar	4 cloves
1 cup water	2 pounds sugar

1. Wash plums and wipe them dry. With a toothpick, prick each plum in 4 or 5 places. Put them all in a big bowl.
2. Bring to a boil vinegar, water, seasonings and

sugar; boil for 5 minutes. Cool syrup and pour over plums. Let stand, covered, for 3 days.

3. On the third day drain off syrup and bring to a boil again. Cool until tepid, pour over plums and cover.

4. On the fourth day drain and bring syrup to a boil again. Place about 1/2 pound of the plums at a time into the syrup and bring them just to a boil. Remove them with a slotted spoon and place in heat-resistant jars, proceed with remaining plums the same way.

5. Boil syrup for another 5 to 10 minutes, remove scum and pour syrup over plums. All the plums should be covered with syrup.

6. When plums are cool, cover jars. Plums in vinegar keep well, but in warm city apartments they are best kept in the refrigerator.

SAUERBRATEN
A South German recipe

3 pounds round or rump of beef
salt
1 large onion, sliced
1/2 bay leaf
3 cloves
6 peppercorns
1 cup cider vinegar or 3/4 cup wine vinegar and 1/4 cup water

To Marinate the Meat

1. Line a glass or earthenware bowl just large enough to hold the meat with several layers of cheesecloth.

2. Pour enough vinegar into the bowl to thoroughly moisten the cheesecloth.

3. Rub a little salt into the meat.

4. Place meat, onion, bay leaf, cloves, and peppercorns, well distributed over the meat, in the bowl.

5. Fold cheesecloth over meat and pour remaining vinegar over it.

6. Cover the bowl and refrigerate for 3 to 5 days. Turn meat several times.

To Braise the Meat

1 to 2 tablespoons oil   1 jigger gin or vodka
                           (optional)

1. Preheat oven to 275°F.
2. Remove meat from bowl and dry it well.
3. Heat oil in a flameproof casserole and brown meat on all sides. Add onion slices from marinade and brown lightly.
4. Save marinade, as you may wish to use a tablespoon or two of it in gravy.
5. Pour gin or vodka over meat and cover casserole immediately.
6. Finish cooking in oven, turning once. Cooking time will be about 2-1/2 hours.
7. Make about 2 cups of gravy (see page 252). Gravy is important for sauerbraten.
8. Serve with potato dumplings or noodles.

YIELD: 8 to 10 servings

JUICY MEAT LOAF

This meat loaf can be mixed in the shallow casserole in which it is to be baked.

- 2 slices rye bread
- 2 slices white bread
- 1 cup water
- 1 medium onion, chopped
- 1 tablespoon chopped parsley
- 3 tablespoons grated Parmesan cheese
- 1 pound lean ground beef
- 1 egg
- 1 teaspoon salt
- 1/4 teaspoon pepper
- 1 teaspoon crumbled oregano
- 2 tablespoons oil

1. Preheat oven to 350°F.
2. Pour water over bread in a shallow 1-quart casserole. When soft, break it up finely with a fork.
3. Combine with onion, parsley, cheese, beef, egg,

salt, pepper, and oregano; mix well. Shape into a rectangle about 1-1/2 inches high and pour oil over the top.

4. Bake 35 to 45 minutes or until done.

YIELD: 6 servings

LONDON BROIL

A tender, juicy, flavorful steak from a lean cut of beef.

| 2-1/2 pounds (about) rump of beef | 2 tablespoons soy sauce |

1. Rub meat with soy sauce on both sides. Let stand in the refrigerator 1 to 2 hours.
2. Broil in a preheated broiler or on an outdoor grill to desired doneness.
3. Transfer to a heated platter and cut into thin slantwise slices to serve.

YIELD: 8 servings

STU'S LONDON BROIL

This was Stu's mother's recipe. He says just thinking about it makes his mouth water.

| 2 pounds flank steak juice of 2 lemons | 1-1/2 tablespoons (about) prepared mustard |

1. Trim off fat and membrane, then score surface of the flank steak.
2. Place steak in a shallow pan and pour lemon juice over it. Let stand in refrigerator overnight or at least 5 hours, turning meat 2 or 3 times.
3. Remove meat from marinade 1 hour before broiling. Spread both sides of steak with mustard.
4. Preheat broiler or outdoor grill. Broil steak to

desired doneness, turning once. Have both sides well browned. Sprinkle with salt and pepper, if desired.

5. To serve, place steak on a carving board. With a sharp knife, slice diagonally across the grain at a 45-degree angle; slices should be about 1/2 inch thick.

YIELD: 5 to 6 servings

CHINESE PEPPER STEAK

1-1/4 pounds tender beef, trimmed (sirloin or flank steak)	1 teaspoon dry sherry or dry vermouth
1-1/2 pounds green peppers	3 tablespoons oil
	1/2 teaspoon salt
	dash of pepper
1-1/2 teaspoons cornstarch	1 teaspoon shredded ginger
1 tablespoon soy sauce	1 clove garlic, crushed

SAUCE

1-1/2 teaspoons cornstarch	1/4 teaspoon monosodium glutamate
1/4 cup cold water	
1 tablespoon soy sauce	1-1/2 cups bouillon

1. Cut beef into 1/8-inch slices. Cut each pepper diagonally into strips 1 inch wide (remove seeds and membranes).
2. Combine beef slices, cornstarch, soy sauce, and sherry; mix well.
3. For the sauce, mix cornstarch with water, soy sauce, and monosodium glutamate; set aside.
4. In a large skillet heat oil, salt, pepper, ginger, and garlic; when garlic is lightly browned, discard it.
5. With the skillet on high heat, sauté beef slices quickly, 2 to 3 minutes; remove them while still rare.
6. Put the peppers in the skillet. Add another tablespoon of oil if necessary. Sauté peppers for about 5

minutes, cover skillet, and turn off heat. Let stand for 2 minutes; peppers will be just at the tender-crisp stage.

7. Combine beef with peppers in skillet.

8. Add bouillon to reserved sauce mixture. Stir well, pour over beef and peppers, and cook, stirring, until juice is thickened, smooth and clear.

YIELD: 4 servings

SHISH KEBAB
From the Near East

2 pounds leg of lamb, trimmed, cut into 2-inch cubes	12 small white onions, parboiled 2 minutes
	3 medium green peppers, seeded, cut into 6 pieces each

Marinade

1/3 cup oil (part olive)	1 bay leaf, crushed
1/3 cup lemon juice	2 teaspoons salt
1 medium onion, thinly sliced	pepper, freshly ground
1 clove garlic, thinly sliced	oregano

1. Combine marinade ingredients. Let lamb cubes stand in marinade from 2 to 12 hours, turning meat several times. Keep covered tightly, in the refrigerator.

2. When ready to broil, arrange meat on skewers, alternating with onions and pepper pieces.

3. Broil over outdoor grill or in oven broiler to desired doneness, turning occasionally.

YIELD: 6 servings

LAMB AND VEGETABLE CASSEROLE

- 3 pounds lamb shanks or shoulder with bone, trimmed and cut into large serving pieces
- 3-1/2 cups boiling water
- 1 large onion, coarsely chopped
- 1 clove garlic, whole
- 1 bay leaf
- 8 peppercorns
- 2 teaspoons salt
- 2 tablespoons oil
- 2 tablespoons flour
- 3 medium potatoes, peeled and quartered
- 4 medium carrots, scraped, cut in halves lengthwise
- 6 small white onions
- chopped parsley

1. Put meat into a wide flameproof casserole, preferably placing it in a single layer; pour boiling water over meat.

2. Add onion, garlic, bay leaf, peppercorns, and salt. Bring to a boil, cover, and simmer very gently for about 1 hour on top of stove. Remove bay leaf after 30 minutes' cooking time.

3. When just tender, remove meat from broth; trim off any visible fat. Strain broth; remove fat.

4. Preheat oven to 350°F.

5. Wash and dry casserole. Heat oil in the casserole, add flour, and cook 2 minutes, while stirring. Gradually add 1-1/2 cups of reserved broth, while stirring, and bring to a boil.

6. Correct seasoning and remove 1/2 cup of sauce for later use. Return meat to remaining sauce in casserole (sauce should not quite reach the top of meat).

7. Arrange potatoes, carrots, and onions on top of meat; spoon remaining 1/2 cup of sauce over vegetables. Cover and heat just to boiling.

8. Transfer to the oven and bake for 40 minutes or until vegetables are tender. Sprinkle with parsley before serving.

YIELD: 4 to 6 servings

TURKISH LAMB AND LENTIL STEW

1 pound lean lamb, cut into 1-inch cubes
1/2 teaspoon salt
1 clove garlic, sliced
1/4 teaspoon ground ginger
1/2 pound lentils
1 large onion, chopped
2 tablespoons oil
2 tablespoons flour
2-1/2 to 3-1/2 cups beef or chicken broth
vinegar (optional)

1. Mix salt, garlic, ginger, mashing all well, between sheets of foil; combine with meat thoroughly.
2. Wash lentils; drain.
3. In a large saucepan sauté onion in oil to a light yellow color. Add meat and sauté, without browning, for a few minutes. Sprinkle flour over meat and onion; cook for 2 minutes, while stirring.
4. Add lentils and 2-1/2 cups hot broth; bring to a boil, stirring gently. Simmer a few minutes.
5. Cover and cook over a very low flame for about 1-1/2 hours or in a 275°F. oven for about the same length of time. Add more broth as needed.
6. Add a little vinegar just before serving or serve vinegar separately at the table.

YIELD: 4 servings

ROAST LOIN OF PORK

Have the butcher crack the bones for easy carving.

4 pounds loin of pork
1 teaspoon rosemary or thyme
2 cloves garlic, slivered
salt and pepper

1. Preheat oven to 450°F.
2. Remove as much of the fat from the pork as possible; then make a few incisions into the meat and

insert garlic slivers. Rub rosemary or thyme lightly into the meat; sprinkle with salt and pepper.

3. Roast at 450°F. for 15 minutes or until roast begins to brown; then reduce the heat to 325°F. Cover with aluminum foil for about 1 hour for special tenderness and flavor.

4. Allow 30 minutes' cooking time to the pound. A meat thermometer inserted in center of loin, away from bone, should register 175°F. when meat is done.

5. When roasted, allow meat to stand at room temperature 15 minutes before slicing to serve. This keeps the juices in the meat.

6. For making gravy, see page 252.

YIELD: 6 servings

MARINATED ROAST LOIN OF PORK OR FRESH HAM

- 4 pounds loin of pork or 3 pounds fresh ham
- 1/2 cup soy sauce
- 1 cup pineapple juice
- 1/2 cup dry white wine or dry sherry
- 2 tablespoons honey or brown sugar
- 1 clove garlic, cut in half
- 2 teaspoons chopped fresh ginger or 1 teaspoon ground ginger

1. Place pork loin or ham in a shallow pan. If using loin, place it meat side down.

2. Combine remaining ingredients and pour over meat. Cover and refrigerate overnight or at least 6 hours. Spoon marinade over meat a few times while it is marinating.

3. Remove from marinade and roast as in preceding recipe for Roast Loin of Pork.

4. Baste with marinade several times while roasting.

YIELD: 8 servings

ITALIAN MEAT BALLS IN TOMATO SAUCE

Meat balls in tomato sauce are a perennial favorite in families with children. If the sauce is ready, the meat balls may be made quickly. This homemade sauce freezes well so double the recipe and freeze enough for another meal.

TOMATO SAUCE

- 3 tablespoons oil (some olive)
- 1 medium onion, chopped
- 1 clove garlic, chopped
- 1 can (6 ounces) tomato paste
- 1 teaspoon flour
- 3 cups water
- salt and pepper

1. Heat oil in a saucepan, add onion and cook until tender (do not brown). Add garlic and cook 1 minute.
2. Add tomato paste and flour, then add water, stirring until well blended. Season and simmer uncovered about 1 hour, stirring occasionally.

ITALIAN MEAT BALLS

- 1 egg, lightly beaten
- 1 pound lean beef, ground
- 1/4 cup fine bread crumbs
- 1/4 cup water or stock
- 1 tablespoon chopped parsley
- 1 tablespoon chopped onion
- 2 tablespoons grated Parmesan cheese
- 1 teaspoon salt
- pepper

1. Combine all ingredients and mix lightly but thoroughly. Shape into balls about the size of a small egg.
2. Place in a frying pan with some hot oil and brown over medium heat. Shake the pan so that the meat balls brown evenly.
3. Remove browned meat balls from pan and place in boiling Tomato Sauce. Simmer for about 1/2 hour.

YIELD: 4 servings

SWEDISH MEAT BALLS

Light in texture—fragrant with allspice. For cocktails, buffet, or main dish. They are delicious served with watermelon pickle or chutney.

- 1 egg, lightly beaten
- 1 teaspoon salt
- 1/2 teaspoon brown sugar
- 1/2 teaspoon allspice
- 1/4 teaspoon pepper
- 1 pound lean beef, finely ground
- 1/2 pound lean pork, finely ground
- 1/2 cup mashed potatoes
- 1 cup fine bread crumbs
- 2 tablespoons margarine
- 2 tablespoons oil

1. Mix egg with salt, sugar, allspice, and pepper.
2. Lightly combine meats, egg mixture, mashed potatoes and 1/2 cup of the bread crumbs. Form balls about 1 inch in diameter and roll them in the remaining 1/2 cup crumbs.
3. Heat margarine and oil in a large, heavy frying pan and brown meat balls well on all sides, then cover the pan with a lid or a steam-vented lid.
4. Cook meat balls thoroughly over low heat about 15 minutes, shaking the pan occasionally so that they will keep their round shape. You may prefer to finish cooking the meat balls after browning in a preheated 350°F. oven.

YIELD: about 3 dozen small meat balls

MEAT BALLS IN MUSHROOM SAUCE

Prepare Swedish Meat Balls as directed above. Instead of rolling the meat balls in bread crumbs, roll them in flour before browning. After browning, add 2-1/2 cups Mushroom Sauce (see page 254) and simmer them in the sauce for about 1/2 hour.

MEAT BALLS IN CAPER SAUCE
Koenigsberger Klops—from Germany

Caper Sauce

- 2 tablespoons oil
- 2 tablespoons flour
- 2-1/2 cups beef or chicken broth
- pinch of paprika
- 1 small onion, stuck with 2 cloves
- 1 tablespoon vinegar
- 1 tablespoon capers
- pinch of sugar

1. Heat oil in a heavy saucepan. Add flour and cook over a low flame, while stirring, until mixture is dry and bubbly.
2. Gradually add broth, bring to a boil and cook until smooth and thickened, stirring throughout.
3. Add remaining ingredients. Cook for 5 minutes, then taste and add salt if needed.

Meat Balls

- 1 small onion, chopped
- 2 tablespoons oil
- 2 slices day-old white bread
- 1/2 pound lean ground pork
- 1/2 pound lean ground beef
- 1 egg
- 1 anchovy or 1/2 inch anchovy paste
- 1 teaspoon salt
- pinch each of pepper and nutmeg
- 1 tablespoon chopped parsley

1. Sauté onion in oil until transparent.
2. Soak bread in water, squeeze dry, and break it up well.
3. Combine all ingredients lightly but thoroughly. Shape into 8 meat balls and place in hot Caper Sauce. Bring to a boil, cover, and simmer about 1/2 hour, shaking pan occasionally. Remove onion stuck with cloves from sauce before serving.
4. Serve with rice, noodles, or mashed potatoes.

NOTE: You may substitute ground veal for the pork, or use all ground beef, or use all ground veal.

YIELD: 4 servings

VEAL, A DELICIOUS, LEAN MEAT

The versatility of veal is yet to be discovered by many Americans. Veal is one of the most appreciated meats in France, Belgium, Italy, Austria and Germany; every part of the calf is used to make interesting dishes. The best known veal dishes here, and often the only ones people have ever eaten, are veal cutlet and scallopine. They are very expensive.

The less tender cuts, such as shank and shoulder, when braised or simmered, bring out the best in veal and are money saving, too. A good veal stew or braised veal shoulder are among the most flavorful meats imaginable. Many seasonings go well with veal—ginger, curry, paprika, bay leaf, garlic and wine. Veal is good with most vegetables, especially with asparagus, cauliflower, carrots, peppers, tomatoes, spinach and salad greens.

A lean meat, veal contains no "marbling," and whatever fat there is can easily be removed.

Try some of the fine recipes in this chapter; you will want to make them often.

VEAL SCALLOPINE WITH MUSHROOMS
Italian style

- 1 pound veal from rump, sliced very thin
- salt and pepper
- 2 tablespoons oil
- 1 clove garlic
- 1 bay leaf
- 2 teaspoons lemon juice
- 2 tablespoons dry white wine or Marsala
- 2 tablespoons margarine
- 1/2 pound mushrooms, sliced

1. Flatten meat to 1/8-inch thickness. Season with salt and pepper. Lightly dredge with flour.
2. In a skillet, heat oil with garlic and bay leaf. Brown meat well over a high flame, about 2 minutes on

each side, and then remove to a hot serving platter. Remove garlic and bay leaf.

3. Mix lemon juice with wine and pour into the skillet. Stir to combine with pan juices, heat, and pour over veal. Keep hot.

4. Melt margarine in the same skillet. Add mushrooms and sauté for about 3 minutes, then pour over veal. Serve immediately.

YIELD: 4 servings

WIENER SCHNITZEL
Breaded veal cutlets from Austria

1-1/2 pounds veal from rump or leg, sliced about 1/4 inch thick	1/2 cup fine bread crumbs
salt and ginger to season	2 tablespoons oil
flour for dredging	2 tablespoons margarine
2 egg whites or 1 egg, beaten lightly	lemon wedges for garnish

1. Season veal with salt and ginger. Dip lightly in flour, shaking off any excess.

2. Dip into beaten egg whites and then into the crumbs. Let stand on a rack or paper towel about 10 minutes before frying.

3. Heat oil and margarine in a heavy frying pan. Have fat hot as you put the meat in the pan, then reduce heat so that it will cook only at moderate heat.

4. Brown veal about 5 minutes on each side.

5. Serve garnished with lemon wedges.

NOTE: Wiener Schnitzel is popular served with German Potato Salad and mixed greens with French Dressing.

YIELD: 4 to 5 servings

POT ROAST OF VEAL

2 pounds boneless veal (shoulder, rump, or leg)
2 tablespoons oil
salt, ginger
paprika
1 onion, sliced
1 carrot, sliced
1/4 cup chicken broth
1 teaspoon lemon juice
1 tablespoon dry sherry (optional)

1. Preheat oven to 300°F.
2. Heat oil in a flameproof casserole and brown veal on all sides.
3. Sprinkle with salt, ginger, and paprika. Add onion and carrot and brown them lightly.
4. Cover and place in the oven; baste meat occasionally with chicken broth mixed with lemon juice. Cooking period will be about 2 hours.
5. Remove veal and keep warm. Strain liquid and withdraw the fat-free portion (see page 251). Return liquid to casserole and cook off the brown particles which have formed; simmer for a few minutes, add sherry, and serve pan gravy with the meat.

YIELD: 6 servings

ROAST RUMP OF VEAL

1. Preheat oven to 325°F.
2. Rub a 2-pound boneless rump of veal with a cut clove of garlic. Brush lightly with oil. Sprinkle with salt, ginger, and a little flour.
3. Place veal in a shallow roasting pan, together with some sliced onion.
4. Roast about 30 minutes to the pound, to the well-done stage. Baste occasionally with a tablespoon of chicken broth.

NOTE: You may wish to brown veal in a flameproof casserole on top of the stove; then roast for the first hour, covered, in the oven and finish roasting to the well-done stage, uncovered. This method brings out the best flavor in veal.

YIELD: 4 to 6 servings

BROWN VEAL GOULASH

- 2 pounds boneless veal (shoulder, rump, or shank), trimmed and cut into 1-1/2-inch cubes
- 2 tablespoons oil
- 2 tablespoons margarine
- salt, pepper, and paprika
- 1/3 cup flour
- 3 cups chicken broth
- 1 onion, peeled and stuck with 3 cloves
- 1 tablespoon vinegar
- 1/2 bay leaf
- 4 tablespoons dry white wine

1. Preheat oven to 300°F.
2. Heat oil and margarine in a flameproof casserole and brown veal cubes on all sides. Sprinkle with salt, pepper, and paprika. Remove browned veal to a dish, cover, and keep warm.
3. Add flour to the casserole in which veal was browned and cook until dry and bubbly. Then, while stirring, add chicken broth, bring to a boil, and simmer for about 5 minutes. Add onion, vinegar, and bay leaf.
4. Return veal to casserole, together with any liquid which has formed. Spoon the sauce over meat to cover all pieces well.
5. Cover and bake for about 1-1/2 hours. Cooking meat in a thickened sauce permits the meat to retain all of its moisture.
6. Before serving, remove onion and bay leaf and stir in wine.

NOTE: Noodles go well with this dish.

YIELD: 6 servings

BLANQUETTE DE VEAU
Veal Stew à la Française

- 2 pounds boneless veal (shoulder or shank), cut into 1-1/2-inch pieces
- 4 cups chicken broth
- 1 onion stuck with 1 clove
- 2 carrots, scraped, cut into 1-inch pieces
- salt
- 1/4 pound mushrooms, quartered
- 1 tablespoon lemon juice
- 2 tablespoons oil
- 1 tablespoon flour
- pinch of nutmeg
- 1 teaspoon chopped parsley

1. Place veal in a large saucepan, cover with cold water, and bring to a boil. Simmer for 2 minutes. Drain veal and rinse under cold water to remove scum.

2. Wash the saucepan in which the veal was blanched and return veal to the pan. Heat chicken broth and pour over meat.

3. Add onion and carrots and simmer, covered, until meat is tender, about 1-1/2 hours. Add salt if necessary after first half hour of cooking.

4. Fish out carrot pieces as soon as they are fork-tender (about 15 minutes), and set aside.

5. While meat is simmering, remove 1/2 cup of the broth, combine with lemon juice in a small saucepan, and bring to a boil. Add mushrooms and simmer 2 to 3 minutes. Set aside.

6. When meat is tender, drain off broth and remove all fat. Combine enough of the broth with the mushroom liquid to make 2-1/2 cups.

7. In another saucepan, heat the oil. Add the flour and cook, while stirring, until dry and bubbly (1 to 2 minutes), over a very low flame.

8. Gradually stir in the broth, bring to a boil, and simmer about 5 minutes, stirring, until thickened. Add nutmeg and correct seasoning.

9. To serve, place the drained meat in a flameproof casserole. Arrange carrots and mushrooms on top, pour the hot sauce over all, and heat very gently.

10. Sprinkle with parsley and serve with noodles, rice, or small boiled potatoes. Save every bit of remaining broth for a fine soup. Traditionally, small onions are added to the meat when it is partially cooked; if you wish to include them, add 10 to 12 parboiled small white onions to the meat along with the other vegetables.

YIELD: 5 to 6 servings

BRAISED VEAL SHANKS
Kalbhaxen—from Germany

One of the most popular dishes in Germany and Italy (Osso buco). This recipe is the South German version.

- 2 veal shanks (2 pounds meat), cut into 3-inch pieces
- 4 tablespoons oil
- 1 onion, sliced
- 1 carrot, scraped, cut into a few pieces
- salt, ginger, paprika
- 2 tablespoons gin or vodka (optional)

1. Preheat oven to 300°F. Trim all visible fat off meat.
2. Heat oil in a flameproof casserole and brown veal on all sides; add onion and carrot, browning them lightly.
3. Sprinkle meat with salt, ginger, and paprika. Pour liquor over it.
4. Cover casserole, place in the oven and cook for 1 to 1-1/2 hours.
5. When tender, remove meat to a shallow baking dish and allow it to crisp in the oven for about 15 minutes. Strain the juice that has formed and remove all fat.
6. Return fat-free liquid to casserole and gently cook off all of the brown particles that have formed.

Serve sauce with the meat. Should you desire a thickened gravy, see page 252.

NOTE: A green salad is traditionally served with this dish.

YIELD: 6 servings

VEAL AND CHICKEN LIVER LOAF

This loaf is as good cold as hot; a fine choice for a picnic.

- 3 chicken livers
- 1 pound veal shoulder, ground
- 1 small onion, chopped finely
- 2 tablespoons finely chopped parsley
- 1/2 clove garlic, mashed
- 1/4 cup fine bread crumbs
- 1/2 cup chicken broth
- 1 tablespoon dry sherry
- 1 egg
- 1 teaspoon salt
- 1/4 teaspoon pepper
- 1/2 teaspoon allspice

1. Parboil chicken livers in a small amount of broth or water for about 3 minutes; remove livers and chop or mash them.
2. Mix lightly the veal, livers, onion, parsley, and garlic.
3. Combine bread crumbs with broth, sherry, egg, salt, pepper, and allspice (do not use broth in which livers have been parboiled as the flavor is too pronounced).
4. Add the veal mixture and blend lightly but thoroughly. If time permits, let stand for 1 hour in the refrigerator before baking; this step improves the texture of the loaf.
5. Bake at 350°F., in an oiled loaf pan, for about 1 hour.

NOTE: This loaf is as good cold as hot; a fine choice for a picnic.

YIELD: 4 servings

VEAL AND PEPPERS
From Italy

- 1 pound boneless veal (rump, shoulder or leg), cut into 1-1/2-inch cubes
- 1 red and 3 green peppers, medium size, seeded and cut into 1-inch strips
- 4 tablespoons oil
- 1/4 pound mushrooms, sliced
- 1 cup canned tomatoes, well drained, broken up slightly with a fork, or use tomato purée
- salt and pepper

1. Preheat oven to 325°F.
2. In a skillet, sauté peppers in 2 tablespoons of the oil for about 10 minutes; the brown and black spots that develop contribute to the good flavor of the dish. Remove peppers from skillet.
3. In this same pan, heat remaining oil and brown veal cubes in it. Add mushrooms and cook about 10 minutes. Add tomatoes and peppers. Season with salt and pepper.
4. Transfer to a casserole, cover, and bake for about 1 hour.

YIELD: 3 to 4 servings

SWEET AND PUNGENT CHICKEN LIVERS

- 3 medium green peppers, seeded
- 3/4 pound chicken livers, quartered
- 1 tablespoon oil
- 1/2 teaspoon salt
- 1 cup chicken bouillon
- 4 slices canned pineapple
- 1 tablespoon cornstarch
- 1 tablespoon soy sauce
- 1/4 cup vinegar
- 1/4 cup sugar

1. Cut each green pepper into 6 pieces. Parboil them in salted water until nearly tender, about 5 minutes; drain.
2. In a heavy, large skillet, brown chicken livers in the hot oil. Add salt. Sauté livers gently until done, then remove to a hot serving dish and keep warm.
3. In the same skillet, combine 1/3 cup of the chicken bouillon, the pineapple, and parboiled green peppers. Cover and cook over a very low flame about 10 minutes.
4. Blend together the cornstarch, soy sauce, vinegar, sugar, and remaining 2/3 cup chicken bouillon. Add this to the skillet and cook, stirring constantly, until thick and clear, about 5 minutes.
5. Pour contents of skillet over chicken livers and serve at once.

YIELD: 4 servings

LIVER AND ONIONS VENICE STYLE

This dish is especially good with rice or noodles.

4 large onions
1/2 teaspoon salt
1 tablespoon oil
1 pound calves' liver
2 tablespoons white wine

1. Cut onions into small pieces, add salt, and sauté in oil until golden in color.
2. Cut liver into 3/4-inch cubes, discarding skin and veins. Add livers to onions and cook, stirring, about 3 minutes.
3. Before serving, add wine and heat through.

YIELD: 4 servings

LIVER DUMPLINGS

From a famous Black Forest resort hotel in Southern Germany

- 1 pound liver (beef, calves' or chicken)
- 1/2 cup fine bread crumbs
- 1/2 cup skim milk
- 2 eggs
- 1 teaspoon salt
- 1/4 teaspoon ground ginger
- 1/4 teaspoon marjoram
- 1 onion, finely chopped
- 3 tablespoons oil
- 1/4 cup finely chopped parsley
- 2 tablespoons margarine
- 1/4 cup fine bread crumbs

1. Grind liver in a meat grinder. If using beef or calves' liver, remove skin and veins before grinding.
2. Mix the 1/2 cup crumbs and milk in a bowl; add eggs, ground liver, salt, ginger, and marjoram and mix well.
3. Sauté onion in oil until golden. Add parsley and sauté 1 minute more, then combine with liver mixture and blend thoroughly. This is a very soft mixture.
4. Refrigerate for 8 to 12 hours.
5. In a large saucepan bring to a boil two quarts of salted water. With 2 soup spoons, form dumplings and place gently in the boiling water; reduce heat to keep water just at simmering point. After dumplings have risen to the top, cook them 5 minutes more.
6. With a slotted spoon, remove dumplings to a serving dish and keep hot.
7. To serve, gently heat margarine in a small frying pan and brown the 1/4 cup crumbs lightly. Stir while browning; this will take just a minute. Sprinkle crumbs over dumplings.

NOTE: Traditionally, these dumplings are served with sauerkraut and mashed potatoes. They are also good in soup, but then make them smaller and after they are cooked in salted water, as above, transfer them to hot chicken or beef broth and sprinkle with chopped chives.

YIELD: 6 servings

CHICKEN LIVERS IN ASPIC

1/2 pound chicken livers, cut in halves	1-1/2 cups chicken broth
1 envelope (1 tablespoon) unflavored gelatin	2 teaspoons lemon juice
	1 teaspoon soy sauce
	1 clove garlic (optional)
1/4 cup cold water	2 tablespoons dry sherry

1. Sprinkle gelatin over cold water; stir to mix.
2. Bring to a boil chicken broth, lemon juice, soy sauce, and garlic. Add chicken livers, bring to a boil, and simmer about 5 minutes until livers are cooked but still pink inside. Remove livers and set aside; remove garlic.
3. Heat broth to a boil, add gelatin, and cook until dissolved; add sherry. Combine with livers and pour into a bowl or mold; refrigerate until firm (several hours).
4. Serve on shredded greens, garnished with olives, sweet pickles, or chutney with thin rye toast. Or serve with Cumberland Sauce (see page 256).

YIELD: 4 servings

KIDNEYS BAKED IN MUSTARD SAUCE

1 pound veal or lamb kidneys	1/2 teaspoon salt
1 small onion, chopped coarsely	1 teaspoon flour
	2 tablespoons water
1 teaspoon prepared mustard	1 tablespoon sherry freshly ground pepper
2 tablespoons oil	1 teaspoon chopped parsley
1 tablespoon soy sauce	

1. Preheat oven to 375°F.
2. Cut kidneys in half lengthwise and remove hard

white portion. Place close together in a flameproof casserole. Sprinkle onion over, around, and under kidneys. Mix mustard, oil, and soy sauce. Spread evenly over kidneys and sprinkle with salt.

3. Cover and bake about 45 minutes (the lamb kidneys, being smaller, need less time).

4. Drain liquid from casserole into a small saucepan. Mix flour and water and combine with liquid in pan. Bring to a boil, stirring, and simmer for 2 minutes. Add sherry.

5. Pour the sauce over the kidneys, cover, and just heat through on top of stove.

6. Sprinkle with pepper and parsley just before serving.

YIELD: 4 servings

POTTED CALVES' HEARTS

2 calves' hearts
2 tablespoons oil
1/2 cup sliced onions
2 carrots, cut into 4 or 5 pieces
1/2 cup chopped celery
few sprigs of parsley, chopped
1 small bay leaf
6 peppercorns
1/2 teaspoon salt
1 cup chicken or beef broth
1 tablespoon flour
3 tablespoons cold water

1. Preheat oven to 325°F.

2. Remove fat from hearts and cut away sinewy parts. Cut hearts into quarters or eighths, or if you prefer, into thin slices.

3. Put oil in a heavy skillet and brown hearts in it. Add remaining ingredients, except the flour and water. Cover and bake for about 2 hours.

4. To thicken gravy, mix flour with water and blend into pot liquid. Bring to a boil and simmer for a few minutes.

YIELD: 4 servings

KIDNEYS IN RED WINE

- 1 pound veal or lamb kidneys
- 1 tablespoon flour
- 1/2 teaspoon salt
- pepper to taste
- 3 tablespoons oil
- 2 shallots or 1 small onion, chopped
- 1 clove garlic, mashed
- 1 cup beef bouillon
- 1 teaspoon Worcestershire sauce
- 2 tablespoons dry red wine (dry white wine or dry vermouth may be used)
- chopped parsley

1. Cut kidneys in half and remove hard white portions. Cut veal kidneys into 4 to 6 pieces but leave lamb kidney halves "as is."
2. Mix flour, salt, and pepper in a bag; add kidney pieces and shake well to cover all lightly with flour.
3. In a heavy pan, brown kidney pieces well in hot oil. Add shallots or onion and sauté 2 minutes. Add garlic and cook 1 minute.
4. Sprinkle remaining flour mixture over kidneys. Stir a minute to cook the flour. Add bouillon, Worcestershire sauce, and wine. Cover and simmer 10 to 15 minutes.
5. Sprinkle with parsley before serving. Serve with rice or noodles.

YIELD: 4 servings

14

Vegetables

The Chinese way with vegetables is one of the oldest, yet modern as tomorrow. This method of preparing them is simplicity itself. Short cooking time preserves nutrients, texture and color. Their crispness and flavor make them attractive the world over.

Food values of most canned and frozen vegetables compare quite favorably to those of fresh. However, a fresh vegetable has no equal and should processed ones be used exclusively, we would miss some of the best things to eat.

Ways to prepare fresh vegetables are many. When serving several with your dinner, for example, you can cook them side by side in a "steamer basket." They all will taste garden fresh.

Perhaps you have used chicory, escarole and Romaine lettuce only as salad greens. Try them braised—Italian style, or sautéed. New flavor experiences will surprise and delight your family.

Use the blender or vegetable mill to make delicious purées. These are especially advantageous when you entertain guests, for they may be prepared well ahead of time. What could be a more tempting combination than a nicely browned roast chicken with fluffy butternut squash, seasoned with a touch of ginger, or roast leg of lamb with a purée of white turnips?

And let's not forget some of the old favorites—a casserole of sweet potatoes and apples, for instance, or stuffed cabbage prepared in a sweet and sour sauce.

Since nature puts most of the vitamins in the dark

green, leafy, and deep yellow vegetables, we have favored these in our selection. But all vegetables are valuable and offer variety and pleasure, when prepared with care.

VEGETABLES COOKED IN STEAM

An easy way to cook fresh vegetables is to *steam* them. They will keep their color, flavor and nutritive value.

A steamer basket which folds up for storing is very handy. The basket is set in a large pot, containing water about 1/2 inch deep. Vegetables will cook in the steam only, as the water does not touch them. You can improvise with a rack, set on a bowl, placed in the pot.

Several vegetables may be steamed at the same time: cauliflower or broccoli flowerets, tiny potatoes, whole carrots, small white turnips cut in half, asparagus stalks, and others.

Bring the water to a boil, cover pot, and reduce heat. Replenish water if it should boil away. Vegetables will be done in 10 to 20 minutes depending on kind and size; when done, gently lift vegetables to a serving dish or individual plates.

Serve "as is" or season with melted margarine to which a few drops of lemon juice have been added, or with mayonnaise or French dressing.

TO SAUTÉ VEGETABLES CHINESE STYLE

Here are some general rules to sauté vegetables such as asparagus, broccoli, Brussels sprouts, cabbage, and carrots.

Cut asparagus and broccoli diagonally into 1-inch sections.

Cut Brussels sprouts in half or quarters.

Slice or shred cabbage.

Cut carrots into thin strips.

For 1 pound of vegetables, heat 2 tablespoons oil in a skillet or pan.

Add vegetable and sauté for about 3 minutes; sprinkle with salt.

If needed, add 2 to 3 tablespoons water. Cover pan and cook for 5 to 10 minutes. Stir occasionally.

VEGETABLES BAKED IN FOIL

The next time you use your oven for poultry, meat or fish, bake your vegetable—one or several kinds. Any temperature that is best for the main dish will be all right for these vegetables. There are many interesting possibilities.

One- or two-portion packets are easy to handle. Use heavy aluminum foil. Put vegetable in center of a piece of foil large enough to enfold it completely. Season the vegetable and fold the foil over it to seal it securely. The cooking time will vary from 20 to 40 minutes depending on kind and size of the vegetable and cooking temperature.

Suggestions for preparing a few vegetables to be baked in foil:

Cut carrots into strips or leave small ones whole; sprinkle with a little brown sugar and a pinch of salt.

Dice zucchini or eggplant, peeled or unpeeled, season lightly with salt, pepper, finely minced garlic, a little oregano or chopped parsley, and sprinkle with a few drops of oil.

Make strips of peeled cucumbers, cut asparagus into pieces about 2 inches long, slice or "French" green beans diagonally. All these taste good even without any seasoning.

TZIMMIS
A Jewish favorite

- 1 pound carrots (about 6 medium carrots)
- 1 pound sweet potatoes
- 2 tablespoons lemon juice
- 2 tablespoons oil
- 1 tablespoon honey or sugar

1. Wash carrots and sweet potatoes. Cook separately in boiling water in their skins until tender. Peel, slice, or mash them.

2. Put them together in a saucepan; add remaining ingredients and mix well. Cover and simmer for about 10 minutes.

YIELD: 4 to 6 servings

MASHED BUTTERNUT SQUASH

If you like butternut squash moist and sweet, select one that has a slender neck and a big round bulb.

1. Wash squash but do not peel; cut into a few large pieces and through lengthwise to remove seeds.

2. Pour about 1/2 inch of water into a pot; add squash, flesh side up (water should not touch the flesh). Cover pot, bring water to a boil, reduce heat and steam 15 to 20 minutes or until squash is soft.

3. Remove squash, scoop flesh from peel, and mash or force through a food mill. Season with a little brown sugar, ginger, salt, and margarine.

4. Put mashed squash in a saucepan; as it heats, beat well with a wooden spoon until light and fluffy.

NOTE: For an oven casserole, prepare mashed squash as above and put in a casserole. Sprinkle with a bit of brown sugar and dot with margarine. Heat and brown lightly in a 350° to 400°F. oven.

MASHED ACORN SQUASH

Prepare as for butternut squash, above. Cut squash in half lengthwise, scoop out seeds and steam, flesh side up, with about 1/2 inch of water, in a covered pot.

Even when you bake acorn squash, steam them first for 5 to 10 minutes. This will reduce baking time and make for a smooth, non-stringy interior.

KOHLRABI
South German style

Buy only young kohlrabi with their tender greens. Two bunches will serve four people generously. To "stretch" the kohlrabi greens, add 1/2 pound fresh spinach.

To Cook the Greens:

1. Strip kohlrabi greens from stems and wash well. Remove stems and roots from spinach and wash leaves.
2. Cook kohlrabi greens in a little water and salt until nearly tender, add spinach, and cook together for a few minutes.
3. Cool, chop and "bind" with a small amount of white sauce (using any remaining cooking liquid or chicken broth); season with salt and pepper and set aside.

To Cook the Bulbs:

1. Peel the bulbs, halve them, and cook until tender in boiling salted water.
2. Make a medium white sauce with the vegetable liquid, adding milk to make about 1-1/2 cups sauce for 2 bunches of kohlrabi.
3. Cut the cooked bulbs into fine slices and combine them with white sauce; season with a bit of nutmeg and heat thoroughly.

To Serve:

Pour the kohlrabi slices in white sauce into a deep serving dish. In the center, carefully spoon the well-heated greens.

SAUTÉED SPINACH WITH GARLIC
Chinese style

1 pound spinach	1 clove garlic, crushed
2 tablespoons oil	1/2 teaspoon salt

1. Remove roots and tough stalks of spinach, wash leaves thoroughly, and drain well.

2. Heat oil in skillet, add garlic (do not brown), spinach, and salt.

3. Sauté, uncovered, for about 5 minutes, stirring gently with a large fork.

YIELD: 3 servings

SAUTÉED BROCCOLI
Chinese style

1 pound broccoli	2 to 3 tablespoons water
2 tablespoons oil	
1/4 teaspoon dry mustard	1/2 teaspoon salt

1. Wash broccoli, cut diagonally into 1-1/2-inch sections and small flowerets.

2. Heat skillet, add oil, stir in mustard, then add the broccoli. Sauté for 1 to 2 minutes, add water, and cover skillet.

3. Cook about 5 minutes, remove cover, sprinkle broccoli with salt, and stir gently with a large fork. If pan becomes dry, add a bit more water.

4. Cover again and cook to the crisp-tender stage, about 5 minutes longer.

YIELD: 4 servings

VEGETABLE PURÉES

Purées are extremely popular. They are mild in flavor, fluffy, and attractive to serve. There never seems to be enough to satisfy all; they appeal even to those who usually show little enthusiasm for vegetables.

Cook the vegetable, then either mash it well, or force it through a fine sieve or food mill, or purée in a blender.

To serve, the purée can be just heated and seasoned or also "bound" (slightly thickened) in several ways:

1. A little flour may be sifted over the hot vegetable, stirred lightly, and cooked about one minute more.

2. Bits of *beurre manié* (margarine blended with

flour) may be added to the vegetable and cooked until the flour taste is gone, for a minute or two, while stirring.

3. A small amount of white sauce may be combined with the purée.

4. A roux may be made, the purée added, then cooked for a few minutes, while stirring. It may be thinned with some broth to the right consistency.

PURÉE OF BROCCOLI

This way of preparing a vegetable purée is popular in Germany and France.

1 pound broccoli	1/2 cup broth (any
boiling water	stock from
2 tablespoons oil	vegetable plus
1 tablespoon	chicken broth)
chopped onion	salt, pepper, nutmeg
a thin slice garlic	few drops lemon
(optional)	juice
2 tablespoons flour	2 tablespoons skimmed
	evaporated milk

1. Wash and trim off woody portions of broccoli; cut into about 1-inch pieces and put in a saucepan. Sprinkle with salt.
2. Pour boiling water over it, to about 1/2 inch depth. Cook, partially covered, to the tender-crisp stage.
3. Cool and chop finely or purée in blender or food mill. Save any leftover broth.
4. In a saucepan, heat the oil; add onion, and sauté until transparent; add garlic and cook a moment longer. Add flour and cook until dry and bubbly (do not brown).
5. Add broccoli, mixing well; cook over low heat about 5 minutes, stirring.
6. Add broth; season with salt, pepper, nutmeg, and lemon juice.
7. Blend in evaporated milk; serve hot.

NOTE: Use this same method for spinach, savoy cabbage, mustard greens, and many other vegetables.

YIELD: 4 servings

CARROT PURÉE

- 1-1/2 pounds carrots
- 1/2 teaspoon sugar
- 1/4 teaspoon salt
- 1 cup water
- 2 tablespoons margarine
- ground ginger or pepper
- dash of lemon juice

1. Wash and scrape carrots, grate coarsely, and place in a medium-sized pot. Add sugar, salt, and water.
2. Cover pot; cook over low heat about 15 minutes or until carrots are tender.
3. Purée carrots in blender or food mill. Reheat purée and stir in margarine.
4. At serving time, season with ginger or pepper to taste and lemon juice.

YIELD: 4 to 6 servings

PURÉE OF WHITE TURNIPS

- 1-1/2 pounds young white turnips
- 1 medium onion, coarsely chopped
- 1 tablespoon oil
- 1/2 teaspoon salt
- 1/4 teaspoon sugar
- 1 cup water
- 1 tablespoon margarine
- ginger or pepper

1. Wash and peel turnips; slice or dice them.
2. Sauté onion in oil until transparent, but do not brown. Add turnips, salt, sugar, and water.
3. Cover pot; cook gently about 20 minutes or until turnips are tender.
4. Purée in blender or food mill. Reheat purée and stir in margarine and seasoning.

NOTE: If you like a thicker purée, sift 1/2 teaspoon flour over purée; cook one minute, while stirring.

VARIATIONS: Mix purée of carrots with white turnip purée and heat.

For a more substantial dish, some potato may be cooked along with either vegetable, before puréeing.

YIELD: 4 to 6 servings

CABBAGE AND GREEN PEPPER, SWEET AND SOUR

- 3 tablespoons oil
- 1 firm, medium head of green cabbage (about 1-1/4 pounds), shredded
- 2 medium green peppers, seeded, sliced
- 1 medium onion, sliced
- 1/2 teaspoon salt
- pepper
- 1/2 cup chicken broth or water
- 1 tablespoon sugar
- 1 tablespoon vinegar

1. Heat oil in a fairly large pot. Add cabbage, peppers, and onion and sauté about 5 minutes, stirring with a large fork. Volume of vegetables should be reduced and vegetables just barely tender.

2. Season with salt and pepper and add broth, sugar, and vinegar. Cover and cook another 5 minutes.

NOTE: If you like a slightly thickened sauce, sift 1/2 teaspoon flour over the cooked vegetables, stir well, and cook 2 minutes more.

YIELD: 4 servings

CHINESE CABBAGE AND MUSHROOMS

- 3 tablespoons oil
- 1/4 pound mushrooms, sliced
- 1 medium head Chinese cabbage, about 3/4 pound
- 1/4 teaspoon salt
- 1/4 teaspoon monosodium glutamate (optional)
- 1 tablespoon cornstarch
- 1/2 cup chicken broth

1. Heat 1 tablespoon of the oil in a skillet and sauté mushrooms in it for 5 minutes; set aside.
2. Cut Chinese cabbage into strips about 2 inches wide.
3. In a large skillet, heat remaining 2 tablespoons of oil; add cabbage and sauté about 3 minutes, until volume has decreased and it is barely tender.
4. To cabbage, add the sautéed mushrooms; sprinkle with salt and monosodium glutamate; cover pan and cook about 5 minutes.
5. Dissolve cornstarch in broth; stir it into the vegetables. Cook about 2 minutes longer or until sauce is slightly thickened and clear.

NOTE: You may add 1 teaspoon soy sauce to the broth, in which case omit salt in recipe.

YIELD: 4 servings

SAVORY RED CABBAGE
From South Germany

- 1 medium head of red cabbage, about 1-1/4 pounds
- 2 tablespoons vinegar
- 1 teaspoon salt
- 1 medium onion, chopped
- 2 tablespoons oil
- 2 tablespoons sugar
- 1 tart medium apple, peeled, diced
- 1 bay leaf
- 3 cloves
- 1 cup hot water
- 1/4 cup syrup from watermelon pickle or 1/4 cup currant jelly
- 1 teaspoon flour
- 2 tablespoons wine

1. Remove core and tough outer leaves of cabbage and shred it.
2. Combine cabbage, vinegar, and salt and mix well. Let stand for several hours or overnight, if time permits.
3. In a large saucepan, sauté onion in oil; add sugar. Cook, while stirring, until onion is transparent; add apple and cook until it is soft.

4. Add cabbage, bay leaf, cloves, water, and syrup or jelly. Cover and cook gently until tender, about 45 minutes.

5. Sift flour over cabbage, stir well, and cook a few minutes more.

6. Add wine before serving.

YIELD: 6 servings

SAUERKRAUT WITH APPLES

- 1 pound sauerkraut
- 2 tablespoons oil
- 1 medium onion, chopped
- 1 tart, medium apple, peeled, diced
- 1 teaspoon sugar
- 1/2 cup water (approximately)
- 1/4 teaspoon flour
- 2 tablespoons dry white wine (optional)

1. Drain sauerkraut of excess moisture.
2. In a well-glazed pot, heat oil and sauté onion until golden.
3. Add sauerkraut, apple, sugar, and water. Cover and simmer until tender, about 1 hour.
4. Sift flour over sauerkraut, stir well, and cook a few minutes longer.
5. At serving time, season with wine.

YIELD: 4 servings

BARRA'S ZUCCHINI ITALIAN

- 1 pound zucchini
- 1/2 medium onion, sliced thin
- salt and pepper
- 2 to 3 tablespoons boiling water
- 2 tablespoons oil
- 1 egg, beaten lightly
- 2 tablespoons grated Parmesan or Romano cheese
- parsley, chopped

1. Wash zucchini well and slice but do not peel.
2. In a small pot, combine zucchini and onion slices. Season with salt and pepper.

3. Add boiling water (just enough to provide some moisture), cover lightly, and cook until tender, 7 to 10 minutes; do not drain.

4. Gradually stir oil into beaten egg; add cheese and a tablespoon or two of the cooking liquid from zucchini. Pour mixture over the zucchini.

5. Over low heat, cook zucchini gently just until sauce has thickened (about 1/2 minute), while stirring gently.

6. Sprinkle with parsley before serving.

YIELD: 4 servings

BAKED ZUCCHINI PUFF

- 3 small zucchini squash (about 1/2 pound)
- 1 teaspoon chopped onion
- 1 tablespoon oil
- 1-1/2 teaspoons flour
- 1 egg
- 1/2 cup milk
- 1/2 teaspoon salt
- pinch of nutmeg and cayenne
- 1 tablespoon grated cheese

1. Preheat oven to 400°F.

2. Wash and peel zucchini, leaving some peel on for color. Dice zucchini.

3. In a saucepan cook onion in oil until transparent. Add squash, cover, and cook until tender (5 to 10 minutes), stirring occasionally.

4. Remove cover, sprinkle flour over zucchini, and cook one minute, while stirring.

5. Beat egg well and add milk and seasonings.

6. Combine egg mixture with zucchini and beat well with electric or hand beater.

7. Pour into an oiled baking dish and sprinkle with cheese. Bake until top is a light brown and slightly puffed, about 25 minutes.

NOTE: This is a delicate dish but with a pronounced zucchini flavor. We find that other "soufflé-type" vegetable dishes may be improved by *reducing* the number of eggs in the recipe, thereby increasing the distinctive vegetable flavor.

YIELD: 2 servings

ZUCCHINI PATTIES

2 small zucchini
1 egg, slightly beaten
1 tablespoon grated cheese (optional)
salt and pepper
2 to 3 tablespoons flour

1. Wash zucchini well; do not peel. Slice and cook until tender in a little salted water. Drain.
2. Let zucchini cool, then mash well with a fork. Add egg and cheese; season with salt and pepper. Add flour and mix thoroughly.
3. In a skillet, heat just enough oil to lightly cover bottom of pan.
4. Drop zucchini mixture, by tablespoons, into the skillet. Sauté patties until browned on both sides; turn once only.

YIELD: 2 servings

FRENCH GREEN PEAS

2 cups shelled young peas (about 2-1/2 pounds in pod)
1/2 medium onion, chopped
1/4 teaspoon salt
1 small head Boston lettuce, shredded
pinch of sugar
boiling water
1 tablespoon margarine

1. In a saucepan combine peas, onion, salt, lettuce, and sugar. Pour about 1/3 cup boiling water over vegetables.
2. Cover and cook until tender. Very young peas take only a few minutes.
3. Add margarine and stir lightly to mix throughout.

YIELD: 4 servings

BRAISED CHICORY
Italian style

- 2 small heads, about 1 pound, tender chicory
- 2 tablespoons oil
- 1 clove garlic, thinly sliced
- 1/4 teaspoon salt freshly ground pepper
- 1/4 teaspoon chopped basil (optional)

1. Wash and drain chicory well; shred coarsely.
2. Heat oil in saucepan; add chicory and all other ingredients.
3. Cook, partially covered, over low heat about 10 minutes or until tender-crisp; stir with a large fork occasionally.

NOTE: Escarole, Romaine lettuce, and spinach are equally good cooked this way. Escarole takes about the same time as chicory. Romaine lettuce and spinach need less time, only about 5 minutes.

YIELD: 4 servings

BROILED TOMATOES

- 4 medium, firm, ripe tomatoes
- 2 tablespoons grated cheese
- 1/2 cup fine bread crumbs
- 2 tablespoons oil (approximately)

1. Cut the tomatoes into halves, crosswise. Season with salt and pepper and a few sprinkles of sugar.
2. Combine cheese and bread crumbs and spread on tomato halves. Sprinkle tops with oil.
3. Arrange tomato halves in a flameproof shallow serving dish. Broil under medium flame or bake at 400°F. until tops are lightly browned and tomatoes are cooked, 10 to 15 minutes.

YIELD: 4 servings

CAULIFLOWER AU GRATIN

1 medium head cauliflower
3/4 cup water
1/2 teaspoon salt

Sauce

3 tablespoons oil or margarine
1 teaspoon finely minced onion
3 tablespoons flour
cooking liquid and milk to make 1-1/2 cups

Topping

3 tablespoons fine bread crumbs
2 tablespoons grated Parmesan cheese (optional)
2 tablespoons margarine

1. Separate cauliflower into good-size flowerets.
2. Bring water and salt to a boil. Add cauliflower, cover pot lightly, and cook until cauliflower is crisp-tender, about 10 minutes. Drain and place in a casserole, saving the cooking liquid for the sauce.
3. In a small saucepan heat oil, add onion, and stir and cook until transparent. Stir flour into pan and cook until bubbly.
4. Gradually add the cooking liquid and milk, while stirring. Bring to a boil and cook a few minutes, stirring until thickened and smooth. Correct seasoning and pour sauce over cauliflower.
5. Sprinkle with crumbs and cheese and dot with the 2 tablespoons margarine. Brown in a moderate oven (375°F.) about 15 minutes.

NOTE: Broccoli can be substituted for cauliflower.

YIELD: 4 servings

BAKED EGGPLANT PAPA ZINGONE

Perfect with baked fish, lamb, or chicken.

1 medium eggplant
1/4 cup Parmesan cheese
3/4 cup thick tomato sauce

1. Preheat oven to 375°F.
2. Cut unpeeled eggplant into slices 3/4 inch thick, crosswise.
3. Parboil eggplant slices in salted water for 5 to 7 minutes; drain well.
4. Transfer eggplant slices to a shallow, oiled baking dish, keeping slices close together. Spoon tomato sauce over eggplant. Sprinkle with cheese.
5. Bake about 20 minutes, until cheese is lightly browned.

YIELD: 3 servings

EGGPLANT, TOMATO, GREEN PEPPER, AND ZUCCHINI CASSEROLE

- 5 tablespoons oil
- 2 cloves garlic, finely chopped
- 1 small eggplant, peeled, diced
- 1/2 pound zucchini, sliced
- 2 medium onions, thinly sliced
- 1 green pepper, seeded, sliced
- salt and pepper to taste
- 1 teaspoon sugar
- 1 teaspoon oregano
- 4 medium tomatoes, peeled, sliced

1. Preheat oven to 375°F.
2. In a large, flameproof, shallow casserole, heat oil and sauté garlic, eggplant, zucchini, onions, and green pepper until vegetables are just tender but still firm.
3. Season with salt, pepper, sugar, and oregano. Place tomato slices on top. Bake until tomatoes are cooked, about 10 to 15 minutes.

YIELD: 4 to 6 servings

GREEN BEANS LYONNAISE

- 1 pound green beans
- 2 medium onions
- 1 tablespoon oil
- 1 tablespoon margarine
- salt and pepper
- 2 teaspoons wine vinegar
- 2 teaspoons chopped parsley

1. Snip ends off beans and cut them into 2 or 3 pieces. Leave them whole if they are small.
2. Cook beans in small amount of salted water until crisp-tender. Drain them well.
3. Cut onions into thin slices and sauté until golden in a mixture of oil and margarine. Combine beans and onions and heat through. Season with salt, pepper, and vinegar.
4. Sprinkle with parsley before serving.

YIELD: 4 servings

BAKED ONIONS VINAIGRETTE

1 pound medium-sized onions
2 tablespoons oil
salt and pepper
2 tablespoons dry white wine
1/3 cup Vinaigrette Sauce

1. Preheat oven to 350°F.
2. Peel onions and cut in half horizontally; place them, cut sides up, in a flat baking dish. Sprinkle with oil, salt, and pepper. Pour wine over onions.
3. Bake about 30 minutes or until tender and slightly browned.
4. Spoon Vinaigrette over onions and serve hot or cold.

YIELD: 4 servings

SPRING CARROTS

These carrots are very good with roast chicken.

1 bunch young carrots (about 1 pound)
1 tablespoon margarine
1/2 teaspoon sugar
pinch of salt

1. Scrape and wash carrots. Cut them into 1-inch pieces (do not split them).
2. Combine margarine, carrots, sugar, and salt in a

heavy saucepan. Cover and cook over very low flame until tender-crisp, about 15 minutes. Shake pan 2 or 3 times so that carrots cook evenly.

3. If desired, leave cover off for last five minutes of cooking time, to brown carrots lightly.

YIELD: 4 servings

SPICED BEETS

1 pound can sliced beets, drained	1 small bay leaf
1/2 cup beet liquid	4 whole cloves
2 tablespoons brown sugar	3 peppercorns
1 teaspoon flour	3 allspice berries
pinch of salt	2 tablespoons vinegar
	1 small onion, thinly sliced

1. Mix sugar, flour, salt, spices, vinegar, and beet liquid; bring to a boil.
2. Add beets and onion and bring to a boil again; reduce heat and simmer about 5 minutes.
3. Serve hot or cold.

NOTE: Spiced beets improve in flavor on standing; refrigerate several hours or overnight. Reheat to serve hot. Chilled beets are fine for a buffet.

YIELD: 4 servings as a hot vegetable; 8–10 servings as a relish.

SWEET AND SOUR STUFFED CABBAGE

1 large head of cabbage (about 2 pounds)

STUFFING

1/2 medium onion, chopped	pepper to taste
3 tablespoons oil	1 egg, lightly beaten
3 tablespoons fine bread crumbs	3 tablespoons water
1 teaspoon salt	1 pound lean beef, finely chopped
1/4 teaspoon cinnamon	1/2 cup white raisins

SAUCE

2 medium onions, chopped	1/4 teaspoon allspice
1/2 cup tomato purée	2 cloves
1 tablespoon honey	1/2 bay leaf
2 tablespoons sugar	juice of 1/2 lemon
1/4 teaspoon ginger	3/4 cup broth
	2 tablespoons oil

1. Carefully separate all the leaves from the cabbage head, cutting close to the stem. Put leaves in a large saucepan and sprinkle with a little salt. Pour boiling water over cabbage. Boil for 3 to 5 minutes or until leaves are somewhat soft and pliable; drain.

2. Place large leaves on a wooden board and reserve. Chop small center leaves to add to stuffing.

3. Sauté onion in oil until transparent. Add bread crumbs, salt, cinnamon, and pepper; mix well.

4. Beat egg and water lightly and thoroughly combine with beef, bread crumb mixture, and chopped cabbage leaves. Roughly divide stuffing into 12 portions in the bowl.

5. To stuff the cabbage leaves (no string or toothpicks are needed), cut a 12-inch square of double cheesecloth.

6. Place a cabbage leaf, large enough to enfold one stuffing portion, on the cheesecloth square. Use two smaller leaves, if necessary—they will hold together well.

7. Put a few raisins and a portion of the stuffing on the cabbage leaf. Now pick up the four corners of the cheesecloth. Gently twist with one hand while the other hand, cupped below the cabbage, holds it in place. Untwist—you will have a perfectly rounded well-filled cabbage leaf. Continue until all leaves are stuffed.

8. Preheat oven to 325°F.

9. In a large flameproof casserole combine the onions, tomato purée, honey, sugar, ginger, allspice, cloves, bay leaf, and lemon juice; distribute all well over the bottom.

10. Place stuffed cabbage leaves, open ends down, in the casserole. Pour broth over the stuffed cabbage leaves and spread a little oil on each.

11. Cover and heat on top of stove, then bake for 1-1/2 hours, basting them occasionally. They will be tender and light brown and the sauce will be slightly thickened.

YIELD: 6 servings (12 stuffed leaves)

STUFFED CABBAGE

This recipe is a happy combination of the German and Provençal methods.

- 1 large head of cabbage (2 pounds)
- 1 medium onion, chopped
- 4 tablespoons oil
- 1 clove garlic, mashed
- 1/4 cup chopped parsley
- 2 slices bread, soaked and squeezed dry
- 1 teaspoon salt
- 1/2 teaspoon thyme
- pepper to taste
- 3/4 pound lean beef or pork, or a mixture of both, finely ground
- 2 eggs, lightly beaten
- 1-1/2 cups broth, approximately

1. Separate cabbage leaves and parboil as in previous recipe. Chop and reserve small leaves.
2. Sauté onion in oil until transparent. Add garlic and parsley and sauté 1 minute more. Combine with bread, salt, thyme, and pepper.
3. In a bowl, thoroughly mix ground meat, eggs, onion mixture, and chopped cabbage leaves.
4. Stuff leaves as directed in previous recipe.
5. Preheat oven to 350°F.
6. Place stuffed cabbage leaves in a shallow oiled baking dish, open ends down. Heat broth and pour over them. Cover lightly with foil.
7. Bake for 1 to 1-1/2 hours, basting occasionally with pan juice. They will be tender and the tops brown.

NOTE: Savoy cabbage is especially good in this dish.

YIELD: 6 servings (12 stuffed leaves)

STUFFED PEPPERS
From a Bulgarian recipe

The Bulgarian cook prepares peppers for stuffing by gently pressing her thumb down, around the stem, to loosen it. Carefully, without tearing the flesh of the pepper, stem and core are pulled out together and the seeds and membranes then removed. Peppers look very attractive this way, but it is easier just to slice partly through the top of the pepper—do not sever it completely, for it will serve as a cover. Remove seeds and membranes. Peppers for this recipe are not parboiled and rice used for stuffing is uncooked.

- 6 medium green peppers
- 1 pound boneless veal, finely chopped (shank or shoulder are excellent)
- 2 medium onions, chopped
- 1/3 cup oil
- 1/4 pound mushrooms, chopped
- 1-1/2 teaspoons salt
- 1 teaspoon chopped dill
- 1/4 cup chopped parsley
- black pepper to taste
- 1 egg, well beaten
- 2 tablespoons uncooked rice
- 1 cup broth or water
- 2 cups tomato purée
- yogurt

1. Prepare peppers for stuffing as directed above.
2. Sauté onions in oil until they start to color slightly. Add mushrooms and cook until tender, about 5 minutes. Add salt, dill, parsley, and pepper.
3. Thoroughly combine egg with veal, onion mixture, rice, and broth. If time permits, let stuffing mixture stand 1 to 2 hours, refrigerated.
4. Stuff peppers and place them upright, close together in a large flameproof casserole. If any stuffing is left over, form into small balls and placed between the peppers.
5. Pour tomato purée over peppers and cover the

pan. Gently heat on top of stove; then bake, covered, about 1-1/4 hours at 350°F.

6. Serve with yogurt.

YIELD: 6 servings

STUFFED ITALIAN PEPPERS

- 12 small red and green tender "frying" peppers (about 1-1/4 pounds)
- 1 tablespoon oil
- 1 small onion, chopped
- 1 clove garlic, chopped
- 1 pound ground lean beef
- 1/4 cup raw rice
- 1/2 teaspoon curry powder
- 1/2 teaspoon grated fresh ginger
- 1 teaspoon salt
- 1 tablespoon brown sugar
- 1 tablespoon lemon juice

1. Carefully seed the peppers and remove membranes.

2. Sauté onion in oil until transparent. Add garlic and cook one minute more.

3. Combine beef, rice, sautéed mixture, and seasonings and blend thoroughly. Stuff peppers with beef mixture.

4. In a large, heavy frying pan heat 1 tablespoon of oil. Gently brown peppers on one side while pan is covered, about 10 minutes. Turn peppers and brown on other side, keeping pan covered.

5. Add just enough water to keep peppers from burning, cover, and cook on very low flame about 45 minutes.

6. Make balls of any leftover meat filling and cook alongside the peppers.

7. Serve with yogurt, if desired.

YIELD: 4 servings

STUFFED EGGPLANT

- 1 large eggplant
- 2 medium-sized onions, chopped
- 3 tablespoons oil
- 1/4 pound mushrooms, chopped
- 1 teaspoon oregano
- 1/2 pound ground cooked beef or other meat (do not substitute raw meat)
- 1 teaspoon salt
- pinch of pepper
- 1/2 cup fine bread crumbs

1. Bake eggplant in foil at 350°F. for 1 hour.
2. Sauté onions in oil until transparent. Add mushrooms and cook until tender, about 5 to 8 minutes.
3. Cut baked eggplant in half, lengthwise; scoop out pulp to 1/2 inch from outside. Mix pulp with sautéed onions and mushrooms, oregano, meat, salt, pepper, and bread crumbs.
4. Stuff the eggplant shells with mixture and bake at 350°F. for 20 to 30 minutes.

YIELD: 4 to 6 servings as a side dish

SPICY STUFFED EGGPLANT
From Armenia

- 2 medium-sized eggplants
- 2 tablespoons oil
- 1 medium onion, chopped
- 1 clove garlic, crushed
- 1/2 pound lean beef or lamb, finely chopped
- 1 egg, well beaten
- 1/2 teaspoon cinnamon
- 1/2 cup fine bread crumbs
- 1/2 cup broth
- 2 tablespoons chopped parsley
- 1/2 teaspoon salt
- pinch of cayenne

1. Peel eggplants lengthwise in strips, alternating peeled and unpeeled strips. Cut crosswise into slices about 3/4 inch thick.
2. Sprinkle slices lightly with salt, place in a colan-

der, and let stand 1 hour. Wipe dry. This step is optional, but improves flavor.

3. Brush slices with oil and broil or sauté lightly on both sides.

4. To make the stuffing, sauté onion in oil until soft. Combine with all remaining ingredients and mix thoroughly. For a smooth, pâté-like stuffing, purée in a blender the sautéed onion, garlic, egg, bread crumbs, and broth, then combine with other ingredients as above.

5. In a casserole, alternate layers of broiled or sautéed eggplant with stuffing.

6. Bake in a 350°F. oven for about 45 minutes. Serve hot or cold.

YIELD: 6 servings

STUFFED ZUCCHINI NIÇOISE

- 4 small zucchini
- 1 small onion, chopped
- 1 tablespoon oil
- 1 clove garlic, minced
- 1 tablespoon chopped parsley
- 1 egg
- 1/4 cup fine bread crumbs
- salt and pepper to taste
- grated cheese
- bread crumbs

1. Scrub zucchini and cut them in half lengthwise. Parboil them for about five minutes in lightly salted water; drain well.

2. Carefully scoop out zucchini centers. Mash pulp and set aside.

3. Sauté onion in oil until soft. Add garlic and cook one minute (do not brown).

4. Combine onion-garlic mixture with zucchini pulp, parsley, egg, and 1/4 cup bread crumbs. Season with salt and pepper.

5. Fill zucchini shells with stuffing. Set them close together in a shallow, oiled baking dish. Sprinkle with grated cheese and bread crumbs.

6. Bake at 375°F. until lightly browned and puffy, about 30 minutes.

NOTE: For a stuffing variation omit garlic and add 2 ounces chopped ham.

YIELD: 4 servings

SWEET POTATO AND APPLE CASSEROLE

- 1 pound sweet potatoes, boiled in their jackets, peeled
- 2 tart, medium-sized apples
- 2 teaspoons lemon juice
- 3 tablespoons brown sugar
- 2 tablespoons oil
- 1 tablespoon margarine

1. Preheat oven to 350°F.
2. Cut sweet potatoes into slices about 1/3 inch thick. Peel apples, core, and cut into thin slices.
3. In a well-greased baking dish, put a layer of apples. Sprinkle with lemon juice, brown sugar, and oil. Cover with a layer of sweet potatoes. Sprinkle with remaining sugar and dot with margarine.
4. Bake for about 1 hour. Cover baking dish for first half hour of baking.

YIELD: 4 servings

HERBED POTATOES IN CASSEROLE

- 1-1/2 pounds new potatoes
- 3 cups thin White Sauce using half milk and half chicken broth
- pinch of nutmeg
- 1 tablespoon chopped parsley
- 1 tablespoon chopped chives or scallions

1. Boil potatoes in their jackets until fork tender. When cool enough to handle, peel and cut them into 1/4-inch slices.
2. Prepare white sauce while potatoes are cooking, preferably in a cook and serve casserole. Flavor sauce with a pinch of nutmeg.

3. Carefully add potatoes to white sauce.
4. Just before serving, fold in parsley and chives.

NOTE: This is a good party dish. It can stand easily for about 1 hour before serving. Reheat on an asbestos plate or in the oven, but add herbs just before serving.

YIELD: 8 servings

ROAST POTATOES

Roast potatoes in a separate pan with any meat or poultry that you have in your oven. They are popular and take no time and effort.

1-1/2 pounds small or medium potatoes	1 tablespoon oil salt and pepper to taste

1. Preheat oven to 325° to 375°F., depending upon oven temperature needed for meat. Peel potatoes, leave them whole.
2. Heat oil in a heavy, flameproof pan. Dry the potatoes and place in the hot oil. Put pan directly on the bottom of oven.
3. Roast potatoes 20 to 30 minutes on each side (time depending on size of potatoes and oven temperature).

Sprinkle with salt and pepper before serving.

YIELD: 4 servings

HAM AND POTATO HASH

1 pound potatoes, cooked in jackets, peeled	1/2 teaspoon chopped onion freshly ground pepper
1/4 pound boiled or baked ham, chopped (about 1/2 cup)	1-1/2 tablespoons oil for frying

1. Crush potatoes well with a fork. Combine with ham, onion, and pepper to taste.

2. In a heavy skillet, heat oil and add the potato-ham mixture. Press down lightly. Cook over low heat until browned on bottom, about 20 minutes. Do not stir.

Fold in half to serve.

YIELD: 4 servings

SOUTH GERMAN POTATO DUMPLINGS

2 pounds potatoes, peeled, cut into large cubes (use Idaho or other mealy potatoes)
1 large hard roll, soaked in water and squeezed dry
3 tablespoons oil
1 small onion, chopped
1 egg
1/2 cup flour (approximately)
1/2 teaspoon salt
1/4 teaspoon nutmeg

For Garnish

2 tablespoons oil
2 tablespoons finely chopped onions or 2 tablespoons fine bread crumbs

1. Boil potatoes in salted water until tender; drain. Place pot with potatoes over low heat to dry them of excess moisture, put potatoes through ricer.

2. In a skillet heat oil, add onion, and sauté until transparent.

3. Mash hard roll well and add to onion in pan. Cook, turning occasionally, until roll is well dried out, has a glassy appearance, and will ball together. This will take about 15 minutes.

4. Thoroughly combine roll mixture with riced potatoes; cool well.

5. *Very shortly before dumplings are to be boiled,*

combine the potato mixture with egg, flour, and seasoning.

6. In a wide pot bring to a boil about 4 quarts of water with 1-1/2 tablespoons salt.

7. On a floured board (or wax paper) form a large roll of dumpling mixture. With a floured knife divide roll into about 20 pieces. With a little flour, lightly roll pieces into round dumplings.

8. Cook dumplings in simmering (not boiling) water about 10 minutes, with pot partially covered. With a slotted spoon, remove dumplings to a hot platter.

For garnish, brown onions or bread crumbs in oil. Sprinkle on dumplings just before serving.

NOTE: Very popular and practical, too, are dumplings cooked a day ahead. They are cut in half and browned on both sides in oil before serving. Viennese restaurants offer their patrons a choice of today's or yesterday's dumplings.

YIELD: about 20 dumplings 2 inches in diameter; light and fluffy

ROESTIS

This is a popular potato dish in Southern Germany and Switzerland.

1. Boil small potatoes in their jackets. Peel and cool them completely, preferably overnight. Slice them thin.

2. Heat a heavy frying pan, pour oil into it, just enough for a thin layer on the bottom of the pan.

3. Add potatoes to pan, with some finely chopped onion, if you like. Sprinkle with salt and pepper or ginger.

4. Fry potatoes over medium heat. Leave them undisturbed for a few minutes while they develop golden brown crusts, then turn them gently with a spatula and let them brown on the other side.

5. Serve them crisp and hot.

HAITIAN BEAN SAUCE

1 cup red kidney beans or pink beans
3 cups water
3 tablespoons oil
1 clove garlic, peeled and cut into a few pieces
1 tablespoon chopped parsley
salt and pepper to taste
optional seasonings: cayenne or chili powder

1. Bring to a boil beans, water, and 1 tablespoon of the oil. Cook for 1 minute; let stand for 1 hour (or longer if desired).
2. Bring to a boil again and simmer for 45 minutes to 1 hour, or until tender. Add more boiling water, if necessary, to keep beans covered.
3. Drain beans and grind about 1-1/2 cups beans with the garlic.
4. Combine ground beans with those left whole. Stir in chopped parsley, salt, pepper, remaining 2 tablespoons of oil, and cayenne or chili powder.
5. Simmer bean sauce for about 1 hour. Add some boiling water (or chicken broth) if sauce seems too dry. Sauce should be medium thick, glossy, light in texture, and rich brown in color.
6. Serve hot on boiled rice, or as a side dish with German red cabbage and roast turkey, capon, duck or pork. It is also very good served cold as a dip.

YIELD: 4 servings

HEARTY BEAN BUFFET DISH
From Sweden

Smoked turkey or ham is especially good served with these beans.

1 cup pink beans or kidney beans
4 cups water
1 tablespoon oil
1/2 teaspoon salt
3 tablespoons molasses
2 tablespoons cider vinegar

1. Boil beans for 2 minutes with water and oil; set aside for 1 hour.
2. Bring to a boil again and cook beans gently for about 2 hours or until tender, adding more boiling water if necessary.
3. Add salt, molasses, and vinegar. Simmer for 20 minutes, stirring gently several times during cooking.

15

Pancakes and Grain Dishes

FEATHERY BUTTERMILK PANCAKES

1 cup sifted flour (scant)
1/2 teaspoon salt
1/2 teaspoon baking soda
3/4 teaspoon baking powder
1 egg
2 teaspoons sugar
3 tablespoons oil
1 cup buttermilk

1. Sift together flour, salt, baking soda, and baking powder.
2. Beat egg with sugar until thick; add oil gradually, while beating. Combine with buttermilk.
3. Gradually stir egg-milk mixture into flour mixture, blending well.
4. Pour batter onto a greased hot griddle or an electric frying pan at 350°F. Use about 2 tablespoons for each pancake. When bubbles appear on cakes and they are browned on bottom, turn and brown the other side. Do not turn a second time.
5. Serve hot, with applesauce, maple syrup, or honey.

YIELD: about 14 5-inch pancakes

BUTTERMILK WAFFLES

1-1/2 cups sifted flour
1 teaspoon baking soda
1/2 teaspoon salt
2 eggs, separated
1/3 cup oil
2 cups buttermilk
2 tablespoons sugar

1. Sift together flour, baking soda, and salt into a bowl.
2. In a separate bowl, beat egg yolks until light. Gradually beat in oil. Stir in buttermilk.
3. Stir egg mixture into flour mixture, just to blend.
4. Whip egg whites until foamy. Add sugar and continue beating until stiff but not dry. Fold into batter.
5. Heat waffle iron. Before baking first waffle, brush iron lightly with oil (this will not be necessary for remaining waffles).

YIELD: 24 4-inch waffles

POTATO PANCAKES (Latkes)

1 pound Idaho potatoes
1 egg
1/2 teaspoon salt
dash each of pepper and nutmeg
dash of cinnamon
1 tablespoon grated onion
1-1/2 tablespoons flour
1/4 teaspoon baking powder

1. Peel potatoes, grate them, and pour off about half of the liquid.
2. Beat egg lightly; combine with potatoes and remaining ingredients.
3. Heat a heavy frying pan. Pour just enough oil into pan to lightly cover the bottom.
4. Into the hot oil, drop potato mixture by heaping tablespoons, about 3 pancakes to a 10-inch pan. Leave about 2 inches of space between pancakes, so that batter can be flattened out with a knife or spatula and pancakes will be thin.
5. Brown pancakes well on both sides, turning them only once. Add more oil as needed.

6. To be truly enjoyed, potato pancakes must be served piping hot, crisp, and brown, directly from the pan. Apple sauce is the traditional accompaniment.

YIELD: 12 pancakes, 3 inches in diameter

GERMAN PANCAKES

German pancakes are large, golden, and tender—a welcome main dish or dessert in many German homes; always a good standby.

1/2 cup flour	pinch of salt
1/2 cup milk	jam or preserves
1 egg, lightly beaten	sugar
1 tablespoon oil	

1. Combine flour with milk and stir until smooth. Add egg, oil, and salt; mix well.
2. Heat about 2 tablespoons of oil in a 9- or 10-inch skillet (the first pancake will take a little more oil than the following ones).
3. Into the hot pan, pour a scant 1/3 cup of batter; tilt pan to distribute batter evenly. Cook over low to medium heat until golden on underside, then turn with a spatula and brown the other side.
4. Spread a tablespoon of preserve in the center of the pancake. Roll up and sprinkle with sugar. Serve hot, straight from the pan.

YIELD: 4 pancakes (2 servings)

SMALL FILLED PANCAKES (Crêpes)

A delightful main dish for brunch, lunch or supper.

1 cup flour, scant	2 eggs
1/2 teaspoon salt	Filling (see following recipes)
1-1/4 cups water	Parmesan cheese
2 tablespoons oil	

1. Combine flour and salt in a bowl. Gradually add water, stirring until smooth. Add eggs and oil and combine thoroughly.
2. Heat a 6-inch skillet and grease lightly with oil. Pour 1/4 cup batter into skillet; tilt pan so that bottom is covered evenly. For even-size pancakes, pour batter from a glass measuring cup with a spout.
3. Cook over medium heat until lightly browned on under side; turn and brown the other side. Proceed until all pancakes are cooked. Add oil to the pan as needed.
4. Preheat oven to 350°F. Put a heaping tablespoon of desired filling mixture on each pancake and roll up. Place pancakes, close together, on a shallow greased baking dish. Sprinkle with Parmesan cheese.
5. Bake until heated through, crisp, and golden brown, about 15 minutes.

NOTE: Pancakes can be made ahead of time. Cool, stack, and wrap them in plastic or foil and refrigerate. Any of the following fillings can also be made ahead.

YIELD: 12 pancakes (4 servings)

FILLINGS FOR SMALL PANCAKES

CHICKEN FILLING

Combine 2 cups of finely diced chicken with 2 cups of medium White Sauce (page 253) made with a well-seasoned chicken broth and flavored with 2 tablespoons sherry or dry white wine.

CLAM FILLING

Combine 2 cups of well-drained canned or fresh-cooked chopped clams with 2 cups of medium White Sauce (page 253) made with well-seasoned chicken or clam broth (or part of each) and flavored with 1/4 teaspoon of poultry seasoning.

SPINACH, COTTAGE CHEESE AND SMOKED SALMON FILLING

Chop finely 1 cup of cooked, well-drained spinach. Mix thoroughly with 1 cup cottage cheese and 2 ounces chopped smoked salmon. Add salt and pepper to taste. All fillings should hold together lightly and be neither stiff nor runny.

YIELD: The preceding recipes yield enough filling for 12 pancakes.

POT CHEESE PANCAKES

1 cup sifted flour
1 teaspoon baking powder
1/4 teaspoon salt
1/2 pound pot cheese, sieved
3 eggs, lightly beaten
margarine and oil for frying

1. Sift together flour, baking powder, and salt.
2. Combine cheese and eggs; stir until smooth. Add flour mixture and stir until blended.
3. In a 10-inch frying pan heat together 1 tablespoon margarine and 1 tablespoon oil; drop the batter by tablespoonfuls into the hot fat. Cook to golden brown on both sides. Turn pancakes once only.
4. Dust pancakes with sugar. Serve them directly from the pan.

NOTE: Stewed fruit, apple sauce, or other fruit sauces are good accompaniments to pot cheese pancakes.

YIELD: 4 to 6 servings

COTTAGE CHEESE OMELET

1 egg, lightly beaten
1 tablespoon milk
pinch of salt
2 teaspoons oil
1 heaping tablespoon cottage cheese
1 teaspoon grated Parmesan cheese (optional)

1. Combine egg, milk, and salt. In a small skillet or omelet pan, heat oil well (but do not brown).

2. Pour egg mixture into pan; tilt pan to distribute mixture evenly. With a spatula, lift sides of omelet to let uncooked portion flow to bottom of pan.

3. When golden brown on the bottom, spoon cottage cheese over center of omelet, sprinkle Parmesan cheese over cottage cheese; turn off heat.

4. Fold omelet over cheese; serve it right away. The hot omelet will soften and melt cheese slightly.

NOTE: A cottage cheese omelet makes a good main dish. You can season the egg mixture with a few sprinkles of dehydrated bouillon and a pinch of curry powder. Serve with a sautéed green vegetable.

YIELD: 1 serving

BARLEY AND MUSHROOM CASSEROLE

1/2 cup chopped onion	1 cup fine pearl barley
1/2 pound sliced mushrooms	2-1/2 to 3 cups well-seasoned chicken broth
1/4 cup oil	salt and pepper

1. Preheat oven to 350°F.
2. In a flameproof casserole, sauté onion and mushrooms in oil until tender.
3. Add barley and cook, while stirring, until barley is a light brown.
4. Heat broth. Gradually, while stirring, add 2 cups to barley mixture, reserving remaining broth for later use.
5. Bring barley mixture to a boil; correct seasoning with salt and pepper.
6. Cover and place in the oven; bake about 1/2 hour. Uncover and stir in enough remaining broth to moisten thoroughly.
7. Finish cooking, uncovered, until tender, 45 minutes to 1 hour.

YIELD: 4 to 6 servings

BULGUR

Bulgur is specially treated wheat grain. Hearty in flavor and nourishing, it is widely used in the Near East countries. It is also grown in the United States and has become popular here.

2 tablespoons oil
1 cup bulgur
1/2 medium onion, chopped
2 cups hot chicken broth
salt and pepper to taste
pinch of oregano (optional)

1. Heat oil in a flameproof casserole or heavy pot. Sauté bulgur and onion together until golden.
2. Gradually add broth. Add seasonings to taste. Bring to a boil, reduce heat, cover, and simmer about 20 minutes or until bulgur is done.
3. Serve with roast poultry, lamb, or pork.

YIELD: 4 servings

RISOTTO WITH CHICKEN LIVERS
From Italy

1 stalk celery, chopped
1 medium onion, chopped
6 tablespoons oil
1 cup rice
2 to 3 cups chicken broth
2 medium onions, thinly sliced
1/2 pound chicken livers
1/4 pound mushrooms, sliced
salt and freshly ground pepper
1 teaspoon chopped parsley
grated Parmesan cheese

1. Sauté chopped celery and chopped onion in 3 tablespoons of the oil until golden. Add rice and cook, while stirring, until transparent.
2. Heat chicken broth; pour 2 cups into rice mixture. Reserve remaining broth to add later, if needed,

to keep rice moist. Cook over low heat, partially covered, stirring gently occasionally, until rice is tender (about 30 minutes).

3. In a skillet sauté sliced onions in remaining 3 tablespoons of oil until transparent.

4. Cut chicken livers into 2 or 3 pieces and add them. Partially cover pan (preferably use a steam-vented lid). Cook livers until done and evenly browned. Remove liver and onion mixture to a dish and keep hot.

5. In the pan in which livers were cooked, sauté mushrooms for about 5 minutes; add more oil if necessary. Combine livers with mushrooms, season with salt and pepper, and sprinkle with parsley.

6. Arrange rice on a deep platter; make a depression in the center and pile livers and mushrooms into it. Sprinkle with Parmesan cheese.

7. Serve with a tossed green salad.

YIELD: 4 servings

CHICKEN LONG RICE

Long rice is also called transparent or cellophane noodles. These are very fine threads, made from bean starch. They are found in markets carrying Oriental foods.

- 4 ounces long rice
- 4 tablespoons oil
- 6 scallions, white part only, thinly sliced
- 2 tablespoons sherry
- 1/2 teaspoon sugar
- pinch of monosodium glutamate
- 1/2 teaspoon salt
- 1 cup cooked chicken, shredded
- 1 cup hot chicken broth
- 2 tablespoons soy sauce
- 2 tablespoons chopped chives

1. Soak long rice in warm water for 10 minutes; drain. With scissors cut into about 3-inch lengths.

2. Put long rice into a large pot of boiling water;

simmer for 5 minutes. Drain and rinse thoroughly with cold water; drain well.

3. Heat the oil in a wide skillet or casserole; add scallions, sherry, sugar, monosodium glutamate, and salt. Gently sauté for 1 to 2 minutes. Add long rice, chicken, hot chicken broth, and soy sauce. Cover and simmer for about 5 minutes or until broth is absorbed. Sprinkle with chives.

YIELD: 4 servings

SHRIMP LONG RICE

- 4 ounces long rice
- 6 tablespoons oil
- 1 cup finely diced celery
- 1/2 cup finely sliced onion
- Marinated Shrimp (see following recipe)
- 1 cup hot chicken broth
- 2 tablespoons chopped chives

1. Soak, cut, simmer, and drain long rice as in preceding recipe; set aside.
2. In a small skillet heat 2 tablespoons of the oil. Sauté celery and onion for 1 to 2 minutes; set aside.
3. Heat a large skillet or shallow casserole; add remaining 4 tablespoons of oil. Sauté marinated shrimp in hot oil for 1 minute; combine with celery-onion mixture, prepared long rice, and hot broth. Cover and simmer for 5 minutes. Sprinkle with chopped chives.

MARINATED SHRIMP

- 1/2 pound raw shrimp
- 1/2 teaspoon sugar
- 1/2 teaspoon salt
  pinch of pepper
- 2 cloves garlic, minced
- 1/2 teaspoon finely shredded ginger
- 2 tablespoons soy sauce

Shell and devein shrimp; cut diagonally into 1/2-inch slices. Combine with marinade ingredients; let stand 1/2 hour.

YIELD: 4 servings

16

Salads and Salad Dressings

A SALAD EVERY DAY

"She serves delicious salads—even makes her own dressings"—a fine compliment and so easy to earn. A beautiful salad sharpens appetites and tempts everyone.

Salads were slow to gain popularity in this country but have taken it by storm during this century. Mixing greens with oil and seasonings was known in Persia and Greece more than two thousand years ago. The talented Romans added their special touch and eventually the art of salad making was introduced to the French by the Medici princess who later became Queen of France.

Each new group of immigrants to the United States brought with them their favorite ways to prepare food. Many also grew those vegetables which were popular in their native lands; thus they contributed to the great variety of our foods.

The shopper for salad greens today has many choices. Widely used Iceberg lettuce adds crunch to the salad bowl. Tender Boston and crisp, flavorful Bibb lettuce are also popular. From their names, we know that many of our favorite greens are of Italian origin—the delicate Romaine, slightly bitter chicory and escarole as well as the pungent arugula. These dark-green varieties are outstanding in vitamin and mineral content.

Delicious salad dressings are easy to make and inexpensive, so why not make your own?

236 THE PRUDENT DIET

Our salad suggestions are of two
general kinds:

1. Vegetable salads that combine raw or cooked vegetables or both. Usually these accompany the main dish, but they may be served as an appetizer or a separate salad course. A cooked vegetable salad with a tart dressing is often a special favorite with men; a convenience to the cook too for it serves as both cooked vegetable and salad and can be made ahead of time.

2. Main-dish salads which contain a substantial portion of protein-rich foods—meat, fish, poultry, egg, cottage cheese and dried legumes.

Many a salad is improved in flavor when combined with a dressing that "does something for it," such as ripe tomato slices with Aunt Iva's Red Oil Dressing, escarole and watercress with Roquefort Dressing or cooked green beans with a Vinaigrette Sauce.

Some Pointers for Success
with Salad Greens

Buy only fresh greens.

Wash and dry salad greens thoroughly—dressing will not cling to wet leaves.

To store washed greens, wrap in paper towels or a terry towel, place in the vegetable crisper or a plastic bag and refrigerate.

Keep greens and salad dressings refrigerated until serving time.

Use a large salad bowl for mixing the salad.

Cut or shred greens shortly before serving time; toss greens lightly but thoroughly with dressing when ready to serve.

Note: You may like to rub the salad bowl with a cut clove of garlic or rub the cut garlic in a piece of dry bread and toss the bread with the salad; remove bread before serving the salad, unless you have a fancier for it.

Some Good Salad Combinations

Romaine lettuce, escarole, chicory, dandelion greens, raw spinach leaves—French or Roquefort dressing

Head lettuce, green peppers, cucumbers, celery, scallions, tomato wedges—Russian or Roquefort dressing

WITH THESE FOLLOWING COMBINATIONS
FRENCH DRESSING IS BEST:

Watercress, Boston lettuce, stuffed olives
Belgian endive and watercress
Belgian endive and sliced fresh cooked or canned beets
Romaine lettuce, tomato wedges, arugula

CARROT AND WALNUT SALAD

This does not sound like a French recipe but it comes from the Côte d'Azur, a region near Nice called "Californie."

4 medium carrots
1/2 cup walnut meats
pinch of sugar
3 tablespoons lemon juice
4 to 5 tablespoons oil (optional)

Scrape carrots and grate them on a coarse grater. Combine with remaining ingredients. Chill until ready to serve.

YIELD: 4 servings

CUCUMBERS IN YOGURT DRESSING

2 medium cucumbers, peeled, sliced very thin
1/4 teaspoon salt
2 ice cubes
3/4 cup plain yogurt
3 tablespoons mayonnaise
1-1/2 tablespoons white vinegar
2 teaspoons sugar
2 medium white onions, sliced wafer thin

1. Put cucumber slices in a bowl and sprinkle with salt; add ice cubes. Mix well and refrigerate about 15 minutes.
2. Mix yogurt with mayonnaise, vinegar, and sugar. Combine with onion slices.
3. Drain cucumbers well; combine with yogurt-onion mixture. Serve well chilled.

NOTE: This salad is excellent with poached salmon, broiled fish of any kind, or salmon patties.

YIELD: 4 to 6 servings

COLE SLAW

- 1/2 cup mayonnaise
- 1/2 teaspoon sugar
- 1/2 teaspoon salt
- 2 tablespoons vinegar
- 1 tablespoon grated onion
- pepper to taste
- 4 cups finely shredded cabbage

Combine mayonnaise, sugar, salt, vinegar, onion, and pepper. Thoroughly mix with cabbage.

NOTE: For variety, substitute 1/2 cup chopped green pepper or shredded carrots for 1/2 cup of cabbage. For Red and White Slaw, combine red and white cabbage in equal parts.

YIELD: 6 to 8 servings

AVOCADO AND GRAPEFRUIT SALAD
From Grace and Sam

This salad may be served as a separate course or accompany the main course.

- 2 grapefruit
- 1 ripe avocado
- 3 to 4 tablespoons French Dressing
- Romaine lettuce or other crisp greens

1. Peel and section grapefruit. Peel and slice avocado into thin half circles; place in a flat refrigerator dish.

2. Place grapefruit sections with all of the juice over the avocado circles. Add French Dressing. Marinate in the refrigerator at least 1/2 hour.

3. At serving time, arrange greens on salad plates and on them place alternating sections of grapefruit and avocado circles.

YIELD: 6 servings

AVOCADO, TOMATO, AND EGG SALAD

A supper or luncheon main-dish.

On a bed of Romaine lettuce, alternate slices of avocado, tomato, and hard-cooked egg. Serve with Aunt Iva's Red Oil Dressing or Russian Dressing.

GREEN BEANS VINAIGRETTE

- 1 pound fresh green beans
- 1/2 cup French Dressing
- 2 teaspoons finely chopped onion
- 1 teaspoon chopped parsley

1. Wash beans and snip the ends. Cut crosswise into 2 or 3 pieces, depending on their size.

2. Cook them in a small amount of salted water until crisp-tender; drain.

3. Combine French Dressing with onion and parsley and pour over beans while they are still warm.

NOTE: This salad is best served at room temperature.

YIELD: 4 servings

ARTICHOKES WITH MUSTARD VINAIGRETTE

1. When buying artichokes, look for those that are a fresh green, fleshy, and have tightly packed leaves.

2. Wash artichokes well under running water. Trim off stems; with scissors cut off the sharp tips of the leaves.

3. Place artichokes, bottoms down, close together in a pot just the right size to hold them. Pour boiling water into the pot, up to one half the height of the artichokes. Sprinkle artichokes very lightly with salt.

4. Cover pot, bring to a boil, and boil for 30 to 40 minutes. Artichokes are done when you can readily pull out a leaf.

5. Remove artichokes from water and drain well, bottoms up.

6. Serve warm or cold with Mustard Vinaigrette (page 247).

CELERIAC WITH MUSTARD VINAIGRETTE

3 medium-sized celeriac (about 1 pound)	1/2 cup Mustard Vinaigrette
	1/2 teaspoon chopped parsley

1. Peel celeriac and cut in julienne (matchsticks). Cover with boiling water and cook one minute. Drain and rinse with cold water.

2. Combine with Mustard Vinaigrette and refrigerate several hours. Before serving sprinkle with parsley.

YIELD: 4 to 6 servings

A SALAD OF CAULIFLOWER AND PEAS

1 medium head cauliflower, separated into flowerets	1 small can green peas (about 3/4 cup)
	2 tablespoons mayonnaise
1/4 cup French Dressing	1 tomato, sliced

1. Cook cauliflower in a small amount of boiling salted water until just tender but still crisp. Drain and combine with French Dressing. Refrigerate for a few hours, mixing gently occasionally. Drain peas well and chill.

2. Just before serving, mix peas with mayonnaise.

Arrange cauliflower in a mound in the center of a platter. Surround cauliflower with small mounds of peas, alternating with the tomato slices. Serve cold.

YIELD: 4 servings

POTATO AND GREEN BEAN SALAD

1 pound new potatoes
1 pound fresh green beans
1/2 tablespoon chopped onion
1/2 cup Mustard Vinaigrette (page 247)
1 teaspoon chopped parsley
tomato wedges
black olives
hard-cooked eggs, quartered
anchovy fillets

1. Boil potatoes in jackets. Peel and cut into 1/2-inch cubes.
2. Snip ends off beans, cut crosswise into 1/2-inch pieces. Boil in a small amount of salted water until crisp-tender.
3. Combine potatoes, beans, and onion lightly with dressing and parsley.
4. At serving time, garnish with remaining ingredients.

NOTE: This salad is best served at room temperature but it may also be served chilled. Prepare it 1 to 2 hours before serving time.

YIELD: 6 servings

SOUTH GERMAN POTATO SALAD

1 pound small new potatoes
1/2 teaspoon salt
freshly ground pepper
1/2 cup chicken broth
1/2 tablespoon finely chopped onion
2 to 3 tablespoons vinegar
1/3 to 1/2 cup oil

1. Boil potatoes in jackets. Peel and slice thin while still warm.
2. Add salt and pepper to chicken broth and bring to a boil. Add onions to the boiling broth; turn off heat.
3. Pour hot broth and onions over potatoes. Combine vinegar and oil and pour over potatoes. Very gently combine all ingredients.
4. Serve at room temperature; do not chill.

NOTE: If desired, add 2 tablespoons mayonnaise at serving time.

YIELD: 4 servings

RICE SALAD CAP FERRAT

Rice cooked "Indian" style (1 cup rice to 1 quart water), drained and rinsed with cold water, is best for this recipe. Rice should be just done, not too soft.

2 cups cooked rice	olives
1 red pepper, thinly sliced	French Dressing to moisten (about 1/3 cup)
1 green pepper, thinly sliced	chopped parsley
1 medium onion, sliced and separated into rings	

Toss rice and vegetables lightly with dressing. Mix in olives. Sprinkle with parsley.

YIELD: 4 servings

WINTER TOMATO SALAD

1 can (16 ounces) whole peeled tomatoes, drained
1 stalk celery, diced
1 medium onion, thinly sliced, separated into rings
1/2 teaspoon salt
1/4 teaspoon pepper
1/4 teaspoon oregano
1/4 teaspoon sugar
1/3 cup oil
2 tablespoons vinegar

1. Buy best grade firm, whole peeled tomatoes. If tomatoes are large, carefully cut them into halves or quarters.
2. In a bowl combine tomatoes, celery, and onion rings.

Thoroughly mix dressing ingredients and pour over tomato mixture. Chill for several hours before serving.

YIELD: 4 to 6 servings

SALAD OLIVIER

2 cups diced roast veal
2 cups diced boiled potatoes
1/2 medium cucumber, peeled, diced
4 scallions, thinly sliced
3/4 cup mayonnaise
1 to 2 tablespoons yogurt
salt and pepper to taste
crisp greens
sliced cooked beets
cooked green peas
hard-cooked egg slices

1. Gently combine the first four ingredients.
2. Thin the mayonnaise with yogurt. Stir this dressing into the meat mixture. Add salt and pepper to taste.
3. Serve on greens. Garnish each serving with the beets, peas, and egg slices.

YIELD: 4 servings

CHICKEN SALAD

Practically unknown in Europe; even the most sophisticated French visitors to America just love it.

- 2 cups cooked chicken, diced
- 1 cup celery, cut fine
- mayonnaise, about 1 cup
- 1/2 cup walnuts, pecans, or toasted almonds
- crisp salad greens
- olives

At serving time lightly toss chilled diced chicken, celery, and mayonnaise. Add nuts. Serve on greens, garnished with olives.

NOTE: You may omit nuts, if you prefer.

YIELD: 4 servings

ITALIAN BEAN AND TUNA SALAD

- 1 cup dried marrow beans
- 1 pound green beans
- 1 small onion, sliced thin
- 2 tablespoons vinegar (preferably wine vinegar)
- 1/3 cup oil
- salt and pepper to taste
- 1 tablespoon chopped parsley
- 1 can (7 ounces) tuna fish

1. Cook the marrow beans until just tender; drain well.
2. Snip off ends of green beans, cut beans into 1-inch pieces, and cook in salted water until crisp-tender; drain well.
3. Combine marrow beans and green beans with onion.
4. Mix vinegar, oil, salt, pepper, and parsley. Pour over bean mixture, toss all thoroughly, and chill well.
5. To serve, arrange tuna in fair-sized chunks over bean salad. Pass extra oil and vinegar at the table.

YIELD: 6 servings

MACARONI AND TUNA SALAD

1 cup elbow macaroni
1 cup canned tuna fish, flaked
1/2 cup diced celery
1/2 cup peas, freshly cooked, canned, or frozen
1/4 cup French Dressing
3/4 cup mayonnaise
chicory, watercress or other crisp greens
paprika

1. Cook macaroni, drain, and rinse with cold water.
2. At serving time, combine macaroni, tuna, celery, peas, French Dressing and mayonnaise.
3. Place on a bed of crisp, well-chilled greens. Sprinkle with paprika.

NOTE: Canned salmon or other cooked fish may be used in place of the tuna. Ham or chicken or a mixture of both may replace the fish.

YIELD: 4 servings

SALADE NIÇOISE

3 small new potatoes
garlic
6 to 8 leaves Romaine lettuce
1 can (2 ounces) anchovies
1 small can tuna (4 ounces)
2 hard-cooked eggs, sliced
2 small tomatoes, cut into wedges
1/2 green pepper, thinly sliced
12 small black olives
1/2 cup French Dressing

1. Boil potatoes in their jackets. Peel and slice (do not chill).
2. At serving time, rub a salad bowl with a cut clove of garlic. On a bed of lettuce, arrange all salad ingredients attractively.
3. Pour French Dressing over all, distributing it well.

YIELD: 4 servings

SHRIMP AND CRAB MEAT SALAD

1 pound shrimp, boiled or steamed, shelled
1/2 pound crab meat, fresh-cooked or canned
1 cup finely sliced celery
2 tablespoons lemon juice
1-1/2 cups mayonnaise (about)
1/4 teaspoon curry powder
crisp greens
black olives and hard-cooked egg wedges for garnish

1. If shrimp are large, halve them lengthwise. Remove any shell and cartilage from crab meat.
2. Lightly combine shrimp, crab meat, celery, and lemon juice.
3. Mix mayonnaise with curry powder.
4. At serving time, combine shrimp and crab meat mixture with mayonnaise. Arrange on greens and garnish with olives and egg wedges.

YIELD: 6 servings

FRENCH DRESSING

3/4 to 1 cup oil
1/4 cup wine vinegar or cider vinegar
1 teaspoon sugar
1 teaspoon salt
pepper

Measure all ingredients into a bottle or jar. Cover tightly and shake well. Keep refrigerated. Shake thoroughly before serving.

NOTE: For variation, add any or all of the following: 1/2 teaspoon paprika, 1/2 teaspoon dry mustard, 1 peeled clove of garlic.

MAYONNAISE

Tom, Iva's husband, always liked commercial mayonnaise. When Iva started to make her own, he even refused to taste it at first. That was many years ago. Since then he has not just accepted her homemade mayonnaise but he prefers it.

- 1 egg yolk
- 2 tablespoons lemon juice
- 1 teaspoon prepared mustard
- 1/2 teaspoon salt
- 1/2 teaspoon sugar
- pinch of pepper
- pinch of curry (optional)
- 1 cup oil

1. Set a bowl with a small bottom on a wet paper towel to prevent spinning. Combine egg yolk, 1 teaspoon of the lemon juice, mustard, salt, sugar, pepper, and curry. Beat mixture until thickened, using a flat wire whisk or electric mixer.

2. Add oil, drop by drop at first, then in a slow steady stream, beating continuously. Add remaining lemon juice. Store covered in refrigerator.

3. For seasoning variations add a pinch of cayenne pepper, a few drops of Worcestershire sauce, or chopped parsley or chives.

NOTE: Combining egg yolk with some lemon juice and seasoning and beating until thickened *before* adding oil greatly helps prevent separation. Should mayonnaise separate, stop adding oil immediately and beat in 1 to 2 tablespoons commercial mayonnaise—just enough to bring it back into emulsion (no need to use traditional method of beating the separated mixture by teaspoonfuls into another egg yolk). Thin mayonnaise to desired consistency with a small amount of skimmed evaporated milk, buttermilk, or yogurt.

YIELD: about 1-1/4 cups

MUSTARD VINAIGRETTE

Vinaigrette is French Dressing without sugar. It is usually made fresh as needed.

- 1 teaspoon prepared mustard
- pinch of salt
- pinch of pepper
- 1 tablespoon vinegar
- 3 to 4 tablespoons oil

In a small bowl combine mustard, salt, pepper, and vinegar. Gradually add oil, combining all thoroughly.

YIELD: 4 servings

BLENDER MAYONNAISE

Make this recipe *only* if you have a blender, the bottom of which may be removed for easy cleaning.

- 1 whole egg
- 3 tablespoons lemon juice
- 1-1/2 teaspoons prepared mustard
- 3/4 teaspoon salt
- 3/4 teaspoon sugar
- 1/4 teaspoon pepper
- 1/4 teaspoon curry powder (optional)
- 1-1/2 cups oil

1. Put the egg, lemon juice, mustard, salt, sugar, pepper, curry powder, and 1/2 cup of the oil into the container of a blender. Cover container and blend at low speed for about 5 seconds.
2. Without stopping the motor, remove cover and pour remaining oil in a thin stream into center of container. Turn off motor as soon as all oil has been added.

NOTE: See preceding mayonnaise recipe for additional information and variations.

YIELD: about 2 cups

TARTAR SAUCE

To 1 cup mayonnaise add 1 teaspoon prepared mustard, 2 tablespoons chopped dill pickles, 2 tablespoons chopped parsley, and 1 tablespoon chopped capers (or chopped stuffed olives).

RUSSIAN DRESSING

To 1 cup mayonnaise add 1/4 cup chili sauce and 1/2 teaspoon Worcestershire sauce.

AIOLI

This garlic mayonnaise is a tradition on Friday in the South of France. It usually accompanies a "boiled dinner" of codfish, potatoes, carrots, leeks, cauliflower or other vegetables. It is worth your try.

Make 1 cup mayonnaise, using part olive oil. Mash finely 2 to 4 cloves garlic. Combine with mayonnaise.

AUNT IVA'S RED OIL DRESSING

Iva Bennett's maternal grandfather, Major George Brinkerhoff, a veteran of the Civil War, named her after his favorite daughter-in-law. When his son Ernest took Iva Maloney as his bride and brought her to live in the sprawling farmhouse, Grandpa was happy. She was a girl after his own heart—bright, spunky and goodlooking, and an excellent cook, too. Some of the most treasured family recipes have come from her kitchen. Red Oil Dressing is one of them.

1 cup oil	1 teaspoon paprika
2/3 cup catsup	1 teaspoon sugar
1/4 cup vinegar	1 teaspoon finely
1 teaspoon salt	grated onion

Mix all ingredients thoroughly. Refrigerate in a covered jar until ready to use. Shake well each time before using.

NOTE: l peeled clove of garlic cut in half may be substituted for the onion.

ROQUEFORT CHEESE DRESSING

2 tablespoons mayonnaise	3/4 cup French Dressing
2 tablespoons Roquefort cheese	1/2 teaspoon Worcestershire sauce

Mix well together mayonnaise and Roquefort cheese, mashing cheese well. Gradually add French Dressing and then Worcestershire sauce. Keep refrigerated.

17

Sauces and Gravies

> "There is no such passion in human nature as the passion for gravy."
>
> CHARLES DICKENS

It has been said that all the world's recipes are descendants of just a few original ones. To no other area of cookery does this idea seem more applicable than to sauce making, which is often considered mysterious and full of secrets. In spite of their unlimited number, most sauces are variations of four basic ones—White Sauce, Brown Sauce (gravy), Tomato Sauce and Hollandaise (a variation of mayonnaise or vice versa).

White Sauce, also called cream sauce or Béchamel sauce, was invented by Louis de Béchamel, steward of King Louis XIV. Sauce "Velouté" (from the French "velvety") is white sauce in which stock (meat, chicken, fish or vegetable stock) is used in place of milk. In the preparation of many foods, such as creamed vegetables, fricassees, cream soups and, of course, all kinds of sauces, it is important to know how to make White Sauce.

A fine gravy or Brown Sauce is the hallmark of a good cook. Smooth, glossy, rich in color and, most important, excellent in flavor, the gravy contributes much to the pleasure of a meal. The principles involved in making a good gravy are explained in detail in this chapter.

Slow, long simmering is necessary for Tomato Sauce. There are good commercial products available, but they do not equal your own flavor-rich sauce.

For a special occasion when you plan to serve fresh asparagus or poached salmon, Hollandaise is the perfect sauce. Its success depends primarily on the right temperature at which the ingredients are combined; it is not difficult to make. Once familiar with these basic sauces, you have taken the "sorcery" out of "saucery."

GRAVY OR BROWN SAUCE

In France they say, *"Courte sauce, bonne cuisine."* Translated freely, it means: you cannot make a large amount of gravy and expect it to be good. This is especially true of meat and fish sauces, where the cooking liquid provides much of the flavor for the sauce.

A fine sauce appeals to eye and palate alike. It should be rich in flavor and color, smooth, glossy and thickened just slightly.

FAT-FREE STOCK

A prudent gravy is made without any fat from the meat. Following are two ways to separate the fat completely from the drippings or juices resulting from pot roasting meats and poultry.

1. For immediate use, strain drippings into a heat-proof glass jar; let stand for a few minutes. The fat will rise to the top and the line between fat and meat liquid will be clearly visible. Insert a baster to the bottom of the jar, draw up the fat-free liquid and empty it into a measuring cup. If it is not sufficient to make the amount of gravy desired, add broth—homemade, canned, or made with concentrate or bouillon cube.

2. If gravy is to be used later, strain and chill the drippings. The fat will rise and harden. It can easily be lifted off and the fat-free liquid used for making the gravy.

BROWN SAUCE I
The roux method

1 tablespoon oil
1 tablespoon flour
1-1/4 cups Fat-free Stock
salt and pepper to taste
1 teaspoon sherry (optional)

1. Heat oil in the pan in which the meat was cooked. Mix in flour and cook, on low heat, while stirring, until dry and bubbly. Scrape down the brown particles from the sides of the pan; they contain concentrated flavor.
2. Gradually add stock, stirring; continue scraping down dry particles that form on the sides of the pan.
3. Simmer until smooth and glossy; correct seasoning with salt and pepper. For a deeper brown color, add a little caramelized sugar. Just before serving, add a teaspoon of dry sherry, if desired.

YIELD: 1 cup gravy

BROWN SAUCE II
Gravy thickened with cornstarch paste

1. Scrape down brown particles from sides of pan in which meat was cooked.
2. Add 1-1/4 cups Fat-free Stock. Simmer to reduce, stirring to make sure all browned, flavor-rich particles are dissolved.
3. Mix 1-1/2 teaspoons cornstarch with 2 tablespoons water and pour into the simmering liquid, while stirring. Cook, stirring, about one minute or until clear and thickened. Correct seasoning with salt and pepper.

YIELD: 1 cup gravy

GRAVY FOR ROASTED MEATS

There will be little or no liquid after roasting meat uncovered. However, use what there is, after removing all

WHITE SAUCE

1/2 teaspoon finely chopped onion	1-1/2 to 2 tablespoons flour
2 tablespoons oil or margarine, or half of each	1 cup milk
	1/4 teaspoon salt
	pepper to taste

1. In a small saucepan sauté onion in fat until just transparent, about 1 minute.
2. Add flour and cook, while stirring, until mixture is dry and bubbly. Have heat low enough for mixture to stay light in color.
3. Gradually stir in milk and bring to boiling point while stirring. Simmer until all starchy taste is gone, 3 to 5 minutes. Season with salt and pepper.

NOTE: For a thin white sauce reduce fat and flour to 1/2 the amounts in above recipe. Broth, vegetable stock or fish stock may be used for all or part of the milk.

The sauce may be flavored with lemon juice, grated nutmeg, curry powder, Worcestershire sauce, chopped chives, dill or parsley.

YIELD: 1 cup

MUSTARD SAUCE

Prepare White Sauce as directed above, using milk or fish stock. Add to the hot sauce 1 tablespoon prepared mustard, a pinch of dry mustard, and 2 tablespoons dry white wine. Simmer for 2 minutes. Serve hot, with poached fish.

MUSHROOM SAUCE

- 1/4 pound mushrooms
- 1-1/2 cups chicken broth
- 1 tablespoon finely chopped onion
- 1 tablespoon margarine
- 2 tablespoons oil
- 3 tablespoons flour
- few drops lemon juice
- salt and pepper
- 2 tablespoons skimmed evaporated milk

1. Clean mushrooms. Cut caps into thin slices; chop stems coarsely.
2. Simmer stems in chicken broth 5 to 10 minutes; strain broth into a 2-cup measure. Add enough broth to again make 1-1/2 cups. Reserve stems to use in soup or stuffing.
3. In a saucepan sauté onion in margarine and oil until transparent. Add mushroom slices and cook until liquid which has formed is evaporated, about 5 minutes.
4. Dust flour over mushrooms. Cook until mixture is bubbly, while stirring.
5. Gradually add broth, stirring. Cook over very low heat about 10 minutes, until sauce is smooth and glossy, stirring occasionally.
6. Correct seasoning with lemon juice, salt, and pepper. Add milk and blend in.

NOTE: This sauce freezes well.

YIELD: about 2 cups

PEACH CHUTNEY

- 4 pounds ripe but firm peaches
- 1 clove garlic
- 1/2 cup chopped onion
- 1 pound light brown sugar
- 1/2 pound dark brown sugar
- 1 tablespoon salt
- 1 teaspoon red chili powder or flakes
- 1/2 cup coarsely grated ginger root
- 2 cups white vinegar
- 2 cups cider vinegar
- 1/4 pound seedless raisins

1. Place peaches, a few at a time, in simmering water for a minute or two; remove them with a slotted spoon and peel. Cut peaches into slices about 1/2 inch thick.
2. Mash garlic with salt.
3. In a big pot (preferably a large, glazed, flameproof casserole) combine garlic with salt, onion, sugars, chili powder, ginger root and vinegars. Bring to a boil.
4. Add sliced peaches and raisins, bring to a boil and boil gently for 1 hour.
5. Spoon chutney into refrigerator jars, cool, and cover tightly. Store in the refrigerator.

YIELD: 4 to 5 quarts

CURRY SAUCE

For cooked meats, poultry, seafood and eggs. Try our recipe for Peach Chutney (see above) to serve with your curry dishes.

- 1/4 cup chopped onion
- 4 tablespoons oil
- 1 clove garlic, crushed
- 1/2 to 1 teaspoon curry powder
- 1 tart, medium apple, peeled, chopped
- 2-1/2 tablespoons flour
- 2 cups broth (vegetable, meat, fish, or chicken)
- 1 tablespoon lemon juice
- salt

1. In a saucepan sauté onion in oil until a light yellow. Add garlic and cook one minute more.
2. Add curry powder and apple and continue cooking over low heat for about 10 minutes. Stir in flour and blend until smooth.
3. Gradually add broth; bring to a boil, stirring continuously. Simmer over low heat about 5 minutes. Add lemon juice and salt to taste.

NOTE: Milk may be substituted for half of the broth.

YIELD: about 2 cups

CUMBERLAND SAUCE

For cold roast meat, poultry, venison, hot or cold ham.

1/2 tablespoon grated orange rind	1 tablespoon lemon juice
1/4 cup currant jelly	1 tablespoon prepared mustard
2 tablespoons port or sherry	1/4 teaspoon cayenne pepper
1 tablespoon orange juice	1/4 teaspoon ground ginger

Combine all ingredients and blend thoroughly. Serve cold.

YIELD: 1/2 cup

HOLLANDAISE SAUCE

Hollandaise Sauce is most frequently served with poached fish, steamed fish pudding, asparagus, cauliflower, or broccoli. It is a rich sauce and small servings are appropriate. If you have some cooking liquid from the food with which you plan to serve this sauce, use it instead of water—it enhances the flavor.

1 egg yolk pinch of salt pinch of pepper	1 tablespoon broth or water
1 tablespoon lemon juice	4 tablespoons safflower oil
	4 tablespoons margarine

1. In a small bowl, beat with a wire whisk the egg yolk, salt, pepper, lemon juice, and broth. Place bowl over a small pot of simmering water and beat yolk mixture until thickened. Remove bowl from hot water.

2. Warm the oil (preferably in a measuring cup with a spout) by placing cup in a pot of simmering water. When oil is warm, add margarine, cut into pieces. As margarine begins to melt, remove cup from hot water.

3. While beating, slowly add oil and margarine mixture to yolk mixture (as in making mayonnaise).

4. Serve sauce just barely warm. It may be kept at the right temperature by placing bowl in warm (not hot) water until serving time.

YIELD: 3/4 cup (scant)

TUNA FISH SAUCE
For pasta

- 1 can tuna fish (7 ounces) packed in oil (preferably olive oil)
- 1 tablespoon oil
- 1/2 onion, chopped
- 1 clove garlic, mashed
- 2 tablespoons chopped parsley
- 2-1/2 cups tomatoes, stewed or canned
- 1/2 cup tomato purée, canned
- salt and pepper to taste
- pinch of oregano

1. Flake tuna and sauté it with its own oil, the 1 tablespoon oil, onion, and garlic, for about 10 minutes.

2. Add parsley, tomatoes, tomato purée, salt, and pepper. Simmer, uncovered, for 40 to 60 minutes, then add oregano and cook 3 minutes more.

3. Serve with spaghetti or other pasta.

YIELD: 4 to 6 servings

WHITE CLAM SAUCE

- 2 dozen little neck clams
- 4 tablespoons oil (part olive)
- 1 clove garlic, chopped
- salt and pepper, if needed

1. Steam clams in a covered pot containing about 1/4 cup water. As soon as they open remove clams from shells and chop them.

2. Save the clam liquor; if it is poured off carefully, straining may not be necessary.

3. Heat oil and garlic. Simmer a few minutes but do not brown. Add chopped clams and some of the clam liquor and heat through. Correct seasoning with salt and pepper.

This sauce is fine on green noodles, sprinkled with cheese.

YIELD: 4 servings

RED CLAM SAUCE
For spaghetti or other pasta

- 2 dozen little neck clams (or one 10-ounce can chopped clams)
- 1 clove garlic, chopped
- 4 tablespoons oil
- 2 tablespoons chopped parsley
- 2 cups tomatoes
- 2 tablespoons tomato paste
- salt and pepper to taste
- pinch of oregano

1. Steam clams open in a covered pot, with a small amount of water.

2. Remove clams from shells, chop them and set aside, saving the clam liquor (if poured off carefully, straining may not be necessary).

3. Sauté garlic in oil for a few minutes but do not brown. Add parsley, tomatoes, tomato paste and about one-half cup of the clam liquor. Simmer uncovered until sauce is thickened, about 40 minutes.

4. Add clams, salt, pepper, and oregano and cook 2 minutes longer.

YIELD: 4 servings

SAVORY BUTTERS

The following combinations are excellent to serve with broiled or poached fish. You can also use them for canapés.

Mustard Butter

Cream 1/2 cup (1 stick) margarine. Combine well with 1 tablespoon prepared mustard, 1 hard-cooked egg yolk, finely mashed (optional), and 3 drops lemon juice.

Anchovy Butter

Cream 1/2 cup (1 stick) margarine. Combine well with 2 teaspoons anchovy paste and 3 drops each lemon juice and onion juice.

Lemon Butter

Cream 1/2 cup (1 stick) margarine; very gradually beat in 2 tablespoons lemon juice. Add salt to taste.

18

Yeast Breads and Quick Breads

HOME BAKING

You start with a few simple ingredients and come up with something beautiful to look at and delicious to eat, a pleasure to all and a souce of pride and satisfaction to the baker. It is fun to bake "from scratch"—a really creative job. As with every handmade product there will always be slight variations which add exciting, interesting components. While the bread or cake is baking, an enticing smell is wafting through the house, a scent that memories are made of.

Some knowledge and experience are necessary to acquire the "feel" of yeast dough, the right texture of cake batter, and the light touch when combining ingredients for pastry crust. From there on, only your interest and imagination will set limits to the endless variations possible.

Many kitchens, equipped with all modern appliances, do not possess an oven thermometer, a very useful and inexpensive item. Most ovens have temperature gauges, but they may not register accurately. The thermometer will help set the correct temperature to assure baking success.

There are experienced bakers who skillfully sift, measure, cream and fold ingredients for delicate cakes and cookies, but are afraid to tackle a yeast bread so much less demanding of precise techniques. No sifting of flour is usually required, and there is some leeway in baking temperatures. Today's yeast is easy to work with; the result is sure to be a winner.

When it comes to bread, the man of the house is often a most willing and able baker. Just watch the proud expression when his knuckles produce that fine hollow sound of the perfectly baked loaf.

The recipes in this chapter have been set up to help you organize your work and to save time and dishes—all important in getting the most enjoyment out of baking.

CHALLAH
Jewish Sabbath Bread

- 2 medium potatoes
- 1 package dry yeast
- 1-1/2 teaspoons salt
- 1-1/4 cups lukewarm water
- 4 to 5 cups flour
- 3 tablespoons oil
- 1 egg yolk mixed with 1 tablespoon water
- poppy seeds

1. Boil potatoes in skins until tender; peel, rice (or mash) them; cool to lukewarm.
2. Dissolve yeast and salt in water.
3. In a large bowl combine potatoes with 2 cups of the flour, the yeast mixture, and oil, mixing thoroughly. Gradually add remaining flour, using only enough to make a firm dough.
4. On a lightly floured board, knead dough until smooth and elastic, 5 to 10 minutes. Transfer to a lightly oiled bowl and turn to coat on all sides. Cover with a towel and let rise in a warm place until doubled in bulk. Punch down and, if there is time, let rise again.
5. Divide dough into one 2/3 portion and one 1/3 portion. Shape the 2/3 portion into an oval loaf and place on a lightly oiled baking sheet. Cut the 1/3 portion into 3 pieces, rolling each piece into a long, round strip. Make a braid of the 3 strips; pinch ends together firmly. Place braid on loaf lengthwise.
6. Let rise again until doubled in bulk and light. Preheat oven to 400°F.
7. Brush dough with yolk mixture; sprinkle with poppy seeds. Bake 35 to 45 minutes or until nicely browned.

CUBAN BREAD

1 envelope dry yeast	3 to 4 cups flour
1 teaspoon sugar	1 teaspoon salt
1-1/2 cups warm water	1/2 egg white
	1 teaspoon water

1. Dissolve yeast and sugar in warm water.
2. Combine yeast mixture with 3 cups of the flour and salt. Add more flour if necessary to make a stiff dough.
3. Knead on a floured board for 10 to 15 minutes.
4. Transfer to an oiled bowl, turn dough until it is coated lightly with oil on all sides, cover with a towel, and let rise in a warm place until doubled in bulk.
5. Punch dough down and divide in half. Shape into 2 long, thin loaves and place them on a lightly oiled baking sheet. Slash tops diagonally in 3 places with a sharp knife.
6. Let loaves set about 5 minutes. Brush them with mixture of egg white, lightly beaten, and water.

Place bread into cold oven; set temperature at 400°F.

Bake for 35 to 45 minutes, until well baked and crusty brown.

FRENCH BREAD

In France they call it *Pain Ordinaire*. It's the popular crusty bread.

1 package dry yeast	1 cup boiled water, cooled to lukewarm
1/4 cup boiled water, cooled to lukewarm	3/4 teaspoon salt
3/4 cup flour	3 cups flour
	1 egg white
	1 tablespoon water

1. Knead the first 3 ingredients into a ball. Make 2 cuts across the top 1/4 inch deep. Set the ball in a large bowl, containing the 1 cup water. Put in a warm place.

2. When the ball floats, add the salt and the 3 cups of flour and mix thoroughly. Use a little extra flour if necessary. Knead 15 minutes on a board.

3. Place in a bowl, cover with a towel and, in a warm place, let rise until double in bulk.

4. Punch down and knead again. Shape into 2 medium or 4 thin loaves, pointed at the ends. Make some diagonal cuts 1/4 inch deep and 2 inches apart across the tops of the loaves. Put the loaves on a lightly greased baking sheet; let rise until double in bulk. Preheat oven to 450°F.

5. Bake 10 minutes at 450°F., reduce heat to 375°F. and bake 35 to 45 minutes more.

6. Beat egg white with the 1 tablespoon water until foamy and brush loaves with mixture. Return bread to oven for 5 minutes to glaze.

YIELD: 2 medium loaves or 4 long, thin ones

DARK, CRUSTY COUNTRY BREAD

This is a moist bread that will keep well.

- 2 medium mealy potatoes
- 1 envelope dry yeast
- 1/4 cup lukewarm water
- 6 tablespoons yellow cornmeal
- 1-1/2 cups cold water
- 3/4 teaspoon salt
- 1 tablespoon brown sugar
- 1 tablespoon oil
- 1 tablespoon caraway seeds
- 2 cups rye flour
- 2 cups white flour

1. Peel potatoes and cut into large cubes. Cook them in lightly salted water until tender. Drain them well; rice or mash them. Cool to lukewarm.

2. Dissolve yeast in lukewarm water and combine with the mashed potatoes; set aside.

3. In a saucepan stir cornmeal into cold water. Bring to a boil, stirring, and cook for 2 minutes. Add salt, sugar, oil, and caraway seeds; cool to lukewarm.

4. In a large bowl, thoroughly combine cornmeal

mixture and yeast mixture. Gradually add rye and white flours. Knead until smooth on a floured board. This will take about 10 minutes.

5. Place dough in an oiled bowl; turn to grease on all sides. Cover bowl with a cloth. Let dough rise in a warm place until double in bulk; punch down.

6. Knead again. You probably will need some extra white flour since this dough is apt to be a bit sticky. Shape loaves to fit your baking pans. Make some diagonal cuts 1/4 inch deep and 2 inches apart across the tops of the loaves. Let dough rest for 5 minutes.

7. Put into greased baking pans; let rise until double in bulk. Preheat oven to 450°F.

8. Bake at 450°F. for 10 minutes; reduce heat to 375°F. and bake about 50 minutes more.

YIELD: 2 medium loaves or 1 loaf and a batch of rolls

BORIS' PUMPERNICKEL

- 1 package dry yeast
- 1 tablespoon brown sugar
- 2 cups warm water
- 1 cup whole wheat flour
- 1-1/2 teaspoons salt
- 1-1/2 teaspoons caraway seeds
- 2-1/2 cups rye flour
- 2-1/2 cups white flour

1. In a large mixing bowl dissolve yeast and sugar in 1 cup of the warm water; add whole wheat flour and beat well with a wooden spoon until smooth. Cover with a towel; let stand in a warm place about 3/4 hour.

2. Add salt and caraway seeds to the remaining cup of warm water and combine with the yeast mixture.

3. Combine rye and white flours and gradually work into the yeast-whole wheat mixture. First use a wooden spoon, then knead the dough until it is smooth and elastic. The amount of flour mixture (5 cups) is approximate. This will take about 10 minutes.

4. Put dough into a greased bowl, turning to grease lightly on all sides. Cover with a towel and let rise until double in bulk.

5. Punch down; knead well about 5 minutes. Divide dough in half, shape, and place into two lightly greased medium-size bread pans. Let rise until doubled, about 25 to 30 minutes. Preheat oven to 400°F.

6. Bake 10 minutes at 400°F.; reduce heat to 350°F. and bake about 35 to 40 minutes more.

NOTE: "Instant" flour on the board helps prevent dough from sticking while you knead.

YIELD: two 1-pound loaves

OATMEAL BREAD

- 2 cups rolled oats
- 2 teaspoons salt
- 2 cups boiling water
- 2 tablespoons oil
- 1 package dry yeast
- 2 tablespoons dark brown sugar
- 3/4 cup lukewarm water
- 1 cup instant nonfat dry milk powder
- 4 to 4-1/2 cups flour

1. Put oats in a large mixing bowl. Add salt to boiling water and stir into oats. Add oil and stir until smooth; cool to lukewarm.

2. Dissolve yeast and sugar in lukewarm water. Combine oat mixture and yeast mixture.

3. Add milk powder and 4 cups of flour; mix thoroughly. Let rise until double in bulk, about 1-1/2 hours.

4. Punch down and place on lightly floured board to knead. If dough is sticky, add a little more flour. Shape into 2 loaves and place in 2 medium-size, greased loaf pans. Let rise in warm place until double in size. Preheat oven to 375°F.

5. Bake 35 to 45 minutes or until bread tests done.

YIELD: 2 loaves

PEANUT BUTTER BREAD

- 1 package dry yeast
- 1 cup milk, lukewarm
- 1/3 cup peanut butter
- 1/4 cup sugar
- 1 teaspoon salt
- 1 egg, beaten
- 3 to 3-1/2 cups flour

1. Dissolve yeast in milk. Combine peanut butter, sugar, salt, egg, and yeast mixture.
2. Stir in 2 cups of the flour and beat until smooth. Stir in eough of the remaining flour to make a firm dough and knead on a lightly floured board until smooth and elastic.
3. Put dough in a bowl; cover with a towel. Let rise in a warm place until double in bulk. Punch down and let rise again.
4. Punch down, shape into a loaf and place in a medium-size, greased loaf pan. Let rise until doubled in bulk and light. Preheat oven to 375°F.
5. Bake 35 to 40 minutes, or until well browned.

CASSEROLE COTTAGE CHEESE AND DILL BREAD

- 1 package dry yeast
- 1/4 cup lukewarm water
- 1 cup creamed cottage cheese
- 1 tablespoon sugar
- 1 tablespoon finely chopped onion
- 1 tablespoon oil
- 2 teaspoons dill seed
- 1 teaspoon salt
- 1/4 teaspoon baking soda
- 1 egg
- 2-1/2 cups flour, approximately

1. Dissolve yeast in water; set aside. Put cottage cheese in a mixing bowl; set over hot water until cheese is lukewarm.
2. Mix thoroughly lukewarm cottage cheese, sugar, onion, oil, dill seed, salt, baking soda, egg, and dissolved yeast.
3. Gradually add flour. Use enough to make a stiff dough, beating well throughout. Cover bowl with a towel and let rise in a warm place until dough has doubled in bulk, about 1 hour.
4. Punch down dough and turn into an oiled 1-1/2- to 2-quart casserole. Let rise until double in bulk and light. Preheat oven to 350°F.
5. Bake 40 to 50 minutes, until bread tests done.

BREAKFAST BUTTERMILK MUFFINS

1-3/4 cups sifted flour
2 teaspoons tartrate baking powder
1/2 teaspoon baking soda
1/2 teaspoon salt
3 tablespoons sugar
1 egg
2 tablespoons oil
1 cup buttermilk
cinnamon-sugar for topping

1. Preheat oven to 425°F. Sift together flour, baking powder, baking soda, salt, and sugar.
2. In a small bowl, beat egg with a fork, add oil and buttermilk, and mix well.
3. Stir egg mixture quickly into flour mixture; mix just to combine (do not beat).
4. Fill well-greased muffin tins about 2/3 full; sprinkle liberally with cinnamon-sugar. Bake at once for 20 minutes or until muffins are browned and done. Remove from tins as soon as baked.

NOTE: Chopped nuts or sesame seeds may be used in place of cinnamon-sugar.

YIELD: 12 2-1/2-inch muffins

ORANGE NUT BREAD

juice of 1 orange
rind of 1 orange
1 cup raisins
2 tablespoons oil
1 teaspoon vanilla
1 egg, beaten
2 cups sifted flour
1/4 teaspoon salt
1 teaspoon baking powder
1/2 teaspoon baking soda
1 cup sugar
3/4 cup broken nut meats

1. Preheat oven to 350°F.
2. Pour orange juice into an 8-ounce measuring cup; add boiling water to fill cup.
3. Remove white membrane from orange rind. Force orange rind and raisins through a food chopper into a mixing bowl, using coarse blade; add diluted orange juice. Stir in oil, vanilla, and egg.

4. Sift together flour, salt, baking powder, baking soda, and sugar. Combine with above mixture until well blended; do not beat. Stir in nut meats.

5. Bake in greased, waxed-paper-lined, 5- by 9-inch loaf pan about 1 hour and 10 minutes. Test for doneness.

HONEY CAKE

This cake is very "honeyish," moist, and chewy. The flavor is best a day or two after baking; it stays fresh for a long time. For a wonderful snack or dessert serve it with the first tart apples and fresh walnuts of the season.

1-1/2-cups unsifted all-purpose white flour	1-1/2 teaspoons baking soda
1-1/2 cups unsifted rye flour	2 teaspoons baking powder
	1-1/2 cups honey
	1/4 cup buttermilk

1. Preheat oven to 300°F.
2. Sift together white flour, rye flour, baking soda, and baking powder.
3. Thoroughly combine flour mixture with honey and buttermilk.
4. Bake in oiled, wax paper-lined loaf pan for about 1-1/2 hours or until it tests done. Cool on a rack.

NOTE: Oil cup before measuring honey, so that it will not stick.

POPOVERS

1 cup unsifted flour
1/4 teaspoon salt
1 cup milk
2 tablespoons oil
2 eggs

1. Preheat oven to 425°F.
2. Combine flour and salt. Gradually add milk and oil and beat until smooth.
3. Add eggs, one at a time. Beat well, preferably with an electric mixer on high speed, for about 1 minute.
4. Oil a muffin tin well and preheat it for about 10 minutes in the oven before filing. Fill cups 2/3 full. Or use oiled custard cups. Fill them 2/3 full and set on a cookie sheet to bake.
5. Bake until puffed and golden brown, about 30 minutes.

YIELD: 8 to 10 popovers

19
Cakes, Pies, and Cookies

No doubt your file of favorite recipes, like ours, bulges at the cake, pie, and cookie sections. To make selections for this book was difficult, but finally we settled on two categories: recipes we just "could not do without," which include some for very special occasions, and recipes selected to appeal to people with varying tastes.

Among the "must have" choices are yeast coffee cakes for Sunday or birthday breakfasts, summertime fruit tarts, traditional pies, a holiday fruit-filled cake, and standbys—moist and flavorful pound and sponge cakes.

To please different palates, recipes are provided for those who like their cookies soft and tender and for those who prefer them light, crisp and chewy. The selection here is small but good: all have excellent keeping quality and are easy to make.

Baking cakes, pies and cookies is fun; you make them with ingredients of your choice, and they are unique—your own.

BASIC YEAST DOUGH

Swedish tea ring, buns, fruit-filled cakes and others elegant enough for dessert—all are based on one of the simple yeast dough recipes which follow. Either of these doughs can be frozen (preferably before rising) for later use, in individual portions if you wish. One entire recipe will make one large tea ring or four fresh fruit-filled cakes or two batches of buns.

CAKES, PIES, AND COOKIES

YEAST DOUGH I

1 package dry active yeast	1/2 teaspoon (scant) salt
1/4 cup warm (not hot) water	1 egg
3-1/2 to 4 cups unsifted flour	1 cup warm milk
1/2 cup (scant) sugar	1/2 cup (1 stick) unsalted margarine
	1 teaspoon vanilla

1. Dissolve yeast in warm water.
2. Put 2 cups of the flour in a large bowl. Add sugar and salt and blend in.
3. Beat egg lightly. Combine warm milk with margarine, cut into pieces. Margarine does not have to melt, only to soften.
4. Combine dissolved yeast, egg, milk-margarine mixture, and vanilla. Stir this mixture into the flour mixture; beat until smooth.
5. Add another 1-1/2 to 2 cups of the flour to make a rather stiff dough.
6. Beat for 3 to 5 minutes or until dough has lost its stickiness and leaves the sides of the bowl.
7. If time permits, refrigerate dough in the bowl, covered, from 2 hours to 2 days. This improves taste and texture of the final product.
8. When ready to use, let dough rise in a warm place, covered with a towel, until double in bulk and light; punch it down. It is now ready to use.

NOTE: Yeast Dough I and Yeast Dough II can be made with oil in place of margarine. Gradually add oil to the beaten egg, beating continuously, then proceed as indicated in the recipes. Use 1/2 cup oil in place of 1/2 cup margarine.

YEAST DOUGH II

Follow the directions for Yeast Dough I (see preceding recipe), with the following changes:
1. Add 1/2 cup nonfat dry milk powder to the dry ingredients and blend in.

2. In place of the 1 cup warm milk use 1/2 cup warm, undiluted skimmed evaporated milk and 1/4 cup warm buttermilk.

LARGE SWEDISH TEA RING, FILLED AND FROSTED

1. Use 1 recipe Yeast Dough I or Yeast Dough II (see previous recipes) risen and punched down.
2. On a lightly floured surface roll out the dough into a rectangle 1/4 inch thick.
3. Spread with one of the following fillings. Roll up tightly.
4. Transfer to a lightly greased baking sheet and form into a ring, pressing to seal the ends. With scissors make rather deep cuts, from outside toward center, at 1-inch intervals. Turn each section on its side.
5. Let rise until double in bulk and light. Preheat oven to 350°F.
6. Bake about 30 minutes. Frost while warm (see recipe below).

NOTE: To make buns, cut filled roll into 1-inch sections and place them close together, cut side up, in a greased pan. Let rise, bake and frost.

Cinnamon-Raisin Filling

Brush rolled-out dough with oil or softened margarine (about 1/4 cup). Sprinkle with a mixture of 3/4 cup brown sugar and 1-1/2 tablespoons cinnamon. Sprinkle with 1/2 cup seedless raisins.

Chocolate Filling

Brush rolled-out dough with oil or softened margarine (about 1/4 cup). Sprinkle with a mixture of 3/4 cup sugar, 4 to 6 tablespoons unsweetened cocoa powder, and 1/2 teaspoon cinnamon.

Filbert Paste Filling

Combine 1-1/2 cups ground filberts (about 6 ounces), 1/2 cup sugar, 1/3 cup milk, and 1 teaspoon vanilla. Spread evenly on rolled-out dough.

Frosting

Blend 1/2 cup confectioners sugar, 1 tablespoon milk (or 1 tablespoon of either brandy or unbeaten egg white), and 1/2 teaspoon vanilla (or a few drops of lemon juice). If you like a liberal amount of frosting, double the above recipe.

BIENENSTICH
(Bee Sting Cake)

A marvelous South German cake with a most unlikely name. It keeps fresh and can be made a day or two ahead of time.

1. Use 1/3 recipe for Yeast Dough II (page 271). You can make the entire recipe and freeze the remaining portion.
2. Let dough rise, punch it down, and roll it out to about 1-1/4-inch thickness. Place in a greased spring form or other cake pan about 10 inches in diameter.
3. Let rise until double in bulk and light. Preheat oven to 350°F.
4. Spread Roast Almond Topping (see recipe below) evenly over risen dough. Bake about 35 minutes.
5. Cool on a rack. Split cake when cold and fill with Vanilla Cream Filling (see page 274). Refrigerate this cake.

ROAST ALMOND TOPPING

1/3 cup unsalted margarine	2 tablespoons milk
1/3 cup sugar	1/2 teaspoon vanilla
1 cup ground blanched almonds (4 ounces)	1/4 teaspoon cinnamon (optional)

1. While dough is rising prepare the topping. In a small heavy pan or skillet heat margarine, add sugar and brown lightly, while stirring, 3 to 4 minutes.

274 THE PRUDENT DIET

2. Add almonds and roast to a light brown, while stirring.

3. Add milk, vanilla, and cinnamon and cook all gently for another 2 minutes. Set aside.

VANILLA CREAM FILLING

1 package vanilla pudding (3 ounces)	1 tablespoon brandy or rum
1-1/2 cups milk	1/2 teaspoon vanilla
1 egg yolk	1/4 cup V.S.S. or unsalted margarine

1. In a small saucepan blend pudding mix with milk. Cook over medium heat, stirring constantly, until pudding thickens and has started to boil. Continue cooking for 1 minute.

2. Beat the egg yolk in a small dish; stir in a few tablespoons of the hot pudding. Combine thoroughly with the remaining pudding.

3. Add brandy and vanilla. Chill pudding thoroughly, stirring frequently. Or cover surface with wax paper to prevent a skin from forming.

4. When pudding is chilled, cream V.S.S. or margarine, gradually add pudding, and mix well.

ZWETSCHGEN KUCHEN

Zwetschgen is the German word for "Italian" plums, also called freestone plums or prunes. Zwetschgen Kuchen is so popular, it must keep its name.

2-1/2 pounds ripe, firm Italian plums	1/4 cup zwieback crumbs
1/4 batch of Yeast Dough I or II, risen and punched down	1/3 to 1/2 cup sugar

1. Cut plums lengthwise to remove pits, but do not separate halves. Make a small incision on opposite ends of plum halves to flatten them out a bit.
2. Preheat oven to 400°F. Grease a 10-inch spring form or other cake or pie pan.
3. Shape dough into a ball and roll out to 1/8 inch thickness. As soon as rolled out, dough should be eased into the prepared pan and filled. Make sure there is ample dough for a 3/4-inch rim. Do not allow dough to rise.
4. Sprinkle crumbs over dough. Arrange plums over it, close together. Distribute one half of the sugar evenly over fruit.
5. Bake on low shelf at 400°F. for 10 minutes, then reduce heat to 350°F. and bake about 35 minutes more.
6. Sprinkle with remaining sugar. Remove from pan to cool on a rack.

NOTE: German Sweet Pastry can be used in place of yeast dough.

YIELD: 1 cake, 10 inches in diameter

FRESH BLUEBERRY CRUMB CAKE

- 1 quart fresh blueberries
- 2/3 cup sugar
- 2 tablespoons cornstarch
- 2 tablespoons minute tapioca
- 2 tablespoons lemon juice
- 1/4 batch of Yeast Dough I or II, risen and punched down
- 1/4 cup zwieback crumbs

1. Combine blueberries with sugar, cornstarch, tapioca, and lemon juice. Let stand about 15 minutes. Preheat oven to 400°F.
2. Roll out dough and place in a prepared pan. Make sure you have ample rim.
3. Sprinkle crumbs over dough and fill with blueberry mixture.
4. Distribute Crumb Topping (see below) evenly over berries.

5. Bake on low shelf at 400°F. for 10 minutes, then reduce heat to 350° and bake about 35 minutes more.

CRUMB TOPPING

2/3 cup zwieback crumbs
1/4 cup softened margarine
4 tablespoons sugar
1/2 teaspoon cinnamon (optional)

Lightly combine all ingredients with a fork.

GUGLHUPF

1 package dry active yeast
1/4 cup warm (not hot) water
1/2 cup undiluted skimmed evaporated milk
1/4 cup buttermilk
1/2 cup (1 stick) unsalted margarine, cut in pieces
1/2 teaspoon salt
1 teaspoon vanilla
grated rind of 1 lemon
2 eggs, beaten
3 cups flour, unsifted
1/2 cup sugar
1/2 cup nonfat dry milk powder
1/2 cup seedless raisins
blanched almonds (optional)
Confectioners Vanilla Sugar (see below), (optional)

1. Dissolve yeast in warm water.
2. In a bowl set over hot water, warm evaporated milk and buttermilk. Add margarine (it does not have to melt), salt, vanilla, and lemon rind.
3. Combine beaten eggs, dissolved yeast, and warm milk mixture.
4. In a large bowl combine flour, sugar, and dry milk powder. Gradually stir into it the egg, yeast, and milk mixture. Beat well until dough has lost its stickiness and leaves the sides of the bowl.
5. Add raisins and combine thoroughly. If time permits cool dough for 2 hours or overnight in a covered bowl in the refrigerator.

6. Let dough rise in a warm place until doubled in bulk. Punch down and fit into a well-greased and floured *guglhupf* form or tube pan, in which almonds have been arranged.

7. Let rise again until light and doubled in bulk. Preheat oven to 350°F.

8. Bake until it tests done, about 45 minutes. Loosen edges and unmold carefully. Cool on rack. While still warm dust with Confectioners Vanilla Sugar, if desired.

CONFECTIONERS VANILLA SUGAR

Use real vanilla bean to flavor confectioners sugar for dusting cakes and cookies and enjoy the difference!

Cut a vanilla bean in half lengthwise, then cut pieces in 2-inch lengths crosswise.

Put 1 cup confectioners sugar in a jar. Bury vanilla bean pieces in the sugar. Keep jar tightly closed. Vanilla fragrance intensifies on standing.

BABA AU RUM

- 1 envelope yeast
- 1/4 cup lukewarm water
- 1/4 cup skimmed evaporated milk
- 3 eggs, beaten lightly
- 2 tablespoons safflower oil
- 1 tablespoon rum
- 2 cups sifted flour
- 3 tablespoons sugar
- 1/4 teaspoon salt
- 1/2 cup (1 stick) unsalted margarine
- 1/4 cup currants (or raisins)
- apricot jam (optional)

SYRUP

- 1 cup sugar
- 1-1/2 cups water
- 1/2 cup rum

1. Dissolve yeast in water; add evaporated milk.
2. Briefly beat together eggs, oil, and rum. Combine yeast mixture with egg mixture.

3. Sift together flour, sugar, and salt. To flour mixture, gradually add yeast-egg mixture; beat well with a wooden spoon.

4. Cut margarine into thin slices; thoroughly incorporate them into the dough, beating until smooth and satiny (this is a soft dough). Stir in currants.

5. Refrigerate in a covered bowl, permitting some room to rise, for about 12 hours. Stir down.

6. Fill greased baba molds or custard cups 1/2 full. Let rise, covered, in a warm place until doubled in bulk. Preheat oven to 350°F.

7. Place molds on a baking sheet; bake babas 30 minutes or until they are golden brown, puffy, and test done.

8. While babas are baking, make the syrup. Combine sugar and water and boil 3 minutes. Cool and add rum.

9. Unmold baked babas and cool slightly on a rack. Prick them with a toothpick in several places. Place babas on rack over a narrow-bottomed bowl; with a baster or spoon pour syrup over babas. Repeat basting once or twice. Reserve remaining syrup in bowl.

10. Spread a thin layer of apricot jam over babas if desired. Just before serving pour remaining syrup over babas.

NOTE: Babas freeze well. Allow baked babas to cool and wrap for the freezer. Before serving, warm in the oven, prick, and add syrup as directed.

YIELD: 12 babas

ENGLISH HOLIDAY TEA CAKE

- 2-1/2 cups sifted flour
- 2-1/2 teaspoons tartrate baking powder
- 1-1/2 pounds seedless raisins
- 1/2 pound mixed candied fruit, diced
- 1 cup V.S.S. (or 2 sticks unsalted margarine)
- 1/2 cup plus 1/3 cup sugar
- 3 eggs, separated
- 3 tablespoons sherry
- 3 tablespoons rum or brandy

1. Preheat oven to 350°F. Line three 1-pound loaf pans with baking paper or grease and line with wax paper.
2. Sift flour with baking powder. In a large bowl sprinkle 1/4 cup of flour mixture over raisins and candied fruit, mix well, and set aside.
3. Cream V.S.S. with the 1/2 cup sugar until light and fluffy.
4. Beat egg yolks until thick; gradually add to creamed mixture, beating well.
5. Stir in flour mixture, alternating with sherry and rum.
6. Whip egg whites until foamy, gradually beat in the remaining 1/3 cup sugar. Continue beating until stiff and glossy.
7. Stir about 1 cup of the egg white mixture into the cake batter to lighten it; fold in the remaining portion.
8. Pour batter over fruit and mix lightly but thoroughly. Fill prepared pans.
9. Bake about 1 hour or until cakes test done. Cool in pans for about 45 minutes, then remove from pans. Remove paper and finish cooling on a rack.
10. Allow cakes to ripen two weeks, well wrapped in foil, in a cool place. This cake keeps fresh for a long time.

YIELD: 3 loaf cakes

CHEESECAKE

This is a flavorful, moist, luscious cheesecake, which lends itself to variations.

- 2 pounds cottage cheese
- 1 cup sugar
- 1/4 cup skimmed evaporated milk
- 3 large eggs
- 1/4 cup safflower oil
- 1/4 teaspoon salt
- 1 teaspoon grated lemon rind
- 1 teaspoon vanilla
- 2 tablespoons lemon juice
- 1/4 cup nonfat dry milk powder
- 1/4 cup flour
- 1/2 cup finely crushed zwieback or graham cracker crumbs

1. Preheat oven to 350°F.
2. Sieve cheese to remove lumps. Dissolve sugar in skimmed evaporated milk.
3. Beat eggs until thick, preferably in an electric mixer. Add oil gradually while beating. Add salt, vanilla, lemon rind and juice, and dry milk powder and mix well.
4. Thoroughly combine egg mixture with cheese, milk-sugar mixture, and flour.
5. Grease a 10-inch pie pan or a 9-inch spring form well. Dust with crumbs. Pour batter into prepared baking pan; bake for 1 hour or until cake tests done.
6. If baked in a spring form, remove sides but not bottom of pan. Cool on a rack, away from drafts, and chill. Cake will drop a little—it is unavoidable.

NOTE: This cheesecake forms its own thin crust; should you wish a crumb shell, see the following recipe.

YIELD: 10 to 12 servings

CRUMB SHELL FOR CHEESECAKE

1-1/4 cups zwieback or graham cracker crumbs
2 tablespoons sugar
1/4 cup safflower oil or melted margarine

1. Combine crumbs and sugar; mix in oil. Reserve 1/2 cup of mixture to sprinkle on top of cheese filling before baking.
2. Press remainder on bottom and up the sides of a 9-inch greased spring form or 10-inch pie pan.
3. Fill and bake as directed in preceding recipe for Cheesecake.

CHEESECAKE ITALIAN STYLE

Follow the recipe for Cheesecake, substituting orange rind for lemon rind and adding 1 tablespoon each of chopped white raisins and candied orange peel; dust baked cake with confectioners sugar.

CHEESECAKE GERMAN STYLE

Use Cheesecake recipe as given above. Add 1/2 cup currants to mixture.

FRANKFURT FILBERT TORTE

This marvelous recipe has been a family secret for generations. It is worthy of your great occasions.

- 6 eggs, separated
- 1 cup sugar
- 1/2 pound shelled filberts, ground
- juice and grated rind of 1 lemon
- 1 medium carrot, scraped, finely grated
- 2 tablespoons graham cracker crumbs
- 1 ounce fine bitter chocolate
- 1 tablespoon V.S.S. or unsalted margarine

1. Preheat oven to 350°F.
2. Beat egg whites with 1/2 cup of the sugar until thick and glossy.
3. With same beater (no need to wash) beat yolks until thick and lemon colored. Gradually add the remaining 1/2 cup sugar, beating until mixture is light and fluffy.
4. Combine yolk mixture with filberts, juice and rind of lemon, and grated carrot.
5. Stir into yolk mixture a few tablespoons of the egg white mixture; blend in the rest.
6. Grease a spring form pan and dust with graham cracker crumbs. Or grease sides of pan and line bottom with baking paper.
7. Pour batter into prepared pan. Bake about 50 minutes or until cake tests done. Cool on a rack.
8. When cold, melt chocolate over hot water, combine with shortening, and spread over top of cake. This topping is just sufficient to provide an elusive extra touch.

DATE NUT TORTE

2 eggs	1 teaspoon baking powder
1/2 cup sugar	3/4 cup coarsely chopped walnuts
1/2 teaspoon vanilla	1 pound pitted dates, cut into pieces
1/2 teaspoon salt	
2/3 cup sifted flour	

1. Preheat oven to 325°F.
2. Beat eggs; add sugar, vanilla, and salt and blend well. Sift together flour and baking powder.
3. With a fork, stir flour mixture lightly into egg mixture. Add nuts and dates.
4. Pour into a well-greased 8- or 9-inch square cake pan. Bake until torte is lightly browned and springs back when touched, about 25 minutes (do not overbake).
5. Serve warm or cold as a dessert, or cut, while warm, into 1-inch squares. Roll squares lightly in granulated sugar. Serve with tea or punch.

YIELD: 6 servings or 20 to 30 1-inch squares

BUTTERMILK LEMON POUND CAKE

This makes a large cake. You can freeze part of it—a fine pound cake is good to have on hand.

3 cups sifted flour	1-1/2 cups sugar
1/2 teaspoon baking soda	4 eggs
1/2 teaspoon baking powder	grated rind and juice of 1 lemon
3/4 teaspoon salt	1 teaspoon vanilla
1 cup V.S.S. or unsalted margarine	1 cup buttermilk
	Confectioners Vanilla Sugar

1. Preheat oven to 325°F.
2. Sift together flour, baking soda, baking powder, and salt.

3. In a large mixing bowl, using an electric beater, cream V.S.S. well; gradually add sugar while beating. Add eggs, one at a time, beating well after each addition until all is light and fluffy.

4. Add rind and juice of lemon (about 3 tablespoons) and vanilla. Combine with flour mixture, alternating with buttermilk. Beat until smooth after each addition.

5. Pour into a well-greased and floured 10-inch tube pan or large loaf pan. Bake for 1 hour and 10 minutes or until cake tests done.

6. Cool on a rack. Dust with Confectioners Vanilla Sugar. Slice thin to serve.

DEVIL'S FOOD CAKE

1/2 cup unsweetened cocoa powder	2 cups sifted flour
1/2 cup hot water	1 teaspoon baking powder
1 cup buttermilk	2 eggs
1 teaspoon baking soda	1/2 cup white sugar
1/4 teaspoon salt	1 cup brown sugar
1 teaspoon vanilla	1/2 cup oil

1. Preheat oven to 350°F.

2. Mix cocoa well with hot water; set aside. Combine buttermilk, baking soda, salt, and vanilla. Sift together flour and baking powder.

3. In a large mixing bowl, beat eggs until thick; gradually add white and brown sugar, beating well; slowly beat in oil. Volume will decrease somewhat.

4. Add flour mixture, alternating with buttermilk mixture, beating until smooth after each addition. Add cocoa mixture, and beat well.

5. Pour into two well-greased and floured 9-inch layer pans or into a large loaf pan. Bake about 30 minutes or until cake tests done.

6. Cool on a rack; fill and cover with Creamy White Frosting or Creamy Chocolate Frosting (see following recipes).

CREAMY WHITE FROSTING

1/4 cup V.S.S. or margarine	skimmed evaporated milk
2 cups confectioners sugar	1 teaspoon vanilla

Cream shortening, gradually sift in sugar, combining thoroughly. Add enough milk to make a good spreading consistency. Blend in vanilla.

CREAMY CHOCOLATE FROSTING

Follow the directions for Creamy White Frosting. Add 3 tablespoons of unsweetened cocoa powder to the confectioners sugar.

SPANISH ORANGE SPONGE CAKE

1-1/3 cups sifted flour	1/3 cup safflower oil
1-1/2 teaspoons baking powder	1 teaspoon grated orange rind
pinch of salt	1/3 cup orange juice
3 eggs, separated	1 tablespoon lemon juice
1 cup fine granulated sugar	1 teaspoon vanilla

1. Preheat oven to 325°F.
2. Sift together flour, baking powder, and salt.
3. In a large mixing bowl, beat egg whites until foamy; gradually add 1/2 cup of the sugar. Beat until stiff and glossy.
4. With the same beater, beat yolks until thick and lemon colored; gradually add remaining 1/2 cup sugar and beat well. Slowly add oil and continue beating. Add orange rind, orange juice, lemon juice, and vanilla.
5. Gently fold egg-yolk mixture into egg-white mixture. Sift dry ingredients over mixture in about 4 portions, folding in lightly but thoroughly after each addition.

6. Turn into a greased and floured tube, spring form, or loaf pan. Bake 40 to 50 minutes or until cake tests done.

7. Cool on rack. Dust with Confectioners Vanilla Sugar (page 277) or frost lightly with Orange Frosting (see following recipe).

ORANGE FROSTING

- 1 teaspoon grated orange rind
- 2 tablespoons orange juice
- 2 tablespoons V.S.S. or margarine
- 1 cup confectioners sugar

Mix orange rind with orange juice. Cream shortening with sugar. Add juice and rind and blend thoroughly.

TWO EGG SPONGE CAKE

- 2 eggs
- 3/4 cup sugar
- 3 tablespoons oil
- 1 teaspoon vanilla
- 1 tablespoon lemon juice
- 1/2 cup milk
- 1 cup sifted flour
- 1 teaspoon baking powder
- 1/4 teaspoon salt
- 1 tablespoon grated nuts or coconut for topping

1. Preheat oven to 325°F.
2. In a mixing bowl, beat eggs thoroughly. Slowly add sugar and continue beating several minutes. Gradually add oil along with vanilla and lemon juice.
3. Heat milk but do not boil. Sift together flour, baking powder, and salt and add to egg mixture, alternating with the milk. Mix only to blend well.
4. Pour into oiled and floured 8-inch square baking pan. Lightly sprinkle top with grated nuts or coconut. Bake for 30 to 40 minutes or until cake tests done.

NOTE: This cake batter will be thin but the cake will be light and tender. No icing is needed.

YIELD: 8 to 10 servings

BOURBON CAKE

An adaptation of a James Beard recipe.

1 pound shelled walnuts or pecans	1/2 cup V.S.S. or margarine
1/2 pound seeded raisins	1-1/8 cups sugar
1-1/2 cups sifted flour	3 eggs, separated
1 teaspoon baking powder	2 teaspoons grated nutmeg
1/4 teaspoon salt	2/3 cup plus 1/2 cup bourbon whiskey

1. Grease 2 1-pound loaf pans. Line pans with greased waxed paper or omit greasing and line pans with parchment baking paper.
2. Chop nuts coarsely. Cut raisins in half with scissors.
3. Combine nuts and raisins in a large mixing bowl and stir in 1/2 cup of the flour. Sift remaining cup of flour with baking powder and salt.
4. Preheat oven to 325°F.
5. Cream V.S.S. with 3/4 cup of the sugar until fluffy. Add the three egg yolks, one at a time, beating well after each addition.
6. Mix nutmeg with the 2/3 cup bourbon and add this, alternating with the dry ingredients, in very small portions, to the creamed mixture.
7. Beat the egg whites until foamy. Gradually add the remaining sugar, beating until stiff and glossy. Stir about 1/2 cup of the egg white mixture into the batter and fold in the rest.
8. Pour batter over nut and raisin mixture; combine gently but thoroughly. Pour into prepared pans and bake about 1-1/4 hours or until cakes test done.
9. Let cool in pans for about 1 hour before removing from pans. When cakes are almost cool, pour the remaining 1/2 cup of bourbon over them.

FLAKY PASTRY

1 cup sifted flour
1/2 teaspoon salt
pinch of cinnamon (optional)
1/4 cup oil
3 tablespoons cold milk or water

1. Sift flour, salt, and cinnamon into a bowl.
2. With a fork, beat oil and milk until creamy and slightly thickened. Pour all at once over flour mixture; toss and mix with a fork (dough will be moist).
3. Form dough into a ball, then shape into a flat round. Roll between two pieces of wax paper or plastic wrap (paper will not slip if table is wiped with a damp cloth).
4. Roll dough out evenly into a circle large enough to fit pie pan and provide for an ample rim. Remove top paper; gently lift bottom paper with pastry and invert it over pie pan. Ease pastry into pan and remove paper.
5. Trim off extra crust and press edge with a fork. Prick surface to prevent bubbles from forming while baking. Chill until ready to use.
6. To make a prebaked pie shell, preheat oven to 400°F. and bake shell for 10 to 15 minutes or until lightly browned. Cool before filling.

YIELD: one 8- or 9-inch shell

TART SHELLS

1. Prepare Flaky Pastry as directed in the previous recipe.
2. Roll dough out between 2 sheets of wax paper to 1/8-inch thickness. Cut into 3-1/2- to 4-inch rounds or squares.
3. Fit over standard size inverted tart molds, inverted muffin pans, or custard pans. Prick well.
4. Bake at 450°F. for 12 minutes or until light brown. Cool slightly, then remove carefully. Cool completely before filling.

YIELD: 8 or 9 tart shells

FLAKY PASTRY MADE WITH V.S.S.

1 cup sifted flour
1/2 teaspoon salt
pinch of cinnamon
1/3 cup V.S.S.
2 to 3 tablespoons cold milk or water

1. Sift flour, salt and cinnamon into a bowl. Cut in V.S.S. and combine thoroughly.
2. Add milk gradually, stirring with a fork, until mixture forms a ball.
3. Roll out as directed in the recipe for Flaky Pastry.
4. To make a prebaked pie shell, preheat oven to 400°F. and bake shell for about 10 minutes or until a light brown.

YIELD: one 8- or 9-inch shell

GERMAN SWEET PASTRY SHELL

1-1/2 cups sifted flour
1/3 cup sugar
1/2 cup V.S.S. or unsalted margarine
1 egg yolk
3 tablespoons brandy, gin, or kirsch

1. Mix flour and sugar. Cut V.S.S. into the mixture.
2. With a fork beat egg yolk and add brandy. Blend egg mixture into flour mixture with a fork or spatula. Lightly shape into a ball and chill. Dough can also be frozen for later use.
3. When ready to bake, preheat oven to 375°F. Roll out dough between 2 pieces of wax paper to about 1/8-inch thickness. Ease dough into a lightly greased tart form, spring form, or pie pan. Should dough break in some places, just mend by patting together with your fingers.
4. Prick dough generously with a fork before baking. Chill until ready to go into oven. Bake until lightly browned, 15 to 20 minutes.

NOTE: Make small tart shells or cut cookies from any leftover dough.

YIELD: one 9- to 10-inch shell

FRUIT TART PASTRY SHELL

Even if you are not "born with the light touch" you are bound to succeed with this excellent and easy recipe.

2 cups sifted flour	2 tablespoons brandy or gin
pinch of salt	
1/2 cup sugar	1/2 cup safflower oil
1 egg	

1. Combine flour, salt, and sugar and mix well.
2. In a small bowl beat egg until thick. Gradually beat in brandy and oil.
3. With a large fork stir egg mixture into flour mixture, combining lightly but thoroughly until dough balls together. Divide it into two portions, wrap in waxed paper and chill.
4. When ready to bake, roll dough out between sheets of waxed paper. Lightly grease a pie pan and ease pastry into it, leaving an ample rim. Prick dough well with a fork; chill again. Bake in a preheated oven at 350°F. to a light brown, 15 to 20 minutes.

YIELD: two 8-inch pie shells or 1 shell with lattice top

FRENCH APPLE TART

1 Fruit Tart Pastry Shell (see preceding recipe)	1/2 cup white wine
	1/2 cup water
	1/4 cup sugar
2-1/2 pounds apples (preferably McIntosh)	granulated sugar

1. Prepare and bake a Fruit Tart Pastry Shell as directed in the preceding recipe, using a 9-inch pie pan. Reserve some pastry for a lattice top. Cool pie shell.
2. Peel and core apples and cut them into eighths. Put apples in a saucepan together with wine, water, and the 1/4 cup sugar. Cook until apples are almost done. Remove apples with a slotted spoon and cool them.
3. Preheat oven to 400°F. Fill the cooled pie shell

with apples and cover with a lattice topping of pastry. Sprinkle granulated sugar over apples and lattice.

4. Bake for 15 to 20 minutes, or until lattice is golden brown.

SOUTH GERMAN STRAWBERRY TART

- 1 German Sweet Pastry Shell
- 1 quart strawberries
- 1/3 cup sugar
- 1 scant tablespoon cornstarch
- 2 tablespoons water
- 1 teaspoon lemon juice

1. Prepare and bake the pastry shell as directed, using a 9-inch pie pan.
2. Hull strawberries and cut in half. Remove 1 cup of halved strawberries and set aside.
3. Sprinkle remaining strawberries with 1 tablespoon of the sugar and arrange berries, cut sides down, attractively, on the baked shell.
4. In a small saucepan, crush the 1 cup of berries with the remaining sugar. Mix cornstarch with water and lemon juice; add to berry mixture in saucepan. Bring to a boil, while stirring; cook for 1 to 2 minutes until liquid is clear.
5. Carefully spoon mixture over berries in tart shell, make sure all are lightly covered with glaze. Chill tart thoroughly before serving.

NOTE: Absolutely fresh, firm-ripe berries are essential for the superior quality of this tart.

VINTNER'S LEMON TART

- 1 8-inch unbaked pie shell
- 3 lemons
- 1 medium-sized tart apple
- 1 cup (about 4 ounces) finely ground blanched almonds
- 1 tablespoon lemon juice
- 1 cup sugar

TOPPING

- 2 tablespoons safflower oil
- 1 egg, lightly beaten
- 2 tablespoons yogurt or buttermilk
- 3 tablespoons evaporated skimmed milk
- 2 tablespoons Confectioners Vanilla Sugar

1. Be sure pastry extends up the sides of the pie pan at least one inch. Prick pastry all over with a fork. Refrigerate until ready to bake.
2. Preheat oven to 425°F. and bake pastry until firm but only lightly browned, 10 to 15 minutes.
3. Peel and section lemons with a sharp knife, eliminating all white parts and membranes. Peel apple and grate finely.
4. Combine apple, almonds, lemon juice, and sugar. Spread over baked pastry, making sure mixture covers entire pastry surface.
5. Arrange lemon sections in cartwheel pattern over almond mixture.
6. Beat oil into the lightly beaten egg. Stir in yogurt and exaporated skimmed milk. Pour mixture over tart and sprinkle with Confectioners Vanilla Sugar.
7. Reduce oven heat to 400°F. and bake tart until lightly browned, about 30 minutes. This tart is best served lukewarm, but is also good chilled.

NOTE: Try using Flaky Pastry Made with V.S.S.

YIELD: 6 servings

FRESH BLUEBERRY TARTS

- 6 baked Tart Shells
- 1 pint fresh blueberries
- 1/2 cup raspberry jam

1. Preheat oven to 400°F.
2. Fill tart shells with the blueberries and cover berries with the raspberry jam, about 1-1/2 tablespoons on each tart.
3. Place on a baking sheet in the oven for 7 to 10 minutes.

4. Serve immediately. Crust will be crisp and the berries hot and fragrant—a very unusual and delicious dessert.

NOTE: In place of the blueberries, fresh ripe peaches, thinly sliced, are also very good.

YIELD: 6 tarts

DEEP DISH APPLE PIE

This pie is especially good served warm.

1 recipe Flaky Pastry
12 medium tart apples (Jonathans, McIntosh, or Greenings)
1 tablespoon oil
1/2 to 3/4 cup sugar, depending on tartness of apples
1/2 teaspoon cinnamon
1/2 teaspoon nutmeg
pinch of salt
evaporated milk

1. Peel, core, and slice apples about 1/4 inch thick. Preheat oven to 400°F.
2. Put oil in a round 9- or 10-inch baking dish; tilt so oil covers bottom. Add apple slices (the dish will be well rounded on top). Mix sugar, spices, and salt and distribute over apples. With a sharp knife cut through the apples in several places, allowing sugar and spices to sift through them.
3. Roll out pastry and cover apples. Brush lightly with evaporated milk; pierce top to allow steam to escape.
4. Bake at 400°F. for about 15 minutes or until crust begins to bake and brown lightly; reduce heat to 325°F. and continue baking about 30 minutes or until crust is browned nicely and apples are tender when pierced with a fork.

YIELD: 6 servings

PECAN PIE

- 1 unbaked 9- or 10-inch pastry shell, chilled
- 1/2 cup sugar
- 1 tablespoon flour
- 3 eggs, slightly beaten
- 1 cup light corn syrup
- 1/4 teaspoon salt
- 1/4 cup melted margarine
- 1 teaspoon vanilla
- 1-1/2 cups pecan halves (6 ounces)

1. Preheat oven to 350°F.
2. In a bowl combine sugar and flour. Blend in slightly beaten eggs. Stir in corn syrup, salt, margarine, vanilla, and pecan halves; mix all well.
3. Pour into pastry shell and bake for about 1 hour and 10 minutes.
4. Chill well before serving.

PUMPKIN PIE

- 1 unbaked 9-inch pastry shell
- 1 cup brown sugar
- 1 tablespoon cornstarch
- 1/2 teaspoon salt
- 1 teaspoon cinnamon
- 1/2 teaspoon nutmeg
- 1/2 teaspoon ginger
- 1/4 teaspoon cloves
- 2 eggs, slightly beaten
- 1-1/2 cups puréed cooked pumpkin, fresh or canned
- 1-2/3 cups (1 tall can) skimmed evaporated milk

1. Preheat oven to 425°F.
2. In a bowl combine sugar, cornstarch, salt, and spices. Blend in eggs and pumpkin. Stir in skimmed evaporated milk.
3. Pour into pastry shell and bake in the hot oven for 15 minutes. Reduce heat to 350°F. and bake 25 to 35 minutes more or until a knife inserted comes out clean.

MOTHER B'S OATMEAL COOKIES

- 2 eggs
- 1 cup soft brown sugar
- 1 cup oil
- 1/3 cup molasses
- 3 tablespoons milk
- 2 cups sifted flour
- 1/2 teaspoon salt
- 1 teaspoon baking soda
- 1 teaspoon cinnamon
- 1/2 teaspoon each of ginger, cloves, and nutmeg
- 1/2 cup raisins (softened in water and drained) or 1/2 cup nut meats
- 2-1/4 cups quick rolled oats

1. Preheat oven to 325°F.
2. Beat eggs well in a large mixing bowl. Add brown sugar and beat until well blended.
3. Slowly pour in oil. In the same cup, measure molasses (then every drop will run out) and combine with mixture in bowl. Add milk and blend in.
4. Sift together flour, salt, baking soda, and spices. Add to mixture along with raisins or nuts; mix just to blend. Add oats and stir lightly.
5. Drop from a teaspoon on ungreased baking sheet. Bake about 20 minutes or until firm and light brown.
6. While warm, pack cookies in a box with a tight-fitting cover, between layers of wax paper. Cover at once.

NOTE: These cookies will keep indefinitely in the refrigerator. However, they taste better when at room temperature, so remove those to be used about one-half hour before serving.

YIELD: about 4 dozen 3-inch, soft, drop cookies

IVA'S DELICIOUS MISTAKE
Oatmeal cookies without oatmeal

One day, while listening to the World Series, Iva was making some oatmeal cookies. This time she was using nut meats in place of raisins in Mother B's Oatmeal Cookie recipe, but forgot to put in the oatmeal. She noticed the batter was somewhat thin, but her mind was on the game. Her favorite team was winning and so she just went ahead and baked the cookies. They were softer and spicier cookies, but just great; everybody liked them. They are now often made this way.

MAPLE CURRANT OATMEAL COOKIES

1 cup quick rolled oats
3/4 cup brown sugar
3/4 cup sifted flour
1-1/2 teaspoons baking powder
1/2 teaspoon salt
1 egg
1/2 cup oil
2 tablespoons maple syrup
3/4 cup currants (or raisins)
1/3 cup chopped walnuts

1. Preheat oven to 375°F.
2. Combine oats and sugar. Sift together flour, baking powder, and salt.
3. Beat egg until thick. Gradually beat in oil and maple syrup.
4. Combine well the egg mixture with the oat mixture; blend in flour mixture. Stir in currants and nuts.
5. Drop by rounded teaspoonfuls on greased (or baking-paper-lined) baking sheet. Bake about 15 minutes.

YIELD: about 3-1/2 dozen

HUNGARIAN APRICOT WALNUT BARS

BOTTOM CRUST

1 egg yolk
1/2 cup safflower oil
1-1/2 cups sifted flour
pinch of salt
2 tablespoons white wine or water

FILLING

1/2 cup apricot preserves

TOP LAYER

4 eggs, separated	2 tablespoons fine dry bread crumbs
3/4 cup sugar	
1-1/2 cups ground walnuts (about 6 ounces)	

1. Preheat oven to 375°F.
2. Beat egg yolk with a wire whisk; add oil slowly, beating well. It does not matter if mixture separates.
3. Mix flour and salt. Combine with egg-oil mixture and stir with a fork gently—just to mix.
4. Sprinkle just enough wine or water over dough to make it hold together. Form a ball, then roll out dough between 2 sheets of wax paper and place in a 9- by 14-inch ungreased baking pan. This dough is apt to be crumbly; just patch and pat down to make an even crust. Cover dough with apricot preserves.
5. Beat egg whites until foamy, slowly adding 1/2 cup of the sugar. Beat until stiff and glossy.
6. With the same beater beat yolks until thick; add remaining 1/4 cup sugar and beat until light.
7. Combine egg white and egg yolk mixtures gently. Fold in nuts and bread crumbs.
8. Pour evenly over layer in pan. Bake for 40 to 50 minutes or until cake tests done and is lightly browned. Cool in pan and cut into 2-inch bars.

YIELD: 28 2-inch bars

BROWNIES

2 eggs	1/4 teaspoon baking soda
1/2 cup dark brown sugar	3/4 cup commercial chocolate syrup
1/2 cup safflower oil	1 cup coarsely chopped nuts
1 teaspoon vanilla	
1 cup sifted flour	

1. Preheat oven to 350°F.
2. Beat eggs until thick and lemon colored; gradually add sugar, beating until light.

3. Gradually pour oil into mixture, beating continuously. Add vanilla.

4. Sift flour with baking soda. Stir into above mixture, alternating with chocolate syrup. Fold in nuts.

5. Grease and line with wax paper a shallow, medium-size, square baking pan. Pour batter into it; bake about 35 minutes. Cool in pan and cut into squares.

YIELD: about 36 1-inch squares

ITALIAN HONEY BISCUITS

- 3 eggs
- 2-1/2 cups sifted confectioners sugar
- 3/4 cup honey
- 1/4 teaspoon nutmeg
- 1/4 teaspoon allspice
- 1/2 teaspoon cinnamon
- 1/4 teaspoon salt
- 1 teaspoon vanilla
- 1/2 teaspoon almond extract
- 1/2 teaspoon (combined) grated orange and lemon rind
- 6 ounces whole filberts
- 4 cups (scant) sifted flour

ICING

- 1 cup confectioners sugar
- 2 tablespoons milk or unbeaten egg white

1. Preheat oven to 325°F.

2. Beat eggs, add sugar, and beat well. Add other ingredients in order given and blend thoroughly.

3. Shape into 3 or 4 loaves (which will be sticky) and place on a greased (or baking paper-covered) cookie sheet. Leave enough room between loaves to spread.

4. Bake about 3/4 hour. Spread while warm with a thin icing of confectioners sugar mixed with milk or egg white.

5. After cooling, cut into 1/2-inch slices with a sharp knife and store in a covered tin. These are hard at first, but will soften after a few hours.

YIELD: about 5 dozen biscuits

OLD-FASHIONED MOLASSES BARS

- 1/2 cup V.S.S. or margarine
- 3/4 cup brown sugar
- 1 teaspoon vanilla
- 2 eggs
- 1/2 cup molasses
- 1-1/2 cups sifted flour
- 1/4 teaspoon salt
- 1/4 teaspoon baking soda
- 1 teaspoon baking powder
- 1 cup chopped nuts (about 4 ounces)

1. Preheat oven to 350°F.
2. Cream fat and sugar until fluffy; add vanilla.
3. Beat in eggs, one at a time. Add molasses and blend well.
4. Sift together flour, salt, baking soda, and baking powder; blend into creamed mixture along with nuts.
5. Bake in a well-greased medium-size baking pan 30 to 35 minutes or until done.
6. Cut into bars while warm. Serve warm or cold.

YIELD: 20 to 24 bars

BELGIAN SPICE COOKIES

- 1-2/3 cups sifted flour
- 1/2 teaspoon baking soda
- 1/4 teaspoon salt
- 1/2 teaspoon nutmeg
- 1 teaspoon cinnamon
- pinch of cloves
- 1/2 cup finely chopped nut meats
- 1 egg, beaten
- 1 cup light brown sugar
- 1 teaspoon vanilla
- 1/2 cup oil

1. Sift together flour, soda, salt, and spices. Add nuts and blend well.
2. In a mixing bowl, beat egg; gradually add sugar and vanilla and beat until fluffy.
3. Slowly add oil, beating well. Add flour mixture and blend well.
4. On wax paper, shape dough into two rolls about 2 inches in diameter; wrap in foil. Place in freezer 3 to 4 hours or longer.

5. When ready to bake, preheat oven to 350°F. Cut cookies into thin slices (about 1/8 inch thick) and place on a lightly greased baking sheet (or baking paper-lined baking sheet); do not crowd.

6. Bake about 10 minutes or until lightly browned. Cool on a rack and place in a jar with a tight cover; refrigerate. These cookies will keep crisp several weeks when refrigerated.

YIELD: about 3 dozen

PEANUT BUTTER COOKIES I

These have a mild peanut butter flavor.

- 1/2 cup V.S.S. or margarine
- 1/2 cup peanut butter
- 1/2 cup white sugar
- 1/2 cup brown sugar, firmly packed
- 1/2 teaspoon vanilla
- 2 eggs, slightly beaten
- 1-1/2 cups sifted flour
- 1/2 teaspoon salt
- 1 teaspoon baking powder
- 1/2 teaspoon baking soda
- cinnamon sugar

1. Mix peanut butter with V.S.S. until well blended. Cream in sugars gradually. Add vanilla and the slightly beaten eggs and blend thoroughly.

2. Sift together flour, salt, baking powder, and baking soda and add to the creamed mixture in three portions; mix well after each addition.

3. Chill dough for 1/2 hour or longer.

4. When ready to bake, preheat oven to 350°F.

5. Drop dough from a teaspoon onto ungreased baking sheets. With a floured fork, press each cookie so that ridges remain. Shake a bit of cinnamon sugar onto each cookie.

6. Bake 10 minutes or until cookies are golden brown. Cool on a rack. Store in a tightly covered box. These will keep indefinitely in the refrigerator.

YIELD: 6 dozen 2-inch cookies

PEANUT BUTTER COOKIES II

These cookies have a pronounced peanut butter flavor.

1-2/3 cups sifted flour
1 cup peanut butter
1 egg
1 tablespoon brandy or rum
1 cup sugar
1 teaspoon vanilla

1. Preheat oven to 300°F.
2. Combine all ingredients in a mixing bowl and beat with an electric mixer until smooth.
3. Roll dough into balls about 1 inch in diameter. Place balls about 1 inch apart on an ungreased cookie sheet.
4. Bake about 25 minutes, until slightly firm to the touch and a light brown.

YIELD: about 36 cookies

BLACK WALNUT COOKIES

2-1/3 cups sifted flour
2 teaspoons baking powder
1/2 teaspoon salt
2 eggs
1 cup oil
1/2 cup brown sugar
1/2 cup light corn syrup
1 teaspoon vanilla
1 cup (4-ounce can) black walnuts, chopped
1/4 cup milk

1. Preheat oven to 375°F.
2. Sift together flour, baking powder, and salt.
3. Beat eggs well. Gradually add oil, sugar, corn syrup, and vanilla, beating well all the time.
4. Fold in nuts. Add sifted dry ingredients alternately with milk.
5. Drop by teaspoonfuls on baking paper-lined baking sheet or greased baking sheet. Bake 20 to 25 minutes.

YIELD: about 60 cookies

CAKES, PIES, AND COOKIES

ITALIAN MACAROONS

These are the "chewy" variety.

- 1/2 pound blanched almonds
- 1 cup superfine sugar or 1-1/2 cups confectioners sugar
- 2 egg whites
- 3 tablespoons Kirsch
- 1 egg white
- Confectioners Vanilla Sugar

1. Grind almonds finely (if available use a Mouli grinder), add sugar and mix well.
2. Beat the 2 egg whites until firm and combine with almond and sugar mixture. Add Kirsch and mix well. This is a stiff dough. Wrap dough in plastic wrap or foil and store in the refrigerator 12 hours.
3. When ready to bake, beat the 1 egg white until stiff and combine with dough. You may need to do this by hand at first.
4. With two teaspoons form oval macaroons and place them 1 inch apart on a baking sheet lined with baking paper or unglazed paper. Dust macaroons with Confectioners Vanilla Sugar. Let stand 1 hour.
5. Preheat oven to 350°F. and bake macaroons until lightly brown and puffed up (15 to 20 minutes). Outside should be firm to the touch, inside still soft. Cool on a rack. If macaroons are baked on unglazed paper, slide paper onto a wet board. Remove after 1 minute. Cool on a rack.

NOTE: For less work buy blanched, slivered almonds. For better control of "just right" consistency of dough add egg white mixture gradually to almonds or other nuts in all macaroon type cookies.

YIELD: about 4 dozen

FILBERT MACAROONS

- 2 egg whites (about 1/4 cup)
- 1 cup brown sugar
- pinch of salt
- 1 teaspoon vanilla
- 1/2 pound finely ground filberts
- 4 dozen whole filberts for garnish

1. Preheat oven to 325°F.
2. Beat egg whites until they hold a peak. Gradually beat in the sugar.
3. Add salt and vanilla. Fold in ground filberts and combine thoroughly.
4. Shape balls the size of a small walnut with 2 teaspoons. Place macaroons on baking sheet lined with baking paper or unglazed paper. Press a whole filbert lightly into the center of each macaroon.
5. Bake until outsides are firm to the touch but centers are still soft, about 15 minutes. Remove from oven and after 1 minute transfer macaroons to a rack to cool.
6. When baking sheet has been lined with unglazed paper, slide the paper onto a wet board. Remove macaroons after 1 minute. Store macaroons in an airtight container. They keep well.

YIELD: about 45 macaroons

PECAN DREAMS

- 1/2 cup V.S.S. or unsalted margarine
- 2 tablespoons sugar
- 1 teaspoon vanilla
- 1 cup sifted flour
- 1 cup ground pecans (about 4 ounces)
- Confectioners Vanilla Sugar

1. Preheat oven to 300°F.
2. Beat fat and sugar thoroughly. Stir in vanilla, flour, and pecans. Mix all lightly but thoroughly.
3. Roll dough into balls 1 inch in diameter. Place balls on a greased (or baking paper-lined) cookie sheet, about 1 inch apart.
4. Bake for 35 minutes. While hot, roll in Confectioners Vanilla Sugar. Handle cookies carefully as they are very tender. When cold roll again in Confectioners Vanilla Sugar.

YIELD: about 36 cookies

MANDELBROT

4 cups sifted flour
2 teaspoons baking powder
1 cup sugar
pinch of salt
3 eggs
1 cup oil
1 teaspoon vanilla
1-1/2 cups coarsely chopped almonds or walnuts

1. Preheat oven to 375°F.
2. Sift together flour, baking powder, sugar, and salt.
3. Beat eggs until thick and add, alternating, the flour mixture and oil. Stir in vanilla and nuts and mix well. This will be a soft moist dough (you may need 1 to 2 additional tablespoons of flour).
4. With floured hands form 3 long strips of the dough. Place the strips on a greased cookie sheet and bake until they test done, about 35 minutes. They will not be brown.
5. Cool slightly and cut strips into slices 3/4 inch wide. Place slices, cut side up, on the cookie sheet; bake at above temperature for about 5 minutes.

YIELD: about 3 dozen cookies

SCANDINAVIAN ALMOND COOKIES

1 cup sifted flour
1/2 teaspoon baking powder
1/2 cup V.S.S. or unsalted margarine
1/3 cup sugar
1 teaspoon vanilla
2 tablespoons brandy, rum, or gin
24 whole blanched almonds

1. Preheat oven to 325°F.
2. Sift together flour and baking powder. Cream fat and add sugar gradually, creaming well. Add vanilla and brandy; mix well. Blend in dry ingredients.
3. Shape dough into small balls. Place on ungreased (or baking paper-lined) baking sheet. Press one whole almond into each cookie.
4. Bake 20 to 30 minutes.

YIELD: about 2 dozen cookies

20
Desserts

Fruit is one of nature's most tempting gifts, sweet, succulent, and fragrant, a dessert *par excellence*. Along with their pleasure some fruits contribute great nutritional values. Vitamin C is abundant in citrus fruit and strawberries. Yellow-fleshed cantaloupes, mangoes (sometimes called the queen of fruits) and papayas supply both vitamin A and vitamin C. Apricots are a rich source of vitamin A.

The word fruit comes from the Latin *fructus,* meaning enjoyment. Nothing could describe it better. Serve fruit at its peak of ripeness, cool but not chilled for best flavor. A dash of lemon juice intensifies the aroma of melons and berries. Just before serving, sprinkle berries very lightly with fine sugar. When summer is a berry festival, combine blueberries, raspberries, and currants for a colorful, flavor-rich treat. Fresh pineapple and kirsch are a time-honored combination; just remember that a little kirsch goes a long way. Is there anything more pleasing, any day, than a bowl of fresh fruit from which one can choose—a bunch of sweet grapes, a tangerine, or a crisp, tart and juicy apple?

Sherbets and frozen custards based on milk and fruit are perennial favorites with young and old. They are excellent desserts, light and refreshing, ideal for hot summer days.

When mood or occasion calls for something different, try an apricot soufflé with almond caramel sauce, macaroon-stuffed baked pears or some light and crisp apple fritters.

APRICOT SOUFFLÉ WITH ALMOND CARAMEL SAUCE

- 1 cup cooked, unsweetened, puréed dried apricots (see Note below)
- 1/4 cup sugar
- 2 tablespoons orange-flavored liqueur (optional)
- 1 teaspoon unflavored gelatin
- 1 tablespoon water
- 1/2 cup skimmed evaporated milk
- 1 tablespoon lemon juice
- Almond Caramel Sauce

1. Chill evaporated milk in freezing compartment.
2. Combine apricot purée, sugar, and orange liqueur; chill.
3. Sprinkle gelatin over water, stir, then dissolve over hot water. Mix with a heaping tablespoon of apricot purée. Keep at room temperature.
4. Whip milk (page 320) and fold in lemon juice. With the same beater, beat dissolved gelatin mixture into remaining apricot purée.
5. Beat purée gradually into whipped milk.
6. Pour into a serving bowl and chill until firm. Serve with Almond Caramel Sauce. (See below.)

NOTE: 1 cup (about 6 ounces) dried apricots will yield approximately 1 cup of purée. In a saucepan bring apricots and 1-1/2 cups water to a boil (water enough to cover apricots). Gently simmer until apricots are tender, 15 to 20 minutes. Force through a food mill or sieve.

YIELD: 4 servings

ALMOND CARAMEL SAUCE

- 1/4 cup unblanched, slivered almonds
- 1/2 cup sugar
- 1/2 cup water
- 1 teaspoon orange-flavored liqueur (optional)

1. On a dry pan, toast almonds to a light brown.
2. In a small, heavy saucepan caramelize sugar over low heat to a rich medium brown (until it starts to foam).
3. Slowly add water; simmer 10 minutes, until slightly syrupy. Combine with almonds and chill. Add liqueur.

LEMON SOUFFLÉ

1 3-ounce package lady fingers (to line pan and to make crumbs for topping)	2/3 cup sugar
	2 boxes (3-1/4 ounces each) lemon pie filling
2 tablespoons oil	1/4 cup water
3-1/2 cups water	4 eggs, separated
grated rind and juice of 1 lemon	1/2 cup sugar

1. Line bottom of a well-oiled 9- or 10-inch spring form with lady fingers, cut in half lengthwise. You may also use thin slices of sponge cake. The spring form makes for easy cutting.
2. In a heavy, large saucepan, combine oil, 3-1/2 cups water, lemon rind and juice, 2/3 cup sugar, and lemon pie filling; allow to stand 5 minutes.
3. Add the 1/4 cup water to the egg yolks. Beat with a fork and add to lemon mixture. Cook directly over medium heat, while stirring, until mixture thickens and lemon capsule breaks; remove from heat.
4. Beat egg whites until foamy, gradually add the 1/2 cup sugar, and continue beating until stiff and glossy.
5. Gently fold the beaten egg whites into the hot lemon mixture, until blended throughout. Pour into cake-lined pan and sprinkle crumbs on top.

6. Cool, then store in refrigerator several hours or overnight.

7. When ready to serve, remove sides of spring form and cut soufflé into desired portions.

NOTE: For one half the recipe, use the same spring form; the soufflé will be only half as high but just as delicious.

YIELD: 12 servings

WHITE WINE CREAM

- 3/4 cup sugar
- pinch of salt
- 4 tablespoons arrowroot or 2 tablespoons cornstarch
- 1/4 cup water
- 1-1/4 cups dry wine (such as white Bordeaux)
- grated rind of 1 lemon
- 1/3 cup lemon juice
- 2 eggs, separated

1. In a saucepan combine 1/2 cup of the sugar, salt, and arrowroot. Stir in water, wine, lemon rind, and lemon juice.

2. Bring to a boil over medium flame, while stirring. Simmer 2 minutes, until clear, slightly thickened and starchy taste has disappeared. Do not overcook.

3. In a small bowl beat the egg yolks. Gradually add a few tablespoons of the hot mixture, then combine with remaining hot mixture; mix well. Cool, stirring occasionally.

4. Beat egg whites until foamy. Gradually add remaining 1/4 cup sugar and beat until stiff and glossy. Gently but thoroughly fold into wine cream; chill.

5. Stir lightly with a fork before serving. Serve with freshly toasted slices of leftover baba or sponge cake, or over stewed pears.

NOTE: If wine used is not dry, reduce amount of sugar in recipe.

YIELD: 6 servings

SNOW EGGS IN VANILLA SAUCE

SNOW EGGS

2 egg whites   1/4 cup sugar

1. Beat egg whites until foamy; gradually add sugar and continue beating until stiff and glossy.
2. In a large, shallow pan, bring to simmer about 1 cup of water.
3. With 2 spoons shape beaten whites into egg shapes. Place in simmering water, cook for 1 minute, turn, and cook for 1 minute on the other side.
4. With a slotted spoon, remove snow eggs to paper towels to dry.

VANILLA SAUCE

1 cup skimmed evaporated milk
1 cup water
2 tablespoons cornstarch
1/4 cup sugar
pinch of salt
1 egg, lightly beaten
1 tablespoon V.S.S. or margarine
1 teaspoon vanilla
1 tablespoon brandy (optional)

1. In a heavy saucepan, scald milk and 1/2 cup of the water.
2. Combine cornstarch, sugar, salt and remaining 1/2 cup water; stir until well mixed.
3. Stir cornstarch mixture into simmering milk. Cook, stirring, until thickened and starchy taste is gone (about 2 minutes; do not overcook).
4. Stir about 3 tablespoons of the hot mixture into the beaten egg. Stir egg mixture into the remaining mixture (egg will cook sufficiently in hot mixture).
5. Add shortening, vanilla, and brandy. Cool, stirring occasionally. Pour into a shallow bowl and float Snow Eggs on top. Chill until ready to serve.

YIELD: 4 servings

CREAMY RICE PUDDING

1/2 cup regular rice	1 egg yolk
6 cups boiling water	1/3 cup sugar
2-1/2 cups milk	3 tablespoons unsalted margarine
pinch of salt	1 teaspoon vanilla

1. Pour rice into boiling water, boil for 2 minutes, then drain.
2. Scald milk in top of double boiler. Stir in rice and salt.
3. Transfer to direct heat and cook on low heat (use asbestos plate if necessary), stirring occasionally, about 20 minutes or until rice is tender.
4. Stir yolk in a small dish; combine with a few tablespoons of the hot rice mixture. Gently but thoroughly combine with the remaining rice.
5. Remove from heat. Gently, with a large fork, incorporate sugar, margarine, and vanilla.
6. Serve hot or cold.

YIELD: 4 to 6 servings

BLUSHING MAIDEN

1 4-ounce box frozen raspberries	2 cups buttermilk
2 envelopes unflavored gelatin	1 teaspoon vanilla
	2 egg whites
1/2 cup water	4 tablespoons sugar

1. Defrost raspberries. Soften gelatin in cold water; dissolve over hot water.
2. Mash berries well with a fork. If desired, strain to remove seeds.
3. Combine berries and buttermilk; add vanilla. Add dissolved gelatin; cool until mixture begins to solidify.
4. Whip egg whites until foamy, add sugar gradually, and beat until stiff and glossy.

5. Fold egg-white mixture into buttermilk mixture. Refrigerate for several hours before serving.

YIELD: 1 quart

APPLE CRISP

3 pounds tart apples (McIntosh or Greenings)
1/2 cup flour
1/2 cup brown sugar
pinch of salt
1 teaspoon cinnamon (optional)
1/4 cup (1/2 stick) margarine

1. Preheat oven to 350°F.
2. Peel and core apples. Slice them into a rather shallow, 9-inch baking dish. If apples are not tart, sprinkle some lemon juice or kirsch over them.
3. Combine flour, sugar, salt, and cinnamon. Cut margarine into flour mixture with a knife or pastry blender. Spread topping over apples.
4. Bake about 30 minutes, or until topping is browned and apples are tender.
5. Serve hot or cold.

YIELD: 6 servings

APPLE FRITTERS

3 medium-size tart apples (about 1 pound)
1 tablespoon sugar
few drops lemon juice
few drops rum (optional)
Batter (see below)

1. Peel and core apples; cut them into 1/4-inch slices. Sprinkle with sugar, lemon juice, and rum, and let stand for about 1 hour. Gently turn them once or twice.

2. With a long-handled fork, dip apple slices into Batter.

3. Fry in deep oil to a golden brown. Sprinkle with sugar before serving.

YIELD: 6 servings

BATTER FOR FRUIT FRITTERS

1/2 cup flour
   pinch of salt
1/4 cup lukewarm
   water
2 tablespoons oil
3 tablespoons rum or
   wine
1 egg, separated

1. Put flour and salt in a small bowl. Stir in water, oil, rum, and egg yolk. Let stand 1 to 2 hours at room temperature.

2. When ready to use, beat egg white until stiff and fold into yolk mixture.

COTTAGE CHEESE FRITTERS
Adapted from a Chamberlain recipe

4 tablespoons cottage
   cheese
1 egg, lightly beaten
   pinch of salt
2 tablespoons flour
oil for deep frying
Confectioners Vanilla
   Sugar

1. Mash cheese until smooth. Stir in the egg and salt and gradually stir in the flour. This should be the consistency of a thick batter.

2. Drop batter by teaspoonfuls into hot oil. When fritters are puffed and golden, remove to a hot plate and sprinkle with Confectioners Vanilla Sugar.

3. Serve at once.

YIELD: 3 servings

CARAMEL-GLAZED CHESTNUT DESSERT
After a recipe of Elizabeth David

- 1 pound fresh chestnuts
- 1/2 cup milk
- 1/2 cup water
- 6 tablespoons sugar, dissolved in 3 tablespoons water
- 4 tablespoons margarine, softened

GLAZE
- 1/2 cup sugar
- 1/4 cup water

1. To cook chestnuts, cut a cross on the flat side of each with a sharp knife. In a saucepan, cover chestnuts with cold water, bring to a boil and simmer for 15 to 20 minutes.
2. Remove a few at a time from the hot water; shell and skin them.
3. Put skinned chestnuts in a saucepan, add milk and water, bring to a boil, and simmer until they are very soft, about 30 minutes.
4. Drain off liquid; put chestnuts through a food mill or sieve.
5. Bring to a boil the sugar and water syrup. Boil two minutes; cool. Combine with puréed chestnuts. Add softened margarine and mix thoroughly.
6. Turn into a lightly oiled refrigerator tray; refrigerate 24 hours or longer.
7. On the day on which it is to be served turn chestnut cake out on a serving platter.
8. To make the glaze, boil sugar and water until syrup starts to foam and is of rich medium brown color; pour it over chestnut cake. With a heated metal spatula or knife smooth glaze over the sides, working fast, as glaze hardens quickly. Refrigerate dessert for several hours.
9. Some time before serving, heat a knife blade well and gently mark dessert into servings. Sugar will melt just enough so that portions can be divided without cracking the glaze.

YIELD: 6 to 8 servings

BAKED STUFFED PEARS

4 firm ripe eating pears
3/4 cup almond macaroon crumbs
1/2 cup dry vermouth
1/4 cup apricot jam

1. Preheat oven to 375°F.
2. Wash, halve and core pears; place them cut sides up, in a shallow baking dish.
3. Mix 1/2 cup of the macaroon crumbs with 1/4 cup of the vermouth and fill pear cavities with this mixture.
4. Combine apricot jam with remaining vermouth and spread over pears. Sprinkle with remaining macaroon crumbs.
5. Bake for 10 to 15 minutes (do not overcook). Serve hot or cold.

NOTE: Large, ripe, peeled peaches can be substituted for pears.

YIELD: 4 servings

MOTHER'S STEWED BLUEBERRIES

Simplicity itself, and delicious.

1 quart fresh blueberries
3 or 4 tablespoons sugar

In a saucepan, gently bring the berries and sugar to a boil. Shake saucepan or stir carefully so berries cook evenly. Boil for about 4 to 5 minutes. Chill.

NOTE: You may add a slice of lemon peel and a piece of stick cinnamon to berries when you cook them, for added flavor.

BAKED DRIED APRICOTS

These apricots keep their shape and taste fresh.

2 cups (about 12 ounces) dried apricots	3 to 4 cups water 1/4 to 1/3 cup sugar

1. Preheat oven to 300°F.
2. In a flameproof casserole, slowly bring apricots and water to a boil. Transfer casserole to the oven and bake, uncovered, about one hour or until apricots are plumped up and tender.
3. Gently stir in sugar and bake 5 minutes more.
4. Cover and let stand until cold; store in the refrigerator.

YIELD: 6 servings

BROILED BANANAS

4 firm, ripe bananas	2 tablespoons honey
1 tablespoon oil	2 tablespoons sesame seeds
1 tablespoon lemon juice	

1. Peel bananas and place them in an oiled, shallow, broiler-proof pan.
2. Brush bananas with oil, then with lemon juice. Drizzle honey over them; sprinkle with sesame seeds.
3. Broil about 4 inches from flame for 5 to 7 minutes, or until heated through and browned and sesame seeds are toasted.

YIELD: 4 servings

FROZEN ITALIAN CUSTARD

- 2/3 cup skimmed evaporated milk
- 1 teaspoon unflavored gelatin
- 2 tablespoons water
- 1 egg, separated
- 3 tablespoons safflower oil
- 2 tablespoons honey
- 1/4 cup chopped, toasted almonds or crushed almond macaroons
- 1/2 teaspoon vanilla
- 1 tablespoon rum, brandy, or sherry
- 2 tablespoons sugar

1. Chill evaporated milk. In a small bowl, soften gelatin with water. Dissolve over hot water; cool to room temperature.
2. In a bowl with a small bottom, beat egg yolk well with wire whisk; slowly add oil, drop by drop, while beating, until mixture becomes smooth and thick.
3. Add honey, almonds, vanilla, rum, and dissolved gelatin; mix well.
4. Beat egg white until foamy, gradually add sugar, and beat until stiff and glossy; fold into yolk mixture.
5. Whip milk until very stiff (see page 320); fold into egg mixture lightly but thoroughly.
6. Pour at once into a chilled freezing tray. Freeze several hours or overnight.

NOTE: A small amount of liquor added to any frozen dessert prevents large crystals from forming.

YIELD: about 1-1/2 pints

FROZEN LEMON CUSTARD

- 2/3 cup skimmed evaporated milk
- 1 egg, separated
- 6 tablespoons sugar
- grated rind of 1 lemon
- 1/3 cup lemon juice
- 1 tablespoon kirsch or gin (optional)

1. Chill evaporated milk in a freezer tray.
2. In a bowl with a small bottom, beat egg yolk well; add 4 tablespoons of the sugar, lemon rind, lemon juice, and kirsch.
3. Beat egg white until foamy, gradually add remaining sugar, and beat until stiff and glossy. Fold into yolk mixture; chill.
4. Whip milk until stiff; fold into egg mixture. Pour at once into chilled freezing tray. Freeze for several hours.

YIELD: about 1-1/2 pints

FROZEN POT DE CRÈME AU CHOCOLAT

- 2/3 cup skimmed evaporated milk
- 1 teaspoon unflavored gelatin
- 1 tablespoon water
- 1/2 cup commercial chocolate syrup
- 1 egg
- 1/4 cup safflower oil
- pinch of salt
- 1 tablespoon brandy or rum
- 1/2 teaspoon vanilla

1. Chill skimmed evaporated milk in a freezer tray.
2. In a small bowl soften gelatin in water; dissolve over hot water. Combine with chocolate syrup; keep at room temperature.
3. Beat egg until thick and lemon colored; very gradually beat in oil.
4. Combine with chocolate mixture, salt, brandy, and vanilla. Refrigerate, but not long enough for mixture to congeal.
5. Whip milk very stiff and fold into egg-chocolate mixture.
6. Pour at once into chilled custard cups or chilled freezing tray. Freeze for several hours. For best flavor and texture allow to ripen 12 to 24 hours before serving.

YIELD: about 1-1/2 pints

ORANGE MILK SHERBET

1 cup skimmed evaporated milk
1 tablespoon lemon juice
1 can (6 ounces) frozen orange concentrate, unthawed
1 tablespoon brandy, rum or orange liqueur

1. Whip evaporated milk until stiff (see page 320). Fold in lemon juice and gently mix in frozen orange concentrate. Add brandy or liqueur.
2. Pour at once into two chilled freezing trays. Freeze for several hours.

NOTE: This is a rather tart sherbet. If you like it sweeter, add some fine sugar along with the orange concentrate.

YIELD: 1 quart

RASPBERRY YOGURT SHERBET

1 box (4 ounces) frozen raspberries
1-1/2 cups plain yogurt
1 tablespoon lemon juice
1 egg white
2 tablespoons sugar

1. In a wide bowl mash slightly defrosted berries well.
2. Add yogurt and lemon juice and mix well. Place in freezer and freeze to a mush.
3. Beat egg white until foamy; gradually add sugar, and beat until stiff and glossy.
4. With the same beater, whip berry mixture until light. Fold in beaten egg white.
5. Pour into chilled freezing tray. Freeze for several hours.

NOTE: You may substitute frozen sweetened strawberries for the raspberries. Use 1-1/2 cups fresh, ripe berries, sweetened with 2 tablespoons sugar, if they are available.

YIELD: 1-1/2 pints

PINEAPPLE YOGURT SHERBET

This takes only five minutes to prepare and is ready to serve in one hour.

- 2 cups plain yogurt
- 1 can (6 ounces) frozen pineapple juice concentrate
- 1 tablespoon lemon juice
- 1 teaspoon each grated lemon and orange rind
- 1 tablespoons kirsch, gin, or sweet liqueur

Gently combine yogurt and frozen concentrate. Add remaining ingredients. Pour into chilled freezing tray and freeze. Stir once during freezing.

NOTE: Should you desire a sweeter sherbet, add two tablespoons of honey along with the other ingredients.

YIELD: about 1-1/2 pints

ORANGE YOGURT SHERBET

Use orange concentrate in place of pineapple concentrate. Add 1 tablespoon lemon juice and 1 tablespoon Scotch whiskey or brandy. Omit lemon and orange rind. Combine and freeze as above.

ORANGES WITH KIRSCH

- 4 good-size eating oranges
- 2 teaspoons sugar
- 2 teaspoons kirsch

1. Peel oranges with a sharp knife. Remove any white portion. Cut them into thin crosswise slices, removing seeds.
2. Arrange orange slices in layers in a bowl. Sprinkle each layer with sugar and kirsch.
3. Chill before serving.

YIELD: 4 servings

BAKED BLUEBERRY DESSERT WITH YOGURT TOPPING

1 pint (2 cups) blueberries	1 teaspoon cornstarch
1 egg, separated	1 teaspoon vanilla
2 tablespoons sugar	1/2 cup yogurt
2 tablespoons safflower oil	confectioners sugar

1. Preheat oven to 400°F.
2. Put the blueberries in a shallow 9-inch baking dish.
3. Beat egg white until foamy, gradually adding the sugar; beat until stiff and glossy. Set aside.
4. With the same beater beat the yolk until thick, gradually adding the oil (as in making mayonnaise).
5. Stir in cornstarch and vanilla. Gently mix in yogurt. Stir in a tablespoon of the egg white mixture, and then fold in the remaining portion.
6. Pour egg-yogurt mixture over blueberries, distributing it evenly. Bake about 30 minutes until golden brown and puffy.
7. Dust lightly with confectioners sugar before serving. Serve hot or cold.

NOTE: 3 cups of cherries with pits (or 2 cups pitted) makes a good substitute for the blueberries.

YIELD: 4 servings

WHIPPED CHEESE TOPPING NO. I

4 marshmallows	1/2 teaspoon vanilla
2 tablespoons water	1 cup creamed cottage cheese
1/4 cup milk	
1 tablespoon lemon juice	

1. Simmer marshmallows in water until dissolved, cool, and pour into blender.

2. Add milk, lemon juice, and vanilla; blend at low speed just to mix well.
3. Gradually add cottage cheese while on low speed; change to high speed for about 30 seconds.
4. Chill for several hours before use.

NOTE: This topping is very smooth and light. It retains its consistency and is particularly useful for decorating fruit tarts, gelatin, and other desserts.

YIELD: about 1-1/2 cups

WHIPPED CHEESE TOPPING NO. II

- 1 tablespoon lemon juice
- 1/4 cup milk
- 3 tablespoons confectioners sugar
- 1/2 teaspoon vanilla
- 1 cup creamed cottage cheese

1. Put lemon juice, milk, sugar, and vanilla in the blender and blend at low speed.
2. Gradually add cottage cheese while blender is on low speed; change to high speed for about 30 seconds. Chill.

YIELD: about 1-1/2 cups

WHIPPED EVAPORATED MILK

1. Pour evaporated milk (undiluted) into a freezing tray, or directly into a bowl for whipping. Chill in freezer compartment until fine crystals begin to form around the edges.
2. Pour into a chilled bowl and whip rapidly with a cold beater until very stiff. Preferably use an electric beater.
3. When properly handled, evaporated milk will whip as stiff as cream. If milk does not whip well, it is not cold enough—just re-chill and whip again.

Glossary

ATHEROSCLEROSIS A disease of the arteries in which deposits of fat and cholesterol in the innermost layer of the arterial walls have thickened and narrowed these blood vessels, restricting normal blood flow. Atherosclerosis is the cause of most heart attacks.

CORONARY HEART DISEASE Atherosclerosis in the coronary arteries (blood vessels that furnish blood directly to the heart muscle), impairing adequate blood supply to the heart.

FATS All fats and oils are compounds of glycerol and fatty acids. Each fat molecule contains saturated, monounsaturated, and polyunsaturated fatty acids in varying proportions, depending upon the type of fat. Chemically the fatty acids differ according to the number of double bonds in their carbon chain.

SATURATED FATTY ACIDS Contain no double bonds. They carry all the hydrogen they can hold.

UNSATURATED FATTY ACIDS Have one or more double bonds.

POLYUNSATURATED FATTY ACIDS Have more than one double bond.

HYDROGENATION A chemical process by which hydrogen is added to various fats and oils under pressure and at high temperature, to change them into a more solid form. Through hydrogenation soft fats and oils can be transformed into hard cooking fats and table spreads.

CHOLESTEROL A fat-like substance present in animal tissues and fluids. Therefore, all food of animal origin also contains cholesterol. The body makes cholesterol which it needs for many important functions. Cholesterol in blood is called blood or serum cholesterol. Cholesterol in food is called dietary cholesterol.

Bibliography

1. Jolliffe, Norman; Rinzler, S. H., and Archer, M. *The Anti-Coronary Club.* Am. J. Clinical Nutrition, vol. 7, July–Aug. 1959
2. Kinsell, L. W.; Partridge, J.; Boling, L.; Margen, S., and Michaels, G. *Dietary Modification of Serum Cholesterol and Phospholipid Levels.* J. Clin. Endocrinol. 12: 1952
3. Bronte-Stewart, B.; Antonis, A.; Eales, L., and Brock, J. F. *Effects of Feeding Different Fats on Serum Cholesterol Level.* Lancet 1: 1956
4. Keys, Ancel. *Diet and the Development of Coronary Heart Disease.* J. Chronic Disease 4: 364. 1956
5. Kannell, W. B.; Dawber, T. R.; Kagan, A.; Rovotskie, N., and Stokes, J. *Risk Factors in the Development of Coronary Heart Disease—6 Year Follow-up Experience. The Framingham Study.* Ann. Int. Med. 55: 1961
6. Kannell, W. B., et al.: *Risk Factors in Coronary Heart Disease, An Evaluation of Several Serum Lipids as Predictors of Coronary Heart Disease, The Framingham Study.* Ann. Int. Med. 61: 1964
7. Jolliffe, Norman. *Fats, Cholesterol and Coronary Heart Disease, A Review of Recent Progress.* Circulation 20: No. 1, July 1959
8. Enos, W. F.; Beyer, J. C., and Holmes, R. H. *Pathogenesis of Coronary Disease in American Soldiers Killed in Korea.* J. Am. Med. Assn. 158. 1955
9. Christakis, G. J. *Nutritional Status of New York City Children.* 3rd Report of the National Vitamin Foundation, New York City, 1964–65
10. Morse, Ellen H.; Merrow, Susan B., and Clarke, Robert F. *Some Biochemical Findings in Burlington, Vermont, Junior High School Children.* Am. J. Clin. Nutrition, vol. 17, Oct. 1965
11. Keys, A.; Kimura, M.; Bronte-Stewart, B.; Larsen, N., and Keys, M. H. *Lessons from Serum Cholesterol Studies in*

Japan, Hawaii and Los Angeles. Ann. Int. Med. 48: 1958
12. Schindel, M. *Change of Serum Total Lipids, Total Cholesterol and Lipidphosphorus in Jewish Yemenite Immigrants after Twenty Years in Israel.* Cited in Keys, A., J. Chronic Dis. 4: 1956
13. ———. *Nat. Diet-Heart Study Final Report.* Circulation, vol. XXXVII, No. 3, Supplement No. 1, March 1968
14. Jolliffe, Norman; Baumgartner, L.; Rinzler, S. H.; Archer, M.; Stephenson, J. H., and Christakis, G. J. *The Anti-Coronary Club—The First Four Years.* N.Y. State J. of Med., vol. 63, No. 1, Jan. 1963
15. Jolliffe, Norman; Maslansky, Ethel; Rudensey, Florence; Simon, Martha; Faulkner, Alice. *Dietary Control of Serum Cholesterol in Clinical Practice.* Circulation, vol. XXIV, No. 6, Dec. 1961
16. Christakis, G. J.; Rinzler, S. H.; Archer, M.; Winslow, G.; Jampel, G.; Stephenson, J. H.; Friedman, G. J.; Fein, H.; Kraus, A., and James, G. *The Anti-Coronary Club—An Approach to the Prevention of Coronary Heart Disease—A Seven Year Report.* Am. J. Pub. Health, vol. 56, No. 2, Feb. 1966
17. Rinzler, S. H. *Primary Prevention of Coronary Heart Disease by Diet.* Bull. N.Y. Academy of Medicine. 44: 936, 1968
18. Keys, A. (Editorial) *Prevention of Coronary Heart Disease—Official Recommendations from Scandinavia.* Circulation, vol. XXXVIII, Aug. 1968
19. Jolliffe, Norman. *Reduce and Stay Reduced on the Prudent Diet.* Simon and Schuster, Inc., New York, N.Y. 1963
20. Wohl, M. G., and Goodhart, R. S. *Modern Nutrition in Health and Disease,* 4th Edit. 1968, Lea & Febiger, Philadelphia, Pa.
    a. Chapt. 18. *Criteria for an Adequate Diet* by Goodhart, R. S.
    b. Chapt. 29 B. *Nutrition in Relation to Atherosclerosis* by Friedman, G. J.
21. Jolliffe, Norman, Editor. *Clinical Nutrition,* Second Edit. 1962, Harper & Brothers, Publishers, New York, N.Y.
    a. Chapt. 1. *The Pathogenesis of Deficiency Disease* by Jolliffe, N.
    b. Chapt. 25. *Dietary Treatment and Prevention of Hypercholesterolemia* by Jolliffe, N.
    c. Chapt. 26. *Obesity* by Jolliffe, N., and Glenn, M. B.
22. Keys, Ancel and Margaret. *Eat Well and Stay Well,* Rev. Edit. 1963, Doubleday and Company, Inc., Garden City, N.Y.

23. Glenn, M. B. *How to Get Thinner Once and for All*. E. P. Dutton & Co., New York, N.Y. 1965
24. Blakeslee, A.; Stamler, J. *Your Heart Has Nine Lives*. Pocket Books, Inc., 1966
25. Kain, Ida Jean, and Gibson, M. B. *Stay Slim for Life*. Doubleday and Company Inc., Garden City, N.Y. 1958
26. Margolius, Sidney. *The Great American Food Hoax*. Walker and Co., Publishers, New York 1971
27. ———. *Recommended Dietary Allowances*. National Academy of Sciences, Seventh Edit. 1968
28. ———. *Agriculture Handbook No. 8, Composition of Foods*. Agric. Research Services, U.S. Department of Agriculture, Rev. Dec. 1968
29. ———. *Nutritive Value of Foods. Home and Garden Bull. No. 72*. Agric. Research Service, U.S. Department of Agriculture. Slightly Rev. Jan. 1971. U.S. Government Printing Office, Washington, D.C. 20402

Index

Acorn Squash, Mashed, 199
Aioli, 249
Almond(s): Caramel Sauce, 305; Cookies, Scandinavian, 303; Mandelbrot, 303; Near East, Roasted, 56; Topping, Roast, 273
Anchovy(ies): Butter, 259; Salade Niçoise, 245; with Tomatoes, 70; Wafers, 61
Animal foods and saturated fats, 12, 13–14
Anti-Coronary Club, 6–11
Apple(s): Casserole, Sweet Potato and, 220; Crisp, 310; Fritters, 310; Pie, Deep Dish, 292; Sauerkraut with, 206; Tart, French, 289
Apricot(s): Baked Dried, 314; Soufflé with Almond Caramel Sauce, 305; Walnut Bars, Hungarian, 295
Arroz con Pollo, 163
Artichokes with Mustard Vinaigrette, 239
Asparagus, *see* Leeks Vinaigrette
Aunt Iva's Red Oil Dressing, 249
Avocado, fat content of, 15; and Grapefruit Salad, 238; Tomato and Egg Salad, 239

Baba au Rum, 277
Bananas, Broiled, 314
Barbecued Chicken, Japanese Style, 160
Barley and Mushroom Casserole, 231
Bean(s): Buffet Dish, Hearty, 225; Soup, Black, 97; Soup, Pink Bean or Red Kidney, 96; and Tuna Salad, Italian, 244; Sauce, Haitian, 224; *see also* Green Beans
Beef, 170–175; Braised, 170; Cabbage, Stuffed, 215; Chinese Pepper Steak, 175; Eggplant, Stuffed, 218; Italian Meat Balls in Tomato Sauce, 180; Italian Peppers, Stuffed, 217; Juicy Meat Loaf, 173; London Broil, 173; Stu's London Broil, 174; Meat Balls in Caper Sauce, 182; Meat Balls in Mushroom Sauce, 181; Pot Roast of, 170; Sauerbraten, 172; Swedish Meat Balls, 181; Sweet and Sour Cabbage, Stuffed, 213; Variation of Scotch Broth, 106
Bee Sting Cake, 273 (Bienenstich)
Beet(s): Soup, 83; Spiced, 213
Belgian Spice Cookies, 298
Beurre Manié, 82
Black Bean Soup, 97
Black Walnut Cookies, 300
Blanquette de Veau, 187
Blender Mayonnaise, 248
Blood cholesterol levels, 4; and diet, 6–10, 17–18
Blowfish, Lemon Broiled, 121
Blueberry(ies): Crumb Cake, Fresh, 275; Dessert with Yogurt Topping, Baked, 319; Mother's Stewed, 313; Tarts, Fresh, 291
Blushing Maiden, 309
Boris' Pumpernickel, 264
Borscht, 83
Bouillabaisse: "Manhattan," 98; "White," 101
Bourride, 101
Brandade de Morue, 123
Bread: Crumbs, Seasoned, 134; planning meals, 32; Boris' Pumpernickel, 264; Casserole Cottage Cheese and Dill, 266;

325

Bread (*continued*)
Challah, 261; as Cocktailers, 55; Croutons, 95; Cuban, 262; Dark, Crusty Country, 263; "diet," 24; French, 262; Oatmeal, 265; Orange Nut, 267; Peanut Butter, 265

Breakfast: Buttermilk Muffins, 267; menus for, 42

Broccoli: Chinese Style, Sautéed, 201; Purée of, 202; Shrimp Balls with, 143; *see also* Cauliflower au Gratin

Brownies, 296

Brown Sauce I, 252; II, 252

Brown Veal Goulash, 186

Buffet Dish, Hearty Bean, 225

Bulgur, 232

Butter, 13; fat content, 14

Buttermilk: Blushing Maiden, 309; Lemon Pound Cake, 282; Breakfast Muffins, 267; Pancakes, Feathery, 226; Waffles, 227

Butternut Squash, Mashed, 199

Butters: Anchovy, 259; Lemon, 259; Mustard, 259

Cabbage: Cole Slaw, 238; and Green Pepper, Sweet and Sour, 204; and Mushrooms, Chinese, 204; Savory Red, 205; Stuffed, 215; Sweet and Sour Stuffed, 213

Cakes: Bee Sting, 273; Bourbon, 286; Buttermilk Lemon Pound, 282; Devil's Food, 283; English Holiday Tea, 278; fat content of, 13; French Blueberry Crumb, 275; Honey, 268; Spanish Orange Sponge, 284; Two-Egg Sponge, 285; *see also* Pastries

Calories, daily allowances, 29; and "diet food," 24; and fat content, 13; in foods, differences in, 27; and frying, 50

Calves' Hearts, Potted, 194

Calves' Liver and Onions Venice Style, 191

Canapé and Canapé Spreads, 55–59: Cheese Dill and Curry, 56; Chicken Liver Pâté, 59; Chicken or Turkey Almond, 57; Chicken Walnut, 57; Fresh Horseradish-Peanut Butter, 59; Ham, 57; Liptauer Cheese, 56; Roquefort Walnut, 57; Shrimp or Crabmeat, 58; Tuna Olive, 58; *see also* Savory Butters

Caper Sauce, Meat Balls in, 182

Caramel-Glazed Chestnut Dessert, 312

Caramel Sauce, Almond, 305

Carp: Baked Fish with Tomatoes, 115; Braised Fish, 115; Gefillte Fish, 78

Carrot: Purée, 203; Soup, 84; Spring, 212; Tzimmis, 198; and Walnut Salad, 237

Casserole Cottage Cheese and Dill Bread, 266

Caviar, red: Taramasalata, 79

Cauliflower: au Gratin, 210; and Peas, a Salad of, 240

Celeriac with Mustard Vinaigrette, 240

Cellophane noodles, *see* Long Rice

Challah, 261

Cheese: Dill and Curry Spread, 56; fat content of, 13, 14; and planning meals, 31; and Prudent Diet, 39–40; Topping No. I, Whipped, 319; No. II, Whipped, 320; Wafers, Roquefort, 61

Cheesecake, 279; German Style, 281; Italian Style, 280

Cherry Tomatoes, Stuffed, 58

Cherry Dessert with Yogurt Topping, Baked, 319

Chestnut(s): Dessert, Caramel-Glazed, 312; Hot Roasted, 55

Chicken: Baked Corn-Crisped, 151; Barbecued, 160; Basic Sautéed, 157; Chinese Braised, 155; Crumb-Baked, 152; with Curry, 157; Escabeche, 164; Filling for Pancakes, 229; Flambé with Mushrooms, 158; Fricassee, Favorite, 160; with Garlic, 156; and Ham Rollups, 155; Hedi's Juicy Roast, 152; Lemon Fried, 151; Long Rice, 233; Milanese, Breast of, 154; with Mushrooms, Sautéed, 159; with Olives Provençale, 161; Paella, 137; Paprika, 162;

Chicken (*continued*)
  Pot au Feu, 104; with Rice, 163; Salad, 244; from Southern Italy, Broiled, 159; Teri Yaki, 153; or Turkey Almond Spread, 57; Variations of Scotch Broth, 106; Walnut Spread, 57
Chicken Breasts, Marinated, 153
Chicken Liver(s): in Aspic, 193; Chopped Liver, 76; Loaf, Veal and, 189; Pâté, 59; Risotto with, 232; Sweet and Pungent, 190
Chickpea Tahini, 74
Chicory, Braised, 209
Chinese: Braised Chicken, 155; Cabbage and Mushrooms, 204; Flavor, Roast Duckling with a, 166; Fried Shrimp Balls, 143; Shrimp Cantonese Style, 145
Chocolate: Brownies, 296; Filling, 272; Frozen Pot de Crème au Chocolat, 316; and the Prudent Diet, 15
Chowder, New England Fish, 103
Chutney, Peach, 254
Cinnamon-Raisin Filling, 272
Clams: Baked Stuffed, 77; Chowder, Manhattan, 102; Filling for Pancakes, 229; Fresh Steamed, 101; Paella, 137; Sauce, Red, 258; Sauce, White, 257; Scalloped, 147; Soup, Cream of, 102
Cocktailers, 54–69: Anchovy Wafers, 61; Cherry Tomatoes, Stuffed, 58; Chicken Liver Pâté, 59; Chinese Fried Shrimp Balls, 68; Cocktail Puffs, 63; Dorothy's Chilled Orange Sections with Cinnamon, 69; Hot Meat Balls, 67; Marinated Swordfish Cubes, 69; Onion and Smoked Salmon Quiche, 66; Pan Bagna, 67; Peanut Butter Curry Wafers, 60; Pizza, 65; Roquefort Cheese Wafers, 61; Sesame Biscuits, 63; Sesame Seed Wafers, 62; Spreads for Canapés, 56–59; Swedish Meat Balls, 181; Yogurt Dip, 58
Cod: Baked Fish with Tomatoes, 115; New England Fish Chowder, 103; Poached Fish, 114; Purée of Salt, 123; Russian Fish Stew, 117; Scandinavian Fish Pudding, 119; Steamed Fish, 116
Codfish: Cakes, Eleanor's Delicious Fresh, 122; Freshening Dried Salt, 123; Soup, Salt, 100; and Spinach Salt, 124; Variation, 124
Cole Slaw, 238
Confectioners Vanilla Sugar, 277
Cookies: Belgian Spice, 298; Black Walnut, 300; Brownies, 296; fat content of, 13; Iva's Delicious Mistake, 294; Maple Currant Oatmeal, 295; Mother B's Oatmeal, 294; Peanut Butter I, 299; Peanut Butter II, 300; Scandinavian Almond, 303; to store, 52
Coquilles Saint Jacques au Gratin, 135
Cottage Cheese: and Dill Bread, Casserole, 266; fat content of, 15, 31; Fritters, 311; Omelet, 230; planning meals, 31; and Prudent Sour Cream, 53; Topping No. I, Whipped, 319; II, 320
Crab Meat: au Gratin, Shrimp and, 139; John's Green Peppers Stuffed with, 148; Lasagna California Style, 148; Salad, Shrimp and, 246; Spread, Shrimp or, 58
Crêpes, 228
Croutons, 95
Crumb: Baked Chicken, 152; Shell for Cheesecake, 280; Topping, 276
Cuban Bread, 262
Cucumber: Tarator, 92; in Yogurt Dressing, 237
Cumberland Sauce, 256
Curry(ied): Chicken with, 157; Sauce, 255; Scallops, 134; Shrimp à l'Indienne, 139
Custards, frozen: Italian, 315; Lemon, 315; Pot de Crème au Chocolat, 316

Date Nut Torte, 282
Deep Dish Apple Pie, 292

328 THE PRUDENT DIET

Dessert Puffs, 64
Devil's Food Cake, 283
Diet: and blood cholesterol, 3–4; and coronary heart disease, 3–4, 5, 6; deficient, 25; "diet foods," 24; pills, 24–25
Dinners, menus for, 43–44
Dips: Haitian Bean Sauce, 224; Yogurt, 58
Duckling: Bigarade, Roast, 165; with a Chinese Flavor, Roast, 166
Dumplings: Liver, 192; for Soup, 91; South German Potato, 222
Duxelles, 88

Eel: in Aspic, 125; Bouillabaisse "Manhattan," 98; Poached Fish, 114; Soup, 98
Eggplant: Chopped, Arabian Style, 73; Chopped, Armenian Style, 72; Charcoal Roasted, 73; Rumanian Style, 73; Papa Zingone, Baked, 210; Stuffed, 218; Spicy, 218
Egg Salad, Avocado, Tomato and, 239
Eggs, fat content of, 14; and planning meals, 31; Cottage Cheese Omelet, 230; and Prudent Diet, 39
Eleanor's Delicious Fresh Codfish Cakes, 122
English Holiday Tea Cake, 278
Evaporated Milk, Whipped, 320

Fats: to avoid, 32; in certain foods, 12–15; polyunsaturated, and Prudent Diet, 7; saturated, 7
Favorite Chicken Fricasse, 160
Filbert: Macaroons, 301; Paste Filling, 272; Torte, Frankfurt, 281
Fillings: Chocolate, 272; Cinnamon-Raisin, 272; Filbert Paste, 272; for Puffs, 56–59; for Small Pancakes, 229; Vanilla Cream, 274
Finnan Haddie in Cream Sauce, 126
Fish
 Anchovy(ies): Butter, 259; Salade Niçoise, 245; with Tomatoes, 70; Wafers, 61

Blowfish, Lemon Broiled, 121
Bouillabaisse "Manhattan," 98
Bourride, 101
Braised, 115
Breading, 113
Broiled, 112; to buy, 108
Cantonese, Steamed, 120
Chowder, New England, 103
Cod, Purée of Salt, 123; Codfish Cakes, Eleanor's Delicious Fresh, 122; Codfish, Freshening Dried Salt, 123; Codfish Soup, Salt, 100; Codfish and Spinach, Salt, 124; Variation, 124
Deep-fried, 113
Eel, in Aspic, 125; Soup, 98
Fat content of, 17
Finnan Haddie in Cream Sauce, 126
Fried, 112
Gefillte, 78
Halibut, Baked in Sherry, 127; Broiled, 126
Herring in Dill Sauce, Schmaltz, 79
Mackerel Fillets, in Wine Sauce, 127; Escabeche, 128; with Mussels, Baked, 118
Pan-fried, 113; and planning meals, 30
Poached, 114
Pudding, Scandinavian, 119
Salmon, Baked in Wine, 129; Broiled, 129; Patties, 130; Quiche, Onion and Smoked, 66
Sardines, Broiled, 125; and Spinach, 125; sauces to serve with, 114; Savory Butters for, 258–259
Shad, Escabeche, 128; Roe, Sautéed, 133
Sole with Mushrooms, Fillets of, 131
Squid, Steamed, 147
Steamed, 116
Stew, Russian, 117
Stock, 78
Striped Bass, Baked Split, 121; Baked Whole, 120
Swordfish, Cubes, Marinated, 69; Lemon Broiled, 131; Soy-Sauce Broiled, 132; on Spits, Turkish Broiled, 132
Taramasalata, 79

INDEX 329

Fish *(continued)*
   with Tomatoes, Baked, 115
   Tuna, Casserole with Noodles, 149; Salad, Italian Bean and, 244; Salad, Macaroni and, 245
   See also Shellfish
Flaedchen Soup, 90
Flaky Pastry, 287; made with V.S.S., 288
Flounder, Russian Fish Stew, 117; Steamed Fish Cantonese, 120
Flour, instant blending, 108
Foil, vegetables baked in, 198
Foods, to avoid, 46; fatty acid composition of, 12–15
French: Apple Tart, 289; Bread, 262; Dressing, 246; Green Peas, 208; Onion Soup, 85
Fritters: Apple, 310; Cottage Cheese, 311
Frosting: Creamy Chocolate, 284; Creamy White, 284; Orange, 285; for Swedish Tea Ring, 273
Fruit: as Cocktailers, 55; desserts, 304–319; Fritters, batter for, 311; and planning meals, 32; Tart Pastry Shell, 289
Frying and calories, 50

Garlic, Chicken with, 156
Gazpacho, 92
Gefillte Fish, 78
German: Pancakes, 228; Sweet Pastry Shell, 288; *see also* South German
Giblets, Variations of Scotch Broth, 106
Ginger, fresh, 145
Grapefruit Salad, Avocado, 238
Gravy: Brown Sauce I, 252; Brown Sauce, II, 252; Prudent, 251
Green beans: Italian Bean and Tuna Salad, 244; Lyyonnaise, 211; Potato and, Salad, 241; Vinaigrette, 240
Green Pepper(s): Chinese Pepper Steak, 175; Stuffed, 216; Stuffed with Crab Meat, John's, 148; Sweet and Sour, Cabbage and, 204; and Tomatoes, Shrimp with, 141; and Zucchini Casserole, Eggplant; Tomato, 211
Guglhupf, 276

Haddock: Baked Fish with Tomatoes, 115; Scandinavian Fish Pudding, 119
Haitian Bean Sauce, 224
Halibut: Baked in Sherry, 127; Broiled, 126; New England Fish Chowder, 103; Poached Fish, 114; Russian Fish Stew, 117; Scandinavian Fish Pudding, 119; Steamed Fish, 116
Ham: Marinated Roast Fresh, 179; and Potato Hash, 221; Roll-ups, Chicken and, 155; Spread, 57
Hash, Ham and Potato, 221
Hearts, Potted Calves', 194
Hedi's Baked Shrimp, 140; Juicy Roast Chicken, 152
Herbed Potatoes in Casserole, 220
Herring in Dill Sauce, Schmaltz, 79
Holiday buffets, 45
Hollandaise Sauce, 256
Honey: Biscuits, Italian, 297; Cake, 268
Horseradish-Peanut Butter Spread, Fresh, 59
Hors d'oeuvre, 70–80; Anchovy with Tomatoes, 70; Chickpea Tahini, 74; Clams, Baked Stuffed, 77; Eggplant, Chopped, 72–73; Gefillte Fish, 78; Herring in Dill Sauce, Schmaltz, 79; Leeks Vinaigrette, 71; Liver, chopped, 76; Mackerel Escabeche, Fillets of, 128; Mackerel Fillets in Wine Sauce, 127; Mushrooms à la Grecque, 71; Pepper Salad, Roasted, 75; Shad Escabeche, Fillets of, 128; Shrimp Batter-Fried, 77; Taramasalata, 79
Hungarian Apricot Walnut Bars, 295
Hypertension and the Prudent Diet, 10

Italian: Bean and Tuna Salad, 244; Custard, Frozen, 315; Honey Biscuits, 297; Macaroons, 301; Meat Balls in To-

330 THE PRUDENT DIET

Italian (continued)
mato Sauce, 180; Peppers, Stuffed, 217; Plums in Vinegar, 171; Plums, see also Zwetschgen Kuchen; Shrimp Buongusto, 146
Iva's Delicious Mistake, 294

Japanese Style, Barbecued Chicken, 160; Chicken Teri Yaki, 153
John's Green Peppers Stuffed with Crab Meat, 148
Jolliffe, Dr. Norman, ix–x, 3; 6

Keys, Dr. Ancel, 4
Kidney bean(s): Haitian Bean Sauce, 224; Soup, Red, 96; Buffet Dish, Hearty, 225
Kidneys, Baked in Mustard Sauce, 193; in Red Wine, 195
Kirsch, Oranges with, 318; Pineapple with, 304
Kitchen helpers, 47–48
Kohlrabi, 200
Kuchen, Zwetschgen, 274

Lamb: Broth, 105; and Lentil Stew, Turkish, 178; Scotch Broth, 105; Shish Kebab, 176; and Vegetable Casserole, 177
Lasagna, California Style, Crab Meat, 148
Leeks Vinaigrette, 71
Legumes, dried, 93
Lemon: Broiled Blowfish, 121; Broiled Shrimp, 144; Broiled Swordfish, 131; Butter, 259; Custard, Frozen, 315; Fried Chicken, 151; Pound Cake, Buttermilk, 282; Soufflé, 306; Tart, Vintner's, 290
Lentil(s): Soup, South German, 95; Stew, Turkish Lamb and, 178
Liptauer Cheese, 56
Liver, Chopped, 76; Dumplings, 192
London Broil, 174; Stu's, 174
Long Rice: Chicken, 233; Shrimp, 234
Lunch, menus for, 42

Macaroni and Tuna Salad, 245

Macaroons: Filbert, 301; Italian, 301
Mackerel: Baked Fish with Tomatoes, 115; Escabeche, Fillets of, 128; Fillets in Wine Sauce, 127; see also Baked Split Striped Bass
Mandelbrot, 303
Manhattan Clam Chowder, 102; see also Bouillabaisse "Manhattan"
Maple Currant Oatmeal Cookies, 295
Margarine: and V.S.S., 52; "diet," 24; fat content of, 15; 17; in recipes, 51
Matt's Poultry Stuffing, 167
Mayonnaise, 246; Aioli, 249; Blender, 248; fat content of, 14; Tartar Sauce, 248
Meal planning, 30–32
Meat Balls: in Caper Sauce, 182; Hot, 67; in Mushroom Sauce, 181; Swedish, 181; in Tomato Sauce, Italian, 180
Meat Loaf, Juicy, 173
Meats: and Anti-Coronary Club, 20; and blood cholesterol, 18; fat content of, 14; and planning meals, 30–31; see also Beef, Calves' Hearts, Calves' Liver, Chicken, Duckling, Ham, Lamb, Pork, Turkey, Veal
Menus, 41–46
Milk, fat content of, 13; and planning meals, 31; and Prudent Diet, 39; in recipes, 51
Molasses Bars, Old-Fashioned, 298
Mother B's Oatmeal Cookies, 294
Mother's Stewed Blueberries, 313
Muffins, Breakfast Buttermilk, 267
Mushrooms: à la Grecque, 71; Casserole, Barley and, 231; Chicken Flambé with, 158; Chinese Cabbage and, 204; Concentrate, 88; Sauce, 254; Sauce, Meat Balls in, 181; Sautéed Chicken with, 159; Soup, Cream of, 88; Veal Scallopine with, 183
Mussels: Baked Fish with, 118; Paella, 137

INDEX

Mustard: Butter 259; Sauce, 253; Vinaigrette, Artichokes with, 239; Vinaigrette, Celeriac with, 240

New England Fish Chowder, 103
Noodles, Tuna Fish casserole with, 149
Nutrition: and the full life, 37; and older persons, 29; and planning meals, 30–32

Oatmeal: Bread, 265; Cookies, Maple Currant, 295; Mother B's, 294; Soup, 90
Oil(s): Dressing, Aunt Iva's Red, 249; and frying, 50; polyunsaturated vegetable, 50; and the Prudent Diet, 21
Old-Fashioned Molasses Bars, 298
Olive(s): Provençal, Chicken with, 161; Spread, Tuna, 58
Omelet, Cottage Cheese, 230
Onion(s): and Smoked Salmon Quiche, 66; Soup, French, 85; Venice Style, Liver and, 191; Vinaigrette, Baked, 212
Orange(s): Sections with Cinnamon, Dorothy's, 69; Frosting, 285; with Kirsch, 318; Milk Sherbet, 317; Nut Bread, 267; Sponge Cake, Spanish, 284; Yogurt Sherbet, 318

Paella, 137
Pan Bagna, 67
Pancakes, 226–230; Feathery Buttermilk, 226; Flaedchen Soup, 90; German, 228; Potato, 227; Pot Cheese, 230; Small Filled, 228
Pasta: Macaroni and Tuna Salad, 245; Noodles, Tuna Fish Casserole with, 149; Red Clam Sauce for, 258; Tuna Fish Sauce for, 257; White Clam Sauce for, 257
Pastries, Baba au Rum, 277; Bienenstich, 273; Blueberry Crumb Cake, Fresh, 275; Cheesecake, 279–280; Date Nut Torte, 282; Filbert Macaroons, 301; Flaky Pastry, 287; Frankfurt Filbert Torte, 281; Guglhupf, 276; Hungarian Apricot Walnut Bars, 295; Italian Honey Biscuits, 297; Italian Macaroons, 301; Mandelbrot, 303; Old-Fashioned Molasses Bars, 298; Pecan Dreams, 302; Pastry Shell, Fruit Tart, 289; Pastry Shell, German Sweet, 288; Pastry Tart Shells, 287; Swedish Tea Ring, Large, 272; Zwetschgen Kuchen, 274; *see also* Cakes
Pâté, Chicken Liver, 59
Peach Chutney, 254
Peanut Butter: Bread, 265; Cookies I., 299; II, 300; Curry Wafers, 60; fat content of, 15; and Prudent Diet, 40
Pears, Baked Stuffed, 313
Peas: and Dumpling Soup, Fresh, 91; French Green, 208; a Salad of Cauliflower and, 240; Soup, Romaine Lettuce and Fresh, 87; Soup, Split, 93
Pecan: Dreams, 302; Pie, 293
Peppers: Salad, Roasted, 75; Steak, Chinese, 175; Stuffed, 216; Stuffed Italian, 217; Veal and, 190
Perch, *see* Steamed Fish
Pies: Deep Dish Apple, 292; fat content of, 13; Pecan, 293; Pumpkin, 293; Pie shell, *see* Flaky Pastry *and* Tart Shell
Pike: Braised Fish, 115; Gefillte Fish, 78; Poached Fish, 114; Russian Fish Stew, 117
Pineapple: Sweet and Pungent Chicken Livers, 190; Yogurt Sherbet, 318
Pink beans: Haitian Bean Sauce, 224; or Red Kidney Bean Soup, 96
Pizza, 65; Filling, Famous, 65
Plums, Italian: in Vinegar, 171; Zwetchgen Kuchen, 274
Polyunsaturated fats: in average American diet, 7; foods containing, 13–15
Pompano: Steamed Fish Cantonese, 120
Popovers, 269
Porgy: Steamed Fish Cantonese, 120

Pork: Marinated Roast Loin of, 179; Meat Balls in Caper Sauce, 182; Meat Balls in Mushroom Sauce, 181; Roast Loin of, 178; Stuffed Cabbage, 215; Swedish Meat Balls, 181

Potatoes: in Casserole, Herbed, 220; Dumplings, South German, 222; fried, and calories, 51; and Green Bean Salad, 241; Hash, Ham and, 221; Pancakes, 227; Roast 221; Roestis, 223; Salad Olivier, 243; Salad, South German, 241; Soup, Watercress and, 86; Soup, White Turnip and, 86

Pot Cheese Pancakes, 230

Pot de Crème au Chocolat, Frozen, 316

Pot Roast of Beef, 170

Poultry, 150–169; fat content of, 15; *see also* Chicken, Duckling, *and* Turkey

Poultry. Stuffing:, Matt's 167; South German, 167; Turkish, 169; Whole Wheat, 168

Protein: daily requirements, 19; and planning meals, 30–31

Prudent Diet: adjustment to, 20–21; and blood pressure, 10; and blood sugar levels, 10; and Dr. Norman Jolliffe, 7; and fish, 17; and heart attacks, 11; and meat, 19; and National Diet-Heart Study, 5; need for good nutrition, 38; and oils, 21; recommendations for, 30–32, 33, 37–40; and strokes, 10

Prudent Sour Cream, 53

Prudent Yogurt, 53

Prunes: Italian Plums in Vinegar, 171; Zwetschgen Kuchen, 274

Pulse, 74

Pumpernickel, Boris', 264

Pumpkin Pie, 293

Purée of: Broccoli, 202; Carrot, 203, 204; White Turnips, 203, 204

Quiche, Onion and Smoked Salmon, 66

Raspberries: Blushing Maiden, 309; Yogurt Sherbet, 317

Red Cabbage, Savory, 205

Red Clam Sauce, 258

Red snapper: Baked Fish with Mussels, 118; Baked Split Striped Bass, 121; Bouillabaisse "Manhattan," 98; Bourride, 101; Steamed Fish Cantonese, 120

Rice: Pudding, Creamy, 309; Risotto with Chicken Livers, 232; Salad Cap Ferrat, 242; Turkish Poultry Stuffing, 169

Risotto with Chicken Livers, 232

Roestis, 223

Romaine Lettuce and Fresh Pea Soup, 87; *see also* Braised Chicory

Roquefort: Cheese Dressing, 249; Cheese Wafers, 61; Walnut Spread, 57

Russian: Dressing, 248; Fish Stew, 117

Safflower oil: fat content of, 14; qualities of, 51; and V.S.S., 52

Salad dressings: Aunt Iva's Red Oil, 249; Blender Mayonnaise, 248; French, 246; Mayonnaise, 247; Mustard Vinaigrette, 247; Roquefort Cheese, 249; Russian, 248

Salad Niçoise, 245

Salads: Artichokes with Mustard Vinaigrette, 239; Avocado and Grapefruit, 238; Avocado, Tomato and Egg, 239; Cap Ferrat, Rice, 242; Carrot and Walnut, 237; of Cauliflower and Peas, 240; Celeriac with Mustard Vinaigrette, 240; Chicken, 244; Cole Slaw, 238; Cucumbers in Yogurt Dressing, 237; Green Beans Vinaigrette, 239; greens for, 236–237; Italian Bean and Tuna, 244; Macaroni and Tuna, 245; Olivier, 243; Potato and Green Bean, 241; Roasted Pepper, 75; Shrimp and Crab Meat, 246; Salade Niçoise, 245; South German Potato, 241; suggestions for, 236–237; Winter Tomato, 243

Salmon: Baked in Wine, 129; Braised Fish, 115; Broiled,

Salmon (*continued*)
129; Patties, 130; Poached Fish, 114; *see also* Baked Split Striped Bass
Sardines: Broiled Canned, 125; and Spinach, Canned, 125
Saturated fats: and coronary heart disease, 7; foods containing, 13–15
Sauces: Brown I, 252; Brown II, 252; Cumberland, 256; Curry, 255; Hollandaise, 256; Mushroom, 254; Mustard, 253; Tartar, 248; to thicken, 82; Tuna Fish, 257; White, 253
Sauerbraten, 172
Sauerkraut with Apples, 206
Savory Butters, 258–259
Savoy cabbage: purée of, *see* Purée of Broccoli; Sweet and Sour Stuffed Cabbage, 213
Scallops: Broiled, 134; Fried, 133; Coquilles Saint Jacques au Gratin, 135; Curried, 134
Scampi, Marinated, 144
Scandinavian: Almond Cookies, 303; Fish Pudding, 119
Schmaltz Herring in Dill Sauce, 79
Scotch Broth, 105–106
Scrod: Russian Fish Stew, 117
Sea Bass: Steamed Fish, 116; Steamed Fish Cantonese, 120
Sesame: Biscuits, 63; Seed Wafers, 62; paste, *see* Chickpea Tahini, 74; tahini, *see* Eggplant, Arabian Style Chopped
Shad: Escabeche, Boned, 128; Roe, Sautéed, 133
Shellfish:
  Clams: Baked Stuffed, 77; Chowder, Manhattan, 102; Fresh Steamed, 101; Scalloped, 147; Soup, Cream, 102
  Crab Meat: John's Green Peppers Stuffed with, 148; Lasagna California Style, 148; fat content of, 14, 17
  Mussels: Baked Fish with, 118; Paella, 137
  Scallops: Broiled, 134; Curried, 134; Coquilles Saint Jacques au Gratin, 135
  Shrimp: Balls with Broccoli, 143; Balls, Chinese, 143; Balls, Chinese Fried, 68; Batter-fried, 77; à la Belle Créole, 142; Boiled, 138; Buongusto, Italian, 146; Cantonese Style, 145; and Crab Meat au Gratin, 139; and Crab Meat Salad, 246; or Crab Meat Spread, 58; with Green Peppers and Tomatoes, 141; Hedi's Baked, 140; à l'Indienne, 139; Lemon Broiled, 144; Long Rice, 234; Marinated, 234; Marinated Scampi, 144; Steamed, 138; Tahiti, 146
Sherbets: Orange Milk, 317; Orange Yogurt, 318; Pineapple Yogurt, 318; Raspberry Yogurt, 317
Shish Kebab, 176
Shortening: hydrogenated, 14, 15; very special ("V.S.S."), 14, 52
Smelts: Deep-fried Fish, 113
Snack foods, fat content of, 15, 25; and Prudent Diet, 43
Snow Eggs in Vanilla Sauce, 308
Soft drinks, 25
Sole with Mushrooms, Fillets of, 131
Sorrel Soup, *see* Tchav
Soufflé: Apricot, with Almond Caramel Sauce, 305; Lemon, 306
Soups: Beet, 83; Black Bean, 97; Borscht, 83; Bouillabaisse "Manhattan," 98; Bourride, 101; Carrot, 84; Chicken Pot au Feu, 104; Cream of Clam, 102; Cream of Mushroom, 88; Cream of Spinach, 89; Eel, 98; Flaedchen, 90; French Onion, 85; Gazpacho, 92; how to make good, 81; Manhattan Clam Chowder, 102; New England Fish Chowder, 103; Oatmeal, 90; Fresh Pea and Dumpling, 91; Pink Bean or Red Kidney, 96; Romaine Lettuce and Fresh Pea, 87; Salt Codfish, 100; Scotch Broth, 105–106; South German Lentil, 96; Split Pea, 93; Tarator, 92; Tchav, 83; to thicken, 82;

Soups (*continued*)
Watercress and Potato, 86; White Turnip and Potato, 86; Zucchini and Rice, 85
Sour Cream, Prudent, 53
Southern Italy, Broiled Chicken from, 159
South German: Bread Stuffing for Poultry, 167; Lentil Soup, 96; Potato Dumplings, 222; Potato Salad, 241; Strawberry Tart, 290; *see also* German
Soy-Sauce Broiled Swordfish, 132
Spice Cookies, Belgian, 298
Spiced Beets, 213
Spicy Stuffed Eggplant, 218
Spinach: Braised, *see* Braised Chicory; Canned Sardines and, 125; Cottage Cheese and Smoked Salmon Filling for Pancakes, 229; with Garlic, Sautéed, 200; purée of, *see* Purée of Broccoli; Salt Codfish and, 124; Salt Codfish and, Variation, 124; Soup, Cream of, 89
Split Pea Soup, 93
Sponge Cake: Spanish Orange, 284; Two-Egg, 285
Spreads for canapés, 56–59; Taramasalata, 79
Spring Carrots, 212
Squash, Mashed Acorn, 199; Butternut, 199
Squid, Steamed, 147
"Steamer basket," 196, 197
Strawberry Tart, South German, 290
Striped Bass: Baked Split, 121; Baked Whole, 120; *see also* Braised Fish *and* Baked Fish with Mussels
Stuffing: Matt's Poultry, 167; South German Bread, 167; Turkish, 169; Whole Wheat, 168
Swedish: Meat Balls, 181; Tea Ring, Large, Filled and Frosted, 272
Sweet potatoes: and Apple Casserole, 220; Tzimmis, 198
Sweet and Sour Stuffed Cabbage, 213
Sweet and Pungent Chicken Livers, 190

Swordfish: Cubes: Marinated, 69; Lemon Broiled, 131; Soy-Sauce Broiled, 132; on Spits, Turkish Broiled, 132
Tahini: Chickpea, 74; Eggplant, Arabian Style, Chopped, 73
Taramasalata, 79
Tarator, 92
Tartar Sauce, 248
Tart Shell, 287; for Fruit Pastry, 289; German Sweet, 288
Tarts: French Apple, 289; Fresh Blueberry, 291; South German, Strawberry, 290; Vintner's Lemon, 290
Tchav, 83
Tomatoes: Broiled, 209; and Egg Salad, Avocado, 239; Gazpacho, 92; Green Pepper and Zucchini Casserole, Eggplant, 211; Sauce, Italian Meat Balls in, 180; Red Clam Sauce, 258; Salad, Winter, 243; Shrimp à la Belle Créole, 142; with Green Peppers and, 141; Stuffed Cherry, 58; Tuna Fish Sauce, 257
Toppings: Crumb, 276; Roast Almond, 273; Whipped Cheese, I, 319; Whipped Cheese II, 320
Tortes: Date Nut, 282; Frankfurt Filbert, 281
Tuna Fish: Casserole with Noodles, 149; Olive Spread, 58; Salad, Italian Bean and, 245; Salade Niçoise, 246; Sauce, 257
Turkey: Almond Spread, 57; to broil a small, 166; Fricassee, *see* Chicken Fricassee; Variations of Scotch Broth, 106
Turkish: Broiled Swordfish on Spits, 132; Lamb and Lentil Stew, 178; Poultry Stuffing, 169
Turnips: and Potato Soup, White, 86; Purée of White, 203; Purée of White, Variation, 204
Tzimmis, 198

V.S.S. (Very Special Shortening), to make, 52
Vanilla: Cream Filling, 274; Sauce, Snow Eggs in, 308; Sugar, Confectioners, 277

Veal: Blanquette de Veau, 187; and Chicken Liver Loaf, 189; Goulash, Brown, 186; Meat Balls in Caper Sauce, 182; and Peppers, 190; Pot Roast of, 185; Roast Rump of, 185; Salad Olivier, 243; Scallopini with Mushrooms, 183; Shanks, Braised, 188; Stuffed Peppers, 216; Wiener Schnitzel, 184

Vegetables: baked in foil, 198; Casserole, Lamb and, 177; as Cocktailers, 55; cooked in steam, 197; planning meals and, 31; as protein sources, 19; purées, 201; Salad Olivier, 244; to sauté, Chinese style, 197; *see also* names of vegetables

Vegetable oils: and diet, 4; and planning meals, 32

Very Special Shortening (V.S.S.), to make, 52

Vitamins: and faulty diet, 25; and planning meals, 30–32

Wafers, Cocktail: Anchovy, 61; Peanut Butter Curry, 60; Roquefort Cheese; 61; Sesame Seed, 62

Waffles, Buttermilk, 227

Walnut: Mandelbrot, 303; Salad, Carrot and, 237; Spread, Roquefort, 57

Watercress and Potato Soup, 86

Weight loss: "aids" to, 23–24; to estimate, 26–27; and Prudent Diet, 10–11

Whipped Cheese Topping No. I, 319; No. II, 320

Whipped Evaporated Milk, 320

Whitefish: Braised Fish, 115; Gefillte Fish, 78; Poached Fish, 114; Russian Fish Stew, 117; *see also* Baked Split Striped Bass

White Sauce, 253

White Turnips: and Potato Soup, 86; Purée of, 203–204

White Wine Cream, 307

Whiting: Bouillabaisse "Manhattan," 98; Bourride, 101; New England Fish Chowder, 103; Steamed Fish, 116

Whole grains: fat content of, 15; planning meals, 32

Whole Wheat Poultry Stuffing, 168

Wiener Schnitzel, 184

Wine Cream, White, 307

Winter Tomato Salad, 243

Yeast Dough I, 271; II, 271

Yogurt: Dip, 58; Dressing, Cucumbers in, 31; and planning meals, 237; Prudent, 53; Sherbet: Orange, 318; Pineapple, 318; Raspberry, 317; Tarator, 92

Zucchini: Casserole, Eggplant, Tomato, Green Pepper and, 211; Italian, Barra's, 206; Niçoise, Stuffed, 219; Patties, 208; Puff, Baked, 207; and Rice Soup, 85; *see also* Romaine Lettuce and Fresh Pea Soup

Zwetschgen Kuchen, 274

ABOUT THE AUTHORS

IVA BENNETT and MARTHA SIMON have had long experience as public health nutritionists in The Department of Health, City of New York, Bureau of Nutrition. From the beginning, they have been deeply involved in the Nutrition Bureau's Anti-Coronary Club, a research project on the prevention of coronary heart disease by diet. For fourteen years Mrs. Bennett was the Voice of Nutrition for the Bureau on the daily WNYC radio program, *Listen to Nutrition*.

Iva Bennett, a graduate of Geneseo State Normal (now a New York State College), has a B.S. in Home Economics Education from Cornell University and an M.A. from Columbia University. Martha Simon has a B.S. in Home Economics from Pratt Institute and an M.S. in Public Health Nutrition from Columbia University. Both authors are excellent cooks.

DO IT!
ALL BY YOURSELF!

- [ ] THE MOTHER EARTH NEWS HANDBOOK
  OF HOMEMADE POWER (8535 • $1.95)
- [ ] AMY VANDERBILT'S EVERYDAY ETIQUETTE
  (8092 • $1.95)
- [ ] SOULE'S DICTIONARY OF ENGLISH SYNONYMS
  (7883 • $1.25)
- [ ] THE RUTH STOUT NO-WORK GARDEN BOOK
  (7763 • $1.25)
- [ ] TREASURY OF CRAFT DESIGN (7683 • $1.95)
- [ ] BUYING COUNTRY PROPERTY (7559 • $1.75)
- [ ] HOW TO BUY STOCKS (7041 • $1.25)
- [ ] THE ILLUSTRATED HASSLE-FREE MAKE YOUR OWN
  CLOTHES BOOK (7029 • $1.25)
- [ ] THE BOOK OF EXPERT DRIVING (5957 • 95¢)
- [ ] THE BANTAM BOOK OF CORRECT LETTER WRITING
  (5673 • $1.00)
- [ ] IT PAYS TO INCREASE YOUR WORD POWER
  (5266 • 95¢)
- [ ] BETTER HOMES AND GARDENS HANDYMAN BOOK
  (4613 • $1.25)
- [ ] THE ART OF MIXING DRINKS (4030 • $1.00)

Buy them at your local bookstore or use this handy coupon for ordering:

Bantam Books, Inc., Dept. DY, 414 East Golf Road, Des Plaines, Ill. 60016

Please send me the books I have checked above. I am enclosing $_____
(please add 35¢ to cover postage and handling). Send check or money order—no cash or C.O.D.'s please.

Mr/Mrs/Miss_____

Address_____

City_____State/Zip_____

DY—6/74

Please allow three weeks for delivery. This offer expires 6/75.

FREE!
Bantam Book Catalog

It lists over a thousand money-saving bestsellers originally priced from $3.75 to $15.00—bestsellers that are yours now for as little as 50¢ to $2.95!

The catalog gives you a great opportunity to build your own private library at huge savings!

So don't delay any longer—send for your catalog TODAY! It's absolutely FREE!

Just send us a post card with the information below or use this handy coupon:

BANTAM BOOKS, INC.
Dept. FC, 414 East Golf Road, Des Plaines, Ill. 60016

Mr./Mrs./Miss_____
(please print)
Address_____
City_____ State_____ Zip_____

Do you know someone who enjoys books? Just give us their names and addresses and we'll send them a FREE CATALOG too!

Mr./Mrs./Miss_____
Address_____
City_____ State_____ Zip_____

Mr./Mrs./Miss_____
Address_____
City_____ State_____ Zip_____

FC—6/74